PRACTICAL DIMMING

Nick Mobsby

**ENTERTAINMENT
TECHNOLOGY PRESS**

Systems Series

This book is dedicated to
Bill Clark, Derek and Muriel Coe, Robert Miles, Poppy and Ken Tattersall.

Front cover: close-up of ETC Matrix II Modular Dimmer Cabinet and Sine Wave Dimmer Modules, original photo: ETC Europe Ltd.

PRACTICAL DIMMING

Nick Mobsby

Entertainment Technology Press

Practical Dimming

© Nick Mobsby

First edition published September 2006
by Entertainment Technology Press Ltd
The Studio, High Green, Great Shelford, Cambridge CB2 5EG
Internet: www.etnow.com

ISBN 1 904031 44 7

A title within the
Entertainment Technology Press Systems Series
Series editor: John Offord

CONTENTS

PREFACE 11

ACKNOWLEDGEMENTS FOR INFORMATION 15

1 INTRODUCTION 19
    1.1 Introduction 20
    1.2 Applications 22
    1.3 Suppliers 23
    1.4 Topics Covered 24
    1.5 Summary 25

2 HISTORY OF DIMMERS 27
    2.1 Introduction 28
    2.2 History of Resistive and Other Types of Dimming .. 29
    2.3 History of Electronic Dimming 37
    2.4 Further Historic Information 57

3 UNDERSTANDING DIMMERS 59
    3.1 General Dimmer Considerations 60
    3.2 Power Control Section 61
    3.3 Interference Suppression 64
    3.4 Acoustic Noise 67
    3.5 Dimmer Law 67
    3.6 Dimmer Sizes 71
    3.7 Heat Dissipation Considerations 72
    3.8 Ratings of Dimmers 74
    3.9 Design Considerations for Building a Dimmer
        Room 77
    3.10 Dimmer Diagnostics and Fault Reporting 82
    3.11 Non Dims, Switches and Relays 84
    3.12 Conclusions 84

4 DIMMING SYSTEM DESIGN..87
   4.1 Introduction 88
   **4.2 Electrical Power Requirements and Venue
      Design Light Levels** 88
   4.3 How to Calculate the Size of Supply Required........88
   **4.4 Example 1: Typical Medium Size School Hall
      Stage**...90
   **4.5 Example 2: Multi-Purpose Large School or
      College Hall Stage**..93
   4.6 Example 3: Medium Sized City or Civic Theatre....97
   4.7 Example 4: High Grade Conference Centre..........103
   4.7 Example 5: News and Current Affairs TV Studio...107
   4.8 Conclusions..110
   4.9 Further Reading..110

5 ARCHITECTURAL DIMMING 113
   5.1 Introduction 114
   5.2 Wall Box Dimmers..114
   5.3 UK Wall Dimmers 115
   5.4 USA Wall Dimmers..117
   5.5 Commercial Lighting Dimmers............................120
   5.6 Commercial Lighting Controllers 125
   5.7 Dimming Fluorescent Lamps 128
   5.8 Conclusions..130

6 TYPES OF DIMMERS...131
   6.1 Introduction 132
   6.2 Individual Dimmers...132
   6.3 Portable Packs – Standard 134
   6.3 Portable Packs – Rack Mount............................136
   6.4 Professional Portable and Rack Mount Packs 149
   6.5 Flight Cased Dimmers 154
   6.6 Medium Density Hard Wired Cabinet Dimmers.163
   6.7 High Density Modular Dimmers 174

6.8 Conclusions 180
6.9 Useful Contact Details 180

7 NEW TECHNOLOGY DIMMERS 183
  7.1 Introduction to Transistor Dimming 184
  7.2 Reverse Phase Transistor Dimming 185
  7.3 Sine Wave Dimming 190
  7.4 Distributed Dimming 196
  7.4.1 Initial Cost? 200
  7.4.2 Required Turn-around Time? 201
  7.4.4 Re-use of Existing Cabling or Fit New Cabling? .. 206
  7.4.5 Is this a new installation or an addition
      to an existing installation? 206
  7.4.6 Quality of Required Dimming Solution and
      Acceptable Acoustic Noise levels? 207
  7.4.7 Other Considerations 209
  7.5 Other Distributed Solutions 209
  7.6 Conclusions 215
  7.7 Useful Contact Details 217

8 ELECTRICAL SYSTEMS 219
  8.1 Introduction 220
  8.2 Electrical Supplies 220
  8.3 Harmonic Distortion and Power Factor 225
  8.4 Electrical Protection and Distribution Boards 229
  8.5 Residual Current and Earth leakage Issues 237
  8.6 Phasing Performance Venue Electrical
      Installations 242
  8.6.1 Example 1: European Black Box Drama
      Studio 243
  8.6.2 Example 2: Large College Stage in the UK 244
  8.6.3 Example 3: Hotel Ballroom used as a
      Performance Space with Three Partitioned
      Areas 247

8.6.4 Example 4: 600-seat Repertory Theatre 248
8.6.5 Example 5: Performance Space within
           Shopping Mall 252
8.7 Socket Outlets and Wall Boxes 255
8.8 Cable Sizes 262
8.9 Earthing 264
8.10 Geographic Layout 264
8.11 Electrical Diversity 267
8.12 Non Dimmed Supplies 270
8.13 Working Lights 271
8.14 House Lights 277
8.15 Conclusions on Electrical Systems 280

9 SETTING UP A SYSTEM AND FAULT FINDING 283
9.1 Introduction 284
9.2 Routine Maintenance 284
9.2.1 Portable Packs in Small Systems 284
9.2.2 Rack Mounted Packs 285
9.2.3 Wall Mounted Dimmer Racks 285
9.2.4 Flight Cased Dimmers 286
9.2.5 High Density Cabinet Dimmers 286
9.2.6 Distributed Dimmer Bars and Packs 287
9.2.7 Other Tests for all Types of Dimmers 287
9.3 Commissioning an Existing System 288
9.4 Commissioning a New System 290
9.4.1 Installed System 290
9.4.2 Temporary System 295
9.5 Conclusions 297

USEFUL CONTACT ADDRESSES 301

GLOSSARY 311

INDEX 343

PREFACE

Having written my first book in 2000/2001 *Lighting Systems for TV Studios* I was in the middle of writing another large tome when an idea dawned on editor John Offord and myself. This followed an experience when for a few minutes I was manning the Entertainment Technology Press stand at an exhibition. Talking with a theatre electrician he explained to me that big reference books were fine for those who had the time to read them but what he wanted was a simpler book that he and his technicians could use to understand day-to-day lighting and related technical issues. So, some five months later followed *Practical DMX;* five months later still I have completed *Practical Dimming,* and I hope this delivers some of the answers that are required by anyone working in the entertainment and related lighting industry where dimmers are now widely used.

Being able to write such a book is only possible due to considerable experience and advice, both good and otherwise, given to me by lighting practitioners from around the world over the past 30 years. They all seem to be from the same very extended family and should be applauded for the lighting they produce in ever diminishing time with ever reducing budgets. To all of them I extend my thanks and admiration. It is one thing to design a system, but a very much higher level of skill is required to produce good theatre and TV show lighting!

To those manufacturers and individuals who have contributed information, pictures and drawings I am extremely grateful. The UK and USA are well serviced by some of the very best manufacturers of lighting equipment in the world. They are highly innovative, operate on the boundaries of technology and compete throughout the world, often delivering solutions in ridiculous time-frames. Having tried this myself I have the utmost admiration for what they do; I applaud them all.

On a more personal note there are a number of extra special people who I want to thank in print.

Rick Dines retired in the late 1990s having been the Senior Project Engineer, BBC Consulting and Projects, looking after lighting systems. The BBC owes Rick a tremendous debt of gratitude for his constant pushing of technology to the limit, exploring new ideas, and constantly returning to basics, having given the BBC some of the best lighting systems of any studios around the world. Rick always gave time to discuss designs, could be persuaded to a different view, managed to get the best from all the individuals on the project and always delivered the goods. His reputation, whilst at the BBC, was somewhat like that of Alfred Hitchcock; he could often be seen making the finishing touches as new studios went on air!

Many of the new dimming advances were pioneered by Rick including the first use of transistor dimmers in a national broadcast TV studio. One lasting impression of working with him was a relatively large scale project in the UK for the BBC for a leading UK political TV programme. We had to replace all the dimmers whilst keeping the studio operational. Having completed everything and tested everything the decision was taken to use the installation on Question Time. Sitting in the control room I overhead the Head of Resources ask when are we going to use the new dimmers? Rick simply said we were tonight! So to Rick a very big thank you for having the patience to guide and teach and for letting me join in all the fun and the heartache too; the lighting world needs your expertise, so try to leave the boat alone - for some of the year at least!

Another BBC supremo is Joe Breslin, Lighting Director at BBC Scotland. Joe can make high quality pictures with a Maglite and a piece of poly board. I first met him some eight years ago and he is another man who has allowed the latest is technological developments to be tried and honed down to provide the right solution. Joe regularly lights many different productions throughout Scotland. Some of the stories he can tell about shows are legendary; the problem is they are real, and they did happen, and he did solve the problem

Having started installing and designing systems immediately after becoming qualified as an electronics and electrical engineer I lacked any formal lighting design and theatrical training. But looking back I have had many lucky breaks – all of which are down to key individuals who have trusted and believed in me. The first of these came in 1972 via Alan Payne, one of the major designers of control desks at Strand Lighting, such as the DDM. He gave me my first chance to work in the theatre: to design and install the dimmable fluorescent under-floor lighting system for *Jesus Christ Superstar* at the Palace Theatre in London's West End with Jules Fisher as the lighting designer.

The second break, in 1979, was courtesy of Alan Bailey and John Gregg from Gregg and Bailey. They entrusted me as the lighting designer on well over 150 events, fashion shows and productions they produced around the world. They had a unique ability to stage a magical show and gave me some incredible opportunities and experiences that I will never forget. John designed sets that allowed light to 'work': Alan choreographed and staged shows that enabled even my poor lighting design to look reasonable! Alan pushed for that something special, extending me to the limit, allowing theatrical innovation and design to become a major part of the show.

I started working in this industry in the early 1970s with a business partner who was considerably senior in years and experience to me. Derek Coe taught me about the wide world of business, commercial engineering, accuracy, standards, quality, communication and other skills far too numerous to mention. Sadly Derek died in 1999 and as each day goes by I miss his input in designing systems and our regular chats. Derek could look at all the angles, the requirements and the problems and yet always find a solution. He was one of the world's gentlemen, commanding respect wherever he went. So posthumously I say a huge thank you to Derek. Without help in the beginning there would be no book to write now. To Derek's lovely wife Muriel I dedicated my first book. Sadly Muriel passed away after this was published but watching her will-power and stamina when fighting through adversity and still be a wonderful grandmother to all of her grandchildren was a joy and an inspiration.

Finally, there are two other people I should mention. One is the man who started my interest in the world of entertainment and particularly television. This was the man who would come home from the Olympics in Japan or The American Presidential Elections, the World Cup in Mexico or the BBC Television Centre with tales and stories that made a young boy's mind wander and dream of being involved. This same man took a young boy around the BBC TV Centre when major events were unfolding, such as Francis Chichester arriving back in the UK after his round the world trip. My father spent his life working for the BBC, being involved in some of the founding issues for a colour television station that became the envy of the world. So to Ray a big thank you for introducing me to what has become a drug!

Finally, to my son Christopher, who is a bit too young now to know what he will do later in life, I extend the hope that just maybe he will find the opportunity and the interest to make his future in the entertainment industry, possibly joining the world of lighting professionals, which for me, has become my extended family.

Nick Mobsby
Horsell
24th August, 2006

ACKNOWLEDGEMENTS FOR INFORMATION

To all of you who have helped with *Practical Dimming* – thank you.

A.C. Lighting Ltd. (UK) – Jonathan Walters and Glynn O'Donaghue
ADB-TTV Technologies (Belgium) – Christian Léonard, Mike Musso,
        André Broucke, and Raph Janssens
Alnetronic GmbH. (Germany) – Reinhard Issac
Andolite Ltd. (UK) – Tony Swayne
Anytronics Ltd. (UK) – Bob Hall
Avolites Ltd. (UK) – Richard Salzedo and Alwyn Fernendas

BBC Resources Ltd. (UK)
BICC Burndy Ltd. (UK)

Clay Paky SPA. (Italy)
Colortran (USA) – for product information
Compulite (Israel) – Anat Tobis, Fred Senator and Danny Redler

Elation (USA) – for product information
ELC (Switzerland) – for product information and assistance.
Electrical Control Systems NI Ltd. (UK) – for electrical distribution
        equipment information
Electron (Greece) – Elena Ekoukiari for product information and
        assistance.
Electronics Diversified Inc. (USA) – for product information.
Electrosonic Ltd. (UK) – Robert Simpson
Entertainment Technology Inc. (USA) – Steve Carson and Jim Crooks
ESTA (USA) – Lori Rubenstein and Karl Ruling
ETC bV. (IES bV.) (Holland) – Jan de Jonge
ETC Europe Ltd. (UK) – Erik Larsen, Mark White, Jeremy Roberts and
        Miranda Hunt

Fred Bentham (UK) – the father of entertainment dimming

Gordon Pearlman (USA) – for some help on the early days of
        Entertainment Technology Inc.

Grey Interfaces Inc. (Canada) – Graham D Likeness

Howard Eaton Lighting Ltd. (UK) – Howard Eaton and Peter Willis

Institute of Electrical Engineers – IEE (UK)
Interactive Technologies Inc. (USA)

Jands (Australia) – for product information
Jim Laws (UK) – for a wealth of useful information and historic data and
    prices
John Offord (UK) – for providing help, proof reading, guidance and
    friendship
John McGraw (USA) – ex Production Arts New York for use of his historic
    literature collection and help

Keith Benson (UK) – one of the best technicians and teachers in the world
Kelsey Acoustics Ltd. (UK)
Kliegl.com – useful source of historic Kliegl information

Lee Lighting Ltd. (UK) – Mark Ackers
Leprecon Inc. (USA) – for product information
Leviton-Colortran Inc. (USA) – Paul Sherbo
Lightfactor Sales Ltd. (UK) – Paul de Ville and Peter Coles
Light-Puter Enterprise Co. – for product information
Light and Sound International Magazine (UK) – Lee Baldock for searching
    the archives
Lightronics Inc. (USA) – for product information
LSC (Australia) – for product and pricing information.
LSI Projects Ltd. (UK) – Russell Dunsire and Andrew Nu
Lutron Inc. (USA) – Melissa Andresko and Kristin Crawford

MA Lighting GmbH (Germany) – for product information.
MK Electric Ltd. (UK) – for data on UK wall box dimmers

Osram Ltd. (UK) for information on DALI, lamps and fluorescent ballasts.

Pathway Connectivity Inc. (Canada) – Graham D. Likeness

PLASA (UK) – Lee Baldock
PRG Europe Ltd. (UK) – Simon Roose
Pulsar Light of Cambridge Ltd. (UK)

Rako Controls (UK) – for help with architectural dimming
Ray Mobsby (UK) – for hours of proof reading and corrections
Rick Dines Associates (UK) – Rick Dines for guidance as ever
Richard Brett (UK) – for some wonderful teaching
Richard Bunting (UK) – for raiding his loft and memory banks
Robert Juliat (France) – François and Jean-Charles Juliat
Russell Dunsire (UK) – for supporting me during difficult times and raiding his loft!

Society of Television Lighting Directors Archive (UK)
Strand Lighting Ltd. (UK) – Peter Rogers, Peter Sherrington and Bethan Dixon
Strand Archive (UK) – Jon Primrose for a history lesson in Strand products
STLD Archive – all STLD members who keep sending me information

Terry Abbs (UK) – for providing some historic Strand information
Theatre Projects Consultants (UK) – Jerry Godden, Alan Russell and Tom Davis
TMB Ltd. (UK)

Zero 88 Ltd. (UK) – Graham Eales

1 INTRODUCTION

It is amazing where you find a dimmer room – production of Taming of Shrew in Perth Botanical Gardens, January 1999
photo: PLASA LSI Magazine, February 1999

Contents:
- **Introduction**
- **Applications**
- **Suppliers**
- **Topics Covered**
- **Summary**

1.1 Introduction

One of the most important parts of any performance-related lighting system is the dimming equipment. This enables the lighting levels to be controlled and balanced as well as providing many lighting changes to create different visual images. Why are dimmers required in performance venues? When using multiple light sources the output must be balanced in order to achieve a well lit and balanced picture for the audience or for a TV camera.

Dimmers are not the only means of controlling light output; devices such as scrims, barndoors, electronic dimmer shutters, irises and filters placed in front of luminaires are all used to control the light output. These devices have a major advantage in that they do not affect the colour temperature of the light output. Controlling the voltage by means of an electrical system, such as a dimmer, has the major disadvantage that the lower the voltage the lower the colour temperature. This tends to make the resulting light output turn yellow and move towards the red end of the colour spectrum. This will also affect the performance of any colour filter applied to the front of the luminaire with resulting major changes to the colour as well as the intensity of the light output, depending on the colour of the filter.

This book looks at the history of dimmer development from the very early days of resistive dimmers, thyratrons and auto-transformer controls to the thyristor and triacs electronic power control devices. In more recent years the transistor dimmer has appeared with the insulated gate bi-polar transistor – what a mouthful and what does it mean? Within this book the different types of dimmers are explained and what this really means to the user. Over the past 30 years a lot of the advances in dimmers have come from large users of power devices such as washing machines, motor speed controls and other devices which really do the same job as a dimmer but in a different form. This has resulted in dimmers changing shape and size, becoming more efficient and now even being small enough to be built into lighting instruments.

Practical Dimming covers the many different aspects of dimming from the early days right up to 21st century systems based around sine wave technology. Not only do we look at the control devices but more practically the different formats that dimmers are produced in. These include the portable packs for the smaller venue, the hard wired wall mounted cabinets for the up to, say, 120 way systems, high density solutions with up to 100 dimmers per cabinet and then distributed packages where dimmers can be mounted close to or within the luminaire.

Fig 1: Kliegl Dimmer Range from Lighting Control Systems Brochure 1961 photo: McGraw Collection USA.

Dimming has made some rapid advances over the past 50 years and some of the history is reviewed within the following chapters. Developments in the major producing countries of the USA and UK are reviewed, together with guidance on products that are available within each product group. To assist potential purchasers current local list prices have been included in local currency. Contact details have been provided within each chapter for companies and suppliers from which further information may be obtained

As dimmers require connection to an electrical supply a chapter has been included on how to consider, specify and connect electrical systems together with related issues such as heat dissipation, acoustic noise, interference and connection to a lighting control network. The companion book *Practical DMX*, also published by Entertainment Technology Press, details with significantly more comprehensive information the different types of lighting network. For those working in TV I have also written a comprehensive guide called *Lighting Systems for TV Studios*, also published by Entertainment Technology Press. For those of you interested in control systems, later in 2006 will follow *Practical Control* which will take an in-depth look at the different control systems from around the world.

1.2 Applications

Dimming now features in our everyday lives from the dimmer on the wall in the lounge through to automatic control systems in shopping malls and hotels that adjust to the time of day. Some brief information on the 'architectural' applications has been included. The theme park, living museums, themed restaurants and other controlled environments are only possible if the illumination can be balanced and altered with the use of dimmers and a suitable control network. Indeed, a lot of new developments have evolved from these new applications for dimmers.

It is probably true that many of those reading this book are simply unaware of how much dimming is built into buildings that we visit regularly. The cruise ship industry packs thousands of dimmer channels onto the modern cruise liner to ensure that we enjoy the cruising experience. Modern TV and theatre presentations require an ever increasing amount of dimmers in order to control the ever larger number of luminaires used in productions. During the course of the book you will see how every 15 years or so the quantity of dimmers in the average size theatre has doubled with the 1950s seeing 30 or a maximum of 60 channels in use where today 360 to 480 dimmers is not an uncommon number in the average venue. On one recent university project I was involved with there where some 10 different size venues and auditoria with a total of over 3000 dimmer channels being specified for the performance and architectural applications.

1.3 Suppliers

The dimming industry is littered with manufacturers who produced industry changing key products and then five or ten years later vanished off the scene. Some details have been included from companies whom I consider have made significant contributions to the 'dimming world'.

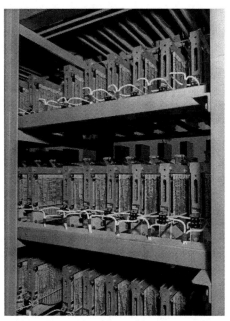

Fig 2: Strand Resistance Dimmer banks 1956, photo: the STLD Archive.

Having worked as a dimmer designer let me tell you that it is not a simple as it might appear. Whilst you may be able to adjust the intensity by packing them into the required size of box, removing all of the interference and heat, making them work reliably with a dirty mains supply as well as keeping them working day after day when they are thrown in and out of trucks is not easy. So next time you look at your dimmers have a thought for the person that designed them.

The industry is fortunate that there are so many good engineers designing products that we have all come to rely on. Recently I was asked to visit a theatre to give them some ideas on how they might upgrade their equipment. After eventually finding the key to the dimmer room it was as if history had stood still. The dimmers had been installed in the early 1970s and they looked like new once the dust was brushed off. 'We never come here,' said the theatre technician, 'we have no need to'. Modern technology allows the dimmers to be installed and forgotten. This requires manufacturers to look carefully at cooling systems as more and more dimmers are crammed into ever smaller spaces the heat dissipation does not change. So today we have 'closed loop' control systems where the temperature is measured and cooling automatically controlled so that they 'manage themselves'.

I have to admit to being fascinated with dimmers from an early age. During my period in education I built unsuccessfully a number of dimmers for my school – progressing through to prototype dimming systems at university which finally did reach manufacturing and saw night after night use on shows such as *Jesus Christ Superstar* in London's West End. Having also toured around the world one got to use many different manufacturers' products, some of these were exceptional; others I have tried to forget. Many of you reading the book will have experiences of problems, the necessity of seeing nails inserted to replace that fuse that just kept blowing and maybe some have suffered the indignity of opening the dimmer room door to see large amounts of smoke emerging from a rather blackened cabinet.

1.4 Topics Covered

Out of necessity some detailing of the way in which dimmers operate has been included together with some simplified diagrams of the different types of power control sections used in the modern dimmer. These have been included

to help with a general understanding and in fault finding when things go wrong.

Like all books covering such a large topic it is not possible to cover every aspect, so generalisations have had to be made. However, I have experience working in many different aspects of lighting so I hope that those working in the theatre, television, event, touring and architectural fields will find the information they require.

The book has been divided into easy-to-use chapters so that you can use it as a quick source of reference or source of information or hopefully enjoy a good read. To

Fig 3: IES Matrix II 2 x 2.5kW Sine Wave Module 2005, photo IES bV (ETC bV).

set the scene a chapter on dimmer history is provided together with some historical pictures that should span all of the different ages of dimming. Then we move onto the different types of packages – portable, wall mount, high density and the latest distributed packages. Next we have details of the necessary electrical supplies and how to estimate and power dimmers, with additional data on control networks. Finally, information on how to test and fault find is provided.

For those experiencing problems I hope that the simple advice provided on fault finding a system helps to solve problems. Out of necessity this cannot cover problems with specific manufacturer's products.

1.5 Summary

Being of an older generation, as many around keep telling me, allows me to comment on many dimming issues as I have passed through the touring circuit, the trade show, the weekly rep and the TV shoot. Hopefully some of these experiences and not too many anecdotes will be found useful.

So without further ado, welcome to *Practical Dimming*. I hope you enjoy reading the book and if you feel I have missed something, make statements with which you disagree or simply wish to send me some comments, then please do. It is often lonely being an author and I welcome your comments! To assist with your communication please free to email me on books@nickmobsby. com. I cannot guarantee to answer every email or include every comment but as the print on demand philosophy of Entertainment Technology Press regularly allows updates I can but try.

Thank you for buying *Practical Dimming*!

Fig 4: One of the latest dimmers launched in 2006, the Strand Lighting low cost installation dimmer called Wallrack, photo: Strand Lighting Ltd.

2 HISTORY OF DIMMERS

A montage of electronic and electro-mechanical dimmers through the ages of 1955 to 2005 photos: Arri GB Ltd, Entertainment Technology, Inc., ETC Europe Ltd., Strand Lighting Ltd., the STLD Archive and the author.

Contents:

- **Introduction**
- **Brief History of Resistive Dimming**
- **History of Electronic Dimming**
- **Patch Panels**
- **Historic Prices**
- **Summary and Contact Details**

2.1 Introduction

Entertainment dimming has progressed from gas lighting dimming systems where the dimmer was actually a gas valve - to resistive dimmers prevalent in the 1920s to 1970s through the choke solutions found in the 1940s to 1970s and thyratrons that were the first 'electronic' solutions found from the 1930s to the 1950s. Probably the most famous of these was General Electric's New York City Radio City Music Hall 3 preset thyratron valve saturated reactor control system installed in 1933. Auto-transformers were seen initially in the 1950s and were still in use in the early 1980s.

The major reduction in size came with the advent of the small power control device called a thyristor. Initially seen in the 1960s they continue today as the preferred power control device in a conventional dimmer. From the washing and motor control world came the triac power controller, which is like two back-to-back thyristors in one electronic package, appeared in the 1970s, again remaining in use in lower cost dimmers today.

The late 1990s saw the advent of the transistor dimmer with the insulated gate bipolar transistors (IGBT's) being used. These are used more like an audio amplifier and have enabled packages without chokes and thus weight and acoustic noise to be produced.

In the 21st century we now have the sine wave dimmer where the amplitude of the sine wave is varied without electrical distortion thus reducing the amount of electrical interference to extremely low levels. This pleases the power generation companies and also audiences as the dimmer buzz or filament 'singing' become things of the past. Whilst the early dimmers were very large and difficult to use and required vast amounts of space, modern dimmers are physically much smaller, even allowing dimmers to be located close to light sources or even within them in the case of moving lights. Vari-Lite is one progressive company using this type of solution.

Early electronic dimmers allowed the use of a control desk located remotely from the dimmer. This was really no different to the earlier resistive solutions save that the age of the transistor rather than the valve allowed the control desk to get smaller and the control signals to move towards standards and the use of low voltage control. Many smaller venues still use analogue controlled dimmers, but since the late 1980s and early 1990s digitally controlled dimmers have become more widely used. These offer many advantages as the firing of the dimmer can be more accurately controlled by use of computerised control, with spare processor capacity being made available for other useful user programmable facilities.

Dimming systems are also one of the most capital intensive parts of any lighting system and care must be taken in choosing the right type of dimmer to suit the venue application. The different types of dimmers and their benefits are discussed later in this book.

Dimmers also require consideration as to how they are to be controlled, how they are to be powered, where they can and should be located, and other general issues.

Before these issues are considered I feel it is appropriate to take a brief historical look at the resistance dimmers with a more in depth view of the electronic dimmer products that have been around over the past 40 or so years.

2.2 History of Resistive and Other Types of Dimming

Thomas Edison is widely credited with having invented the incandescent lamp; he certainly made the principle reliable and found methods of mass producing these early lamps. It would seem that Edison's first successful lamp used carbonised cotton thread as a filament, installed in a glass bulb, with all the air could be removed. On the afternoon of October 21, 1879, Edison's prototype had lasted 45 hours. The next day Edison began to experiment using cardboard as a filament. The cardboard filament was even more successful, and in a couple of months, production of his lamps had increased. On New Year's Eve, December 31, 1879, Edison gave his first public demonstration of his new invention, at Menlo Park, New Jersey. Special trains were run on the Pennsylvania Railroad to accommodate the masses of visitors. About 100 cardboard filament lamps were used in this demonstration, lighting the streets, the laboratory, and the station at Menlo Park. Each lamp was rated at 16 candlepower and consumed about 100 watts (average life was about 100 hours).

In 1880 Edison experimented with other materials for filaments, including wood, grasses, hair and bamboo. Of the over 6000 specimens tested by his laboratory, bamboo became commonly used for filaments. In 1880, on January 17, Patent number 223,898 was issued to Edison for the T.A. Edison Electric Lamp.

In 1881, two years after the first incandescent lamp left Edison's workshop, the steamship 'Columbia' was fitted with a thousand of them. Within another two years, there were over 300 electric power stations in existence, feeding over 70,000 incandescent lamps, each with an average life of 100 hours.

To those born in the UK our history teachers suggest that Joseph Swan should be credited with inventing the incandescent lamp. Swan demonstrated a carbon filament lamp to about 700 people in Newcastle-upon-Tyne in the North East of England on February 5, 1879. Swan's development of the incandescent lamp was reported in the October 29th, 1880 issue of *Engineering*, and this quoted him as follows: "Electric lighting by incandescence is just as simple as arc lighting is difficult, all that is required is a material which is not a very good conductor of electricity, highly infusible and which can be formed into a wire or lamina, and is neither combustible in air, or if combustible, does not undergo changes in a vacuum". The first premises to be illuminated by the new Swan lamp were those of Sir William Armstrong at Cragside near Newcastle in December 1880.

Electric lights manufactured by Edison and Joseph Swan were quickly being adopted by the theatres of the time. One enterprising manager, Richard D'Oyly Carte, of the new Savoy Theatre in London, saw an opportunity to use this new technology. In 1881 he opened the theatre and advertised that "the Savoy was the first public building lighted entirely by electricity". In fact, there were a total of 1158 of the new Swan lamps, used to light the auditorium, the dressing rooms, the corridors and the stage. The electrical and dimmer system was supplied by Siemens Brothers and Company, one of the early pioneers in stage lighting control systems. There were six dimmers in all.

In an article published in *Engineering* on March 3rd 1882 it was reported: "In an artistic and scenic point of view nothing could be more completely successful than the present lighting of the Savoy Theatre – the illumination is brilliant without being dazzling, and while being slightly whiter than gas, the accusation of "ghastliness", so often urged against the light of the electric arc, can in no way be applied. In addition to this the light is absolutely steady, and thanks to the enterprise of Mr. D'Oyly Carte, it is now possible for the first time in history of the modern theatre

Fig 1: Kliegl 1903 Electric lighting installation at Metropolitan Opera House, NYC photo: Kliegl Bros, USA.

to sit for a whole evening and enjoy a dramatic performance in a cool and pure atmosphere." The first USA theatre installation appears to have been in 1882 at the Bijou Theatre in Boston.

In 1903 Kliegl Bros from the USA installed a 96 dimmer stage lighting system at the Metropolitan Opera House in New York City. *Fig 1* shows a poor quality image of the installation that comprised of eight sets of 'border' lights flown from above the stage and four sets of wing lights mounted on the stage sides. The 'switchboard' was located in the basement with the operator (just visible in the photograph) standing in the 'prompters' box.

One of the earliest forms of dimming appears to have been based around the conductivity of liquid. Basically two electrodes were inserted into liquid as the distance between these electrodes increased so the water's 'electrical resistance' increased and less current flowed. The electrodes were controlled by steel wire rope type wires being activated by a set of control levers. The system was relatively cheap but was messy as the liquid pots had to be constantly topped up and were physically very large. One of the most significant early developments in entertainment lighting control in the USA was the General Electric 1933 system for Radio City Music Hall. This was of equal stature, based on being an all electric system rather than the electromechanical systems prevalent in Europe at the time. This control system was really the first control system that allowed the operator to sit close to the action and see what the audience were viewing.

In Europe during this period, probably the most significant control system development was being undertaken by Fred Bentham of the Strand Electric and Engineering Co. Ltd. This was to become the now famous Light Console that looked like, and whose operating philosophy was based on, a Wurlitzer organ. The Light Console was connected to a series of clutch operated dimmers similar to those shown in *Fig 5*. The clutch was invented by Moss Mitchell in 1929 and was to become the basis of most of the UK manufactured dimming systems for decades to come.

Prior to the launch of the Light

Fig 2: General Electric Radio City Music Hall Thyratron System from 1933 photo: General Electric Company, Inc.

Fig 3: Grand Master switchboard circa 1946
photo: The Strand Archive

Console in 1935 the stage dimming solution had been the Grand Master switchboard. These were physically very large and were almost always located in a perch position on stage with the usual poor sightline problems. In this period the better equipped theatres usually had 60 to 80 channels with Fred Bentham confirming in his book *The Art of Stage Lighting* in 1968 that "I have never held Grand Master controls in anything but contempt as a contribution to lighting and, in consequence, as I became active in this field, set about providing an alternative". This resulted in the now famous Light Console although the Second World War really only saw this move into a large number of venues once the war was over. *Fig 3* shows a Grand Master 'switchboard' believed to be at the Royal Court Theatre in Liverpool in the late 1940s. The photograph clearly shows the physical size of the unit helping to explain perhaps why Fred Bentham was less than enthusiastic about these solutions that Strand manufactured for well over two decades.

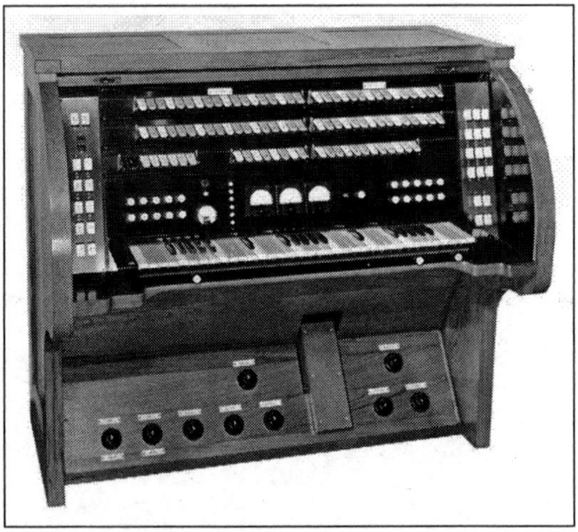

I started my career in stage lighting at school at the age of 15. This was in the 1960s and at that time Strand Electric had very cleverly produced a dimming system that was at a low enough cost that enabled schools to purchase equipment and perhaps have 4, 8 or 12 dimmers controlling

Fig 4: Light Console from 1935
photo: the STLD Archive.

Fig 5: Strand CD Dimming system at BBC Riverside Studios, London 1956 photo: the STLD Archive.

the famous Patt 23, 45 and 123 instruments. This was the Junior 8 dimmer bank with four dimmers and eight outlets controlled by a changeover switch per channel.

Anthony Lord (left) with Nick Mobsby, who were responsible for the lighting

Fig 6: Author First Press Photo 1968
photo: Surrey Advertiser.

The Strand Electric catalogue of the time stated: "To ensure that every stage, however restricted the funds available, should have a switchboard capable of carrying out basic lighting cues, Strand Electric introduced in 1950 the Junior HA switchboard which has sold in thousands and which is still listed. However, Strand now offers an entirely new solution, the Junior 8. This is an extraordinarily compact, lightweight control which can without alteration be used fixed or as a portable. Both the HA and the Junior 8 ensure that dimmers are not wasted for channels that are full-on or off. Thus eight channels can be controlled from four dimmers which, as the dimmer is the most expensive component, effects a real economy. In the case of the Junior 8 the circuitry allows all eight channels to be switched to the dimmers for simultaneous fade-out or fade-in. Furthermore, all board channels terminate in socket outlets which allow lighting circuits to be "patched" in any order and permit circuit substitution at the control".

Fig 6 was the author's first 'press call' when lighting a school production of the *Caucasian Chalk Circle* in 1968 with Junior 8's! When launched in 1963 these

Fig 7: The Strand Junior 8
– complete with a piece of 2" x 1"
as the master fader circa 1964
photo: The Strand Archive.

DIMMER BOARDS

Motor Operated

Kliegboards using motor-driven autotransformer dimmers have proved highly satisfactory for architectural lighting control in churches, auditoriums, restaurants, night clubs, homes and similar applications. These rugged units are almost completely foolproof and easy to operate. The control console, containing miniature finger tip controls, can always be placed in the most convenient location while the motor-operated dimmer bank can be remotely situated.

There are two methods used for remote control of Kliegl Motor Operated Autotransformer Dimmer Boards:

1. POTENTIOMETER CONTROL
Each motor is controlled by a sensitive low-voltage potentiometer. This form of control permits pre-selection of desired intensity, pre-setting, proportional mastering, etc.

2. UP/DOWN CONTROL
Each motor is controlled by an up/down toggle switch instead of potentiometer control as detailed above.

Motor-operated autotransformer dimmers can be easily incorporated with other types of boards. They may be combined with SAF-PATCH or ROTOLECTOR cross-connect systems to increase their flexibility and use. In addition to controlling incandescent lights, motor-operated autotransformer dimmers can be used to control cold cathode lamps and hot cathode rapid-start fluorescent lamps when used with the proper ballasts.

OUTSTANDING FEATURES

- U/L Approved—
- Built to individual requirements—
- Furnished with necessary fusing, main and transfer switches, etc.—
- Available in 2, 2.5, 6, 6.6 and 8 KW capacities—
- Speed ranges from 6 to 45 seconds as selected—

- Full loading range from fractional watts to rated capacity—
- No warm-up time required—
- Can be operated remotely—
- Potentiometer type control amenable to scene presetting—
- Safe, economical, efficient—
- Cool, quiet operation

Fig 8: Kliegl Motorised Auto-transformer Dimmer Catalogue 1961
photo: McGraw Collection USA.

had a list price of £45 for an 8-way 4-slider portable dimmer system. Many of these systems continued until the concern over asbestos forced their removal.

In the USA Kliegl were still marketing motorised auto-transformers in the middle of the 1960s at the same time as they had launched their silicon controlled rectifier (SCR) electronic dimmers. It appears that many users still preferred the reliability and stability of the electromechanical solutions to the new electronic versions. In Europe the same also appears to have been true

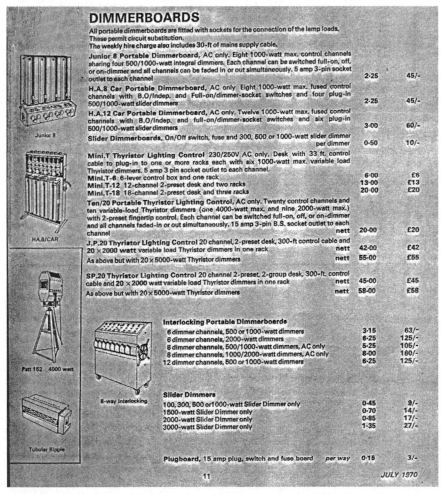

DIMMERBOARDS

All portable dimmerboards are fitted with sockets for the connection of the lamp loads. These permit circuit substitution.
The weekly hire charge also includes 30-ft of mains supply cable.

Junior 8 Portable Dimmerboard, AC only. Eight 1000-watt max. control channels sharing four 500/1000-watt integral dimmers. Each channel can be switched full-on, off, or on-dimmer and all channels can be faded in or out simultaneously. 5 amp 3-pin socket outlet to each channel	2-25	45/-
H.A.8 Car Portable Dimmerboard, AC only. Eight 1000-watt max. fused control channels with B.O/Indep. and Full-on/dimmer-socket switches and four plug-in 500/1000-watt slider dimmers	2-25	45/-
H.A.12 Car Portable Dimmerboard, AC only. Twelve 1000-watt max. fused control channels with B.O/Indep. and full-on/dimmer-socket switches and six plug-in 500/1000-watt slider dimmers	3-00	60/-
Slider Dimmerboards. On/Off switch, fuse and 300, 500 or 1000-watt slider dimmer per dimmer	0-50	10/-
Mini.T Thyristor Lighting Control 230/250V AC only. Desk with 33 ft. control cable to plug-in to one or more racks each with six 1000-watt max. variable load Thyristor dimmers. 5 amp 3 pin socket outlet to each channel.		
Mini.T-6 6-lever control box and one rack	6-00	£6
Mini.T-12 12-channel 2-preset desk and two racks	13-00	£13
Mini.T-18 18-channel 2-preset desk and three racks	20-00	£20
Ten/20 Portable Thyristor Lighting Control, AC only. Twenty control channels and ten variable-load Thyristor dimmers (one 4000-watt max. and nine 2000-watt max.) with 2-preset fingertip control. Each channel can be switched full-on, off, or on-dimmer and all channels faded-in or out simultaneously. 15 amp 3-pin B.S. socket outlet to each channel nett	20-00	£20
J.P.20 Thyristor Lighting Control 20 channel, 2-preset desk, 300-ft control cable and 20 x 2000 watt variable load Thyristor dimmers in one rack nett	42-00	£42
As above but with 20 x 5000-watt Thyristor dimmers nett	55-00	£55
SP.20 Thyristor Lighting Control 20 channel 2-preset, 2-group desk, 300-ft. control cable and 20 x 2000 watt variable load Thyristor dimmers in one rack nett	45-00	£45
As above but with 20 x 5000-watt Thyristor dimmers nett	58-00	£58

Interlocking Portable Dimmerboards		
6 dimmer channels, 500 or 1000-watt dimmers	3-15	63/-
6 dimmer channels, 2000-watt dimmers	6-25	125/-
8 dimmer channels, 500/1000-watt dimmers, AC only	5-25	105/-
8 dimmer channels, 1000/2000-watt dimmers, AC only	8-00	160/-
12 dimmer channels, 500 or 1000-watt dimmers	6-25	125/-

Slider Dimmers		
100, 300, 500 or 1000-watt Slider Dimmer only	0-45	9/-
1500-watt Slider Dimmer only	0-70	14/-
2000-watt Slider Dimmer only	0-85	17/-
3000-watt Slider Dimmer only	1-35	27/-

Plugboard, 15 amp plug, switch and fuse board	per way	0-15	3/-

11

JULY 1970

Fig 9: UK Rental List and Weekly Hire Charges from July 1970, data: Terry Abbs.

as Siemens and AEG were continuing to manufacture two-valve thyratrons or magnetic amplifier dimmers right through to the mid 1970s.

Whilst researching information for this book I came across a hire catalogue from a UK rental company dated July 1970. This shows the weekly hire charges in decimal as well as the older pounds, shillings and pence. The list of items and prices is shown in *Fig 9*. What is noticeable is that portable rental equipment of this time was mainly electromechanical, with the first generation of thyristor dimmers just beginning to appear.

The first generation of dimmers took us from gas until the mid to end of the 1960s. During the later period we saw the beginnings of more complex music shows, the need to flash and chase lights as well as control lighting for professional theatre and television productions. The 1960s saw major revolutions in electronic components enabling completely new types of dimmer to be designed and manufactured. These could be portable, were smaller and allowed more dimmers to be installed in venues as the control systems to drive the dimmers also changed dramatically.

2.3 History of Electronic Dimming

Concentrating on dimmers featuring thyristors takes us to the 1960's. The thyristor or silicon controlled rectifier revolutionised theatrical and entertainment venue dimming. The physical size of the device enabled smaller cabinets to be manufactured, moving the whole world of dimming into a new arena.

Once the physical size had been curtailed, the designer was able to produce a wide variety of dimming solutions. Strangely, these formats remain almost the same today and are often based on the size of the electrical supply or whether a single or 3 phase supply was in use.

The late 1960s and early 1970s were probably the period where the different formats started to be developed. It was also the breeding ground for many companies who still manufacture dimmers to suit the different market sectors today. Sadly, it also saw the demise of other leading manufacturers.

One of the most interesting reports I unearthed was a sales promotion brochure produced by Kliegl Bros of the USA, documenting how they completed an installation in 1968 that converted, in record time, from 1926 resistance dimmers to SCR – silicon controlled rectifier based 'electronic' dimmers. What is equally interesting is what the new control and dimming solution did in 1968 what has now become common place. That is to say that the space

Fig 10: Original Resistance Dimmer Board designed for borders, foot and houselights, photo: Kliegl Bros.

Fig 11: Additional portable road-boards and operators were needed to light any show creating cueing problems photo: Kliegl Bros.

Fig 12: The new master 100 channel light console controlling remote 10 scene preset consoles mounted adjacent to this master control photo: Kliegl Bros.

Fig 13: Kliegl dimmer rack with front door open showing 7kW rated module, photo: Kliegl Bros.

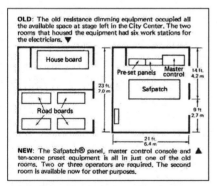

OLD: The old resistance dimming equipment occupied all the available space at stage left in the City Center. The two rooms that housed the equipment had six work stations for the electricians. ▼

House board

Pre-set panels | Master control | 14 ft. 4.2 m

Safpatch

Road boards

23 ft. 7.0 m

9 ft. 2.7 m

21 ft. 6.4 m

NEW: The Safpatch® panel, master control console and ▲ ten-scene preset equipment is all in just one of the old rooms. Two or three operators are required. The second room is available now for other purposes.

Fig 14: Layout drawing showing space occupied by old and new installation complete with patch bay photo: Kliegl Bros.

required with the original installation was reduced by 50% with the new solution, whilst also reducing the manpower required. Figs 10 to 14 provide a historic record of before and after the installation.

Interestingly, whilst this was going on in New York we saw the beginnings of the strive towards bigger is better! 1968 was the year when a number of the independent companies started to be acquired by multi-nationals. The Strand Electric Company was purchased by the Rank

Organisation. One year later Century Lighting became Strand Century and a further part of the Rank Organisation.

Arguably the most successful installation dimmer in Europe at this time was the Strand JTM cabinet introduced in 1965. This was based around a thyristor module housed on a paxolin back plate complete with a drive card and choke assembly that was then bolted to the rear of the cabinet. The modules used germanium transistors and were prone to drift out of trim resulting in a fairly regular maintenance requirement to set the upper and lower trim potentiometers. They utilised a Reyrolle Lloyds register marine fuse mounted on the front panel. The dimmers were in modules of 20 channels matching to the then JP control desks. Typical channel sizes during this period were 60, 80, 100 and sometimes 120 channels. Later on, Strand revamped this range, re-coloured the outer case work from silver to green, changed to silicon transistors and called the updated cabinet STM. This extended the service life well into the next decade, making this range Strand's most successful dimmer of all time.

In 1977 Strand took the dimmer module from the STM range and re-packaged this into a portable pack called Mini 2. Its familiar green case with 5 and 15 Amp round pin sockets on the front of the product

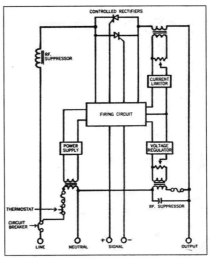

Fig 15: Circuit diagram of R66 dimmer, drawing: Kliegl Bros.

Fig 16: Strand STM Dimmer Cabinet, photo: Strand Lighting Ltd.

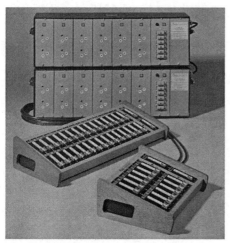

Fig 17: Strand Mini 2 Plus portable
dimmers circa 1975
photo: Strand Lighting Ltd.

brought dimming to the smaller venue, allowed touring systems to be created and a new world was born. At one stage Strand had tried touring versions of the JTM racks for the Olivier Theatre at the Royal National Theatre in the UK. *Fig 17* shows the later derivative of Mini 2 called Mini 2 Plus that once again extended the service life of a well designed product. The JTM, STM and Mini 2 and Mini + dimmers all operated on a unique Strand −ve 10 volt control input that forced users to work within the Strand control domain.

During this period other manufacturers were looking at providing product to meet the growing market not only in theatre but television, night clubs and discos, colleges, schools and for the relatively new rental and touring market. The Mini 2 set the standard for the new '6 pack' market where products were added during the 1970s and 1980s from the likes of Anytronics, Colortran, Leprecon, Multiform, Pulsar and Zero 88.

Fig 18: Green Ginger Micropack 2.5 circa 1985, photo: the author

In the early 1980s a couple of young engineers from Hull University in the UK launched a new company called Green Ginger Ltd. Eventually based in Milton Keynes, Buckinghamshire Green Ginger broke away from the format of 6 channels and designed a product more suited to the limited power supplies available in schools called Micropack – see *Fig 18*. This was available in 4 channels of 1kW with 5 Amp sockets or 4 channels of 2.5kW with 15 Amp sockets. The product was small, lightweight, used BS1362 easily replaceable cartridge fuses and sold at a price level that took the market by storm. The 2.5kW packs were bought in large numbers by rental companies and became the standard for touring productions. The pack was based around use of triacs for power control and was one of the earliest to go down this route. With only one power device per channel, a relatively small choke and heatsink, this contributed to a reduction in package size. What also helped the sales figures was the launch of a Green Ginger three preset three group manual control desk – Microset 20 – that was of an equally small size. This again received wide acclaim and usage in the rental and touring markets.

During 1973 the author was working, as part of his university industrial training, with Alan Payne at his company called Stafford King Controls. Alan was the designer of the Strand DDM control system and allowed the author considerable leeway to develop products. One of these is shown in *Fig 19*. This was a 6 channel pack called 'Minipack', which was based on triac power controls. Fortunately, this was never placed on the market! However some of my other designs did appear, such as the fluorescent dimmable under-floor lighting

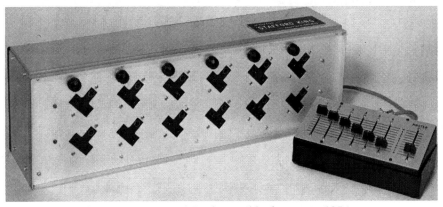

Fig 19: The author's attempt at a 6 Pack portable dimmer in 1974
photo: the author.

system for the musical *Jesus Christ Superstar*. The show was lit by Jules Fisher and ran for many years at the Palace Theatre in London's West End.

The dimming system was actually based around a DC (direct current) dimmer with a 2N3055 power transistor as the current drive controller for the fluorescent tubes. To keep these tubes struck, a high voltage at low current was always present across the tubes. Heaters were used at each end of the tube to maintain the arc. Each floor box was equipped with four blue, four red and four white tubes. In one famous scene where the 69 lashes are applied each of the floor boxes could be illuminated separately or as a group. Incidentally, for the entire run of the show (1972 to 1980) the conventional lighting was controlled on a Strand CD system as shown in *Figs 4 and 5*, with all of the effects operated on a couple of Green Ginger Microset 20 control desks driving their Micropack dimmers.

Whilst the portable pack market was developing, the cabinet dimmer market was expanding with the requirement to try and include more dimmers in one cabinet. The TV and opera/professional

Fig 20: Dimmable Under Floor Lighting at
Jesus Christ Superstar 1972
photo: MCA Records Inc.

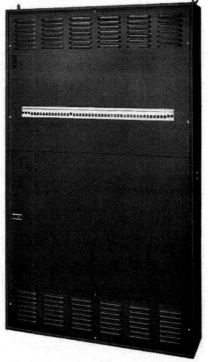

Fig 21: Strand PIP Dimmer 1975
photo: Strand Lighting Ltd.

theatre world was looking for plug-in or modular dimmers making dimmer replacement as easy as plugging in a new module. One should remember that during this period the electrical protection devices, the thyristor technology and the electronics were not as reliable as they are today and maintenance was a very important issue. Most of these early dimmers were fitted with germanium transistors, and these were particularly sensitive to temperature change and often resulted in the upper and lower trim levels drifting. Sometimes, with the dimmer turned off, you could see some lamps 'bleeding through' at a glow in a rig when this happened. Some fires were caused when lamps were left 'turned off' close to curtains, only to heat up and burn the material. Alternatively, as the dimmer was faded up to full it would sometimes switch off due to the control circuit inverting and turning off the thyristors.

One of the most successful products of the 70s in this field was the Thorn modular dimmer, usually sold with the Thorn control systems such as the Q File. Like Strand, the rack was designed to accept up to 20 modules, and was typically fed from a single phase electrical supply. The Thorn systems operated initially on a +ve 5 volt dc control input with later versions operating on what was eventually to become the analogue control standard of + 10 volts dc. Some of these dimmer racks are still in service in 2006 in theatre and TV installations. In fact only a few months ago I was part of a team installing a new Strand 300 Series console with DMX output that was connected, via demultiplexers to well over 100 channels of Thorn modular dimmers that had been installed in 1980, some 25 years previously, and still performing very well!

Thorn had a long period of success, eventually ending when their control desks fell out of popular usage. The Thorn Q file had also been successful in the USA where they had been marketed through Kliegl Brothers – see my forthcoming companion book *Practical Control*. At this point one of their service agents, DEW, took over the manufacturing of the range, making some improvements that allowed the dimmers to continue being sold through to the early 1990s. DEW is continuing to support and maintain these dimmers to the present day. Whilst Thorn was being successful, Strand tried a number of different modular dimming solutions including the MCM and PIP systems. Neither of these proved to be very successful in the theatrical world but were sold in reasonable numbers to new colour television studios that were being built around the 220/240 volt world. My last viewing of an MCM system was in the UK in 2002 just prior to being part of a team that replaced them with some new sine wave dimmers. I understand that a few of these MCM dimmers

Fig 22: Thorn Modular Dimmer 'grey' cabinet, circa 1977, photo: the author.

are still operating in the UK with a further system in Dubai in the UAE.

In parallel to advances in theatrical and portable dimming the television dimmers had gone through a similar evolutionary process. By this time the resistance dimmers used in the early monochrome studios were making way for the advent of colour systems with a greater degree of control. By the 1970s the professional studios were using modular dimmers usually rated at 5kW or 10kW due to the relative lack of sensitivity of the camera with the Thorn dimmer shown in *Fig 22* containing 20 x 5kW or 10 x 10kW dimmers. These were also different in that the dimming curve was specially matched to the camera performance. This ensured that the majority of control was between 50 and 100% where the colour temperature of the lamp was within the working range of the camera.

During the course of the 1970s, and more so in the 1980s, as control system costs started to fall, usage of electronic technology allowed the number of control channels to increase. This matched the expansion of lighting design where the number of luminaires (fixtures) and the types of luminaires available increased, resulting in more venue or touring dimmers being required. However, dimmers at this stage were still relatively expensive and system designers were forced to find ways of increasing lighting system flexibility.

This often forced the use of 'patch panels'. These are units where the number of outgoing circuits is higher than the number of incoming dimmer circuits. They allow the user to 'patch' any outgoing circuit to any dimmer. In some systems more than one patch cord could be patched to a dimmer. This allowed considerable flexibility as luminaires could be patched together before being connected to a dimmer. In the USA and in parts of Europe patch panels were very common during this period. As the cost of dimmers started to fall we saw their usage drop away as a point was reached when custom made patch panels became more expensive than adding additional dimmers. Patch panels are still used in smaller systems where low cost units can be manufactured.

One of the problems with patch bays was trying to maintain phase segregation within the UK electrical regulations, problems that do not seem to have existed in parts of Europe and the USA. This often required different patch panels to be provided for each phase to restrict the cords being cross phase patched. *Fig 24* shows a typical UK installation of three separate phase patch panels where phase coloured patch cords immediately identified any cross phase patching. During this period ERMA (Swiss) patch cords were being widely used. These had a major advantage in that they could be stacked on top of

Fig 23: The author with patching system at Sola Kulturhus in Norway 1988 photo: John Offord.

Fig 24: 3 Phase Patching System at Connaught Theatre Worthing 1985 photo: the author.

one another helping to limit the overall physical size of the patch panel. The disadvantage here was there was no electrical limit to the stacking and so dimmers could become overloaded – always assuming that the cords did not fall out of the patch socket!

The early 1980s saw increases in bands touring across the world with particular growth in the USA in this sector. Transistors had produced a similar affect on sound amplifiers and audio mixers allowing significantly improved touring sound systems to be produced. This period also saw large volumes of American artists touring shows into Europe. This resulted in many UK rental companies adding US manufactured controls such as the Kliegl Performer into their stock.

Companies such as Lighting Methods (LMI) from the USA were leaders in producing reliable and moveable touring dimmers but these were still large in comparison to the Avolites dimmer racks that were prevalent in Europe at this time. It should not be forgotten that with a USA supply voltage of 110 volts a 2.5kW dimmer has to be able to dim a load of around 22 Amps – equal to the load capacity of a 5kW dimmer in 230 volt countries. Hence the electrical load being handled, the size of the feeder supply cables and the amount of heat dissipated all require a 'bigger box'. The launch of the Par Can started a new development in touring systems and resulted in new methods for cabling systems back to dimmer racks. Multiway connectors and multicore cables allowed developments of items such as the 6 lamp bar, meat

Fig 25: Avolites Art 2000 Touring Dimmer and Celco Fusion Touring Dimmer photos: Avolites Ltd. and Celco Ltd.

racks, etc. whilst requiring manufacturers to re-address their designs to cope with the new formats. This led to a whole series of new formats introduced by Aldeham, Avolites, Colortran, Green Ginger with their Microrack, Lumo, LMI, Pulsar, Strand and White Light to name a few producing different solutions. Probably Avolites and LMI were the two major contributors to moving the concept forward. More details of flight-cased dimmers are provided later in this chapter. *Fig 25* shows some touring racks from Avolites and Celco from the 1990s.

The market growth produced two major developments in terms of packaging during the 1980s into the 1990s. Firstly, the very earliest digital technology started to emerge, multiplexed control formats were developed in different formats by many manufacturers and the low cost portable packs began to emerge and eventually flooded the bottom end of the market. The second major issue was the universal adoption of one digital control protocol called DMX in 1990. This allowed users to interconnect different pieces of equipment from different manufacturers onto one data network.

During the 1980s, primarily due to the touring world, manufacturers spent some time developing ways of sending the ever increasing number of control channels down smaller cables from the console to the dimmers. ADB, AVAB, Compulite, Colortran, ETC, Kliegl, Strand and others had their own unique systems that required demultiplexing boxes to convert from the data protocol to the analogue dimmer inputs. Only when the USITT had taken matters to task and produced the first version of the universal DMX standard, in the early 1990s, was everyone able to buy a console from one source and a dimmer from another. DMX dramatically opened the market potential and allowed specifiers to pick and choose their solutions. This was the really the birth of the early 'system integrators' with companies such as Production Arts in the USA, Eurolight and White Light in the UK all beginning to mix and match products to give their clients the best rental or fixed installation solution.

The domination of the larger manufacturers started to erode at this point with customers beginning to buy products that were more suited to their needs. This allowed a number of distribution companies to start up across the world, feeding products to the ever hungry rental and end-user markets. And it led to companies such as Production Arts and Barbizon Lighting in the USA and AC Lighting, Stage Electrics and Lighting Technology in the UK offering one-stop shopping for the entertainment lighting industry.

Looking at the portable packs we saw the first DMX controlled packs become available via companies such as ADB, Green Ginger, Colortran, Electronics

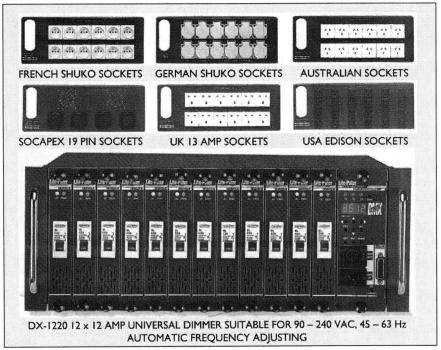

FRENCH SHUKO SOCKETS   GERMAN SHUKO SOCKETS   AUSTRALIAN SOCKETS

SOCAPEX 19 PIN SOCKETS   UK 13 AMP SOCKETS   USA EDISON SOCKETS

DX-1220 12 x 12 AMP UNIVERSAL DIMMER SUITABLE FOR 90 – 240 VAC, 45 – 63 Hz
AUTOMATIC FREQUENCY ADJUSTING

Fig 26: Lite Puter DX 1220 12 channel Universal Voltage modular dimmer pack with different output socket variants, photo: Lite Puter Enterprise Co., Ltd.

Diversified, Pulsar and Zero 88. Most of these products were produced in the USA or the UK due to the large number of venues present in these countries creating a large market demand.

Portable packs developed to suit many different markets. In the USA and the UK many were purchased by schools and colleges who could only afford to buy a small system initially, adding more packs as fund raising allowed. Schools in the UK were initially buying 1kW (5A) rated channels eventually progressing to the now common 10 Amp as it became uneconomic for manufacturers to produce two different types of pack. Europe has suffered badly in the portable pack market because European harmonisation has yet to reach the electrical industry. The standard connector in television has for many years been the BS4343 CEE 17 16 or 32 Amp. This is fine for TV but when you move to theatre or rental applications we see different connectors in Belgium, Germany, France, Switzerland, Spain, Italy and of course the UK. No one will take the risk of standardising as this would kill local country-by-country manufacturing,

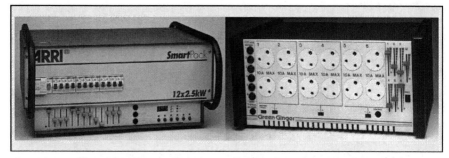

Fig 27: Arri SmartPack circa 1995,   Fig 28: Green Ginger Micropack
photo: Arri GB Ltd.   610DMX circa 1988, photo: the author.

and would result in an almost impossible change in each country of all of the plugs and sockets. So the problem for the manufacturer continues in that they have to produce many different variants economically! *Fig 26* shows what one manufacturer has to do in terms of connector provision to meet the demands of producing a world market product.

Across the world there are many manufacturers producing solutions, and while the pack price can be low one must not forget the allied installation costs and how the outgoing load circuits may safely connect to the packs. Many packs have more than one socket per channel enabling a degree of 'load patching', discussed earlier in this chapter, to take place. Inevitably this can result in a tangled mess of cables, unless some means of managing the cabling can be introduced. In the UK a typical solution is to use a cord patch unit, with cords that connect directly to the sockets on the dimmers such as the pack shown in *Fig 28*. Here the installed cables from the lighting bars or socket boxes are wired through electrical containment of cable tray back to the cord patch where they are interfaced with hanging patch cords that are numbered corresponding to the socket outlet. The cords hang within an organised 'comb', allowing the user to pick a cord and patch this into the dimmer outlet. Where luminaires need to be paired this is achieved if the pack has more than one socket per channel or if safe adapters can be used.

Packs are in common usage in smaller capacity systems prevalent in schools, colleges, amateur theatres, exhibition centres or generally where low cost or flexibility is required. Rental companies are heavy users as packs can be hired out to end-users for that once-a-year production at low cost. Care must be taken in picking packs as there are many different versions, explained in more detail in Chapter 6. Historically, the early Strand Mini 2 format still prevails today, albeit with a digital input for DMX and a few more user friendly controls such as a local fader per channel, preheat to warm up lamps, prolonging lamp life or channel test. Current 2006 list prices for these packs remain at around the £500 to £600 ($900 to $1100) per 6 pack with more sophisticated and higher specification versions reaching £1200 to £1900 ($2100 to $3400) for 12 channel variants suitable for rack mounting or free standing applications.

Once again the format, introduced by Strand in 1965, of an installed dimmer has also made a comeback – that is the wall or free standing cabinet containing hard wired dimmers that link directly to the installed cabling infra-structure. They have made a comeback as electrical safety issues have come more to the fore in buildings such as schools and theatres where inexperienced personnel want to use equipment but may not be suitably qualified. These cabinets are manufactured across the world as the safety issues are global ones.

The 1980s and 90s saw European companies such as ADB with Eurorack, ARRI with their SmartRack, ETC with Unison, Green Ginger with their

Wallrack, Pulsar with their Datarak, Strand with initially Permus and later with LD90, all produce 24 channel cabinets, and initially these were all analogue devices with external demultiplexers. The 1990s saw DMX inputs being added and the analogue formats of control being replaced with fully digital dimmers providing significant user benefits. These included the ability to store back-up memories locally, different voltage outputs for connecting 120 or 230 volt lamps, different dimmer laws to match lamp characteristics, soft patching to cope with different phasing requirements and generally items belonging to dimmers being programmed at the dimmer rather than the control desk.

Fig 30: Colortran i48 Dimmer Rack circa 1995, photo: Colortran Inc.

Digital technology allowed the cabinets to get physically smaller with a typical cabinet now being 1000mm high x 500mm wide x 200mm deep.

In 2006 a standard 24 channel theatre grade cabinet with 2.5kW or 3kW rated dimmers has a list price of around £3500 ($6200). ETC have taken this one step further and offer a Unison cabinet which is able to accept a variety of plug-in modules providing different dimmer ratings, switchable non-dim contactors and an intelligent processor able to control general architectural lighting by means of push button control stations shown in Chapter 5. ADB and Strand offer similar facilities on their Eurorack and LD90 cabinets. This enables these types of dimmers to be sold into many different dimming applications with everyone benefiting from significant cost reductions as the volumes have risen.

As electrical safety has become such a critical issue other companies have tried to reduce costs even further with ADB, Anytronics and Strand producing lower specification installed cabinets that bring better safety into the lower end of the dimming market for schools, colleges and the smaller venue. The Anytronics Contractor rack delivers 24 channels of triac dimming at a UK list price of around £1700 ($3000), well below the £100 ($180) per channel of a portable pack. This accepts DMX signals directly, has the option of RCD protection, discussed

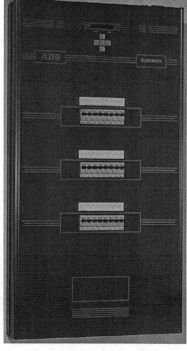

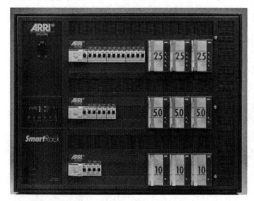

Fig 30: Arri SmartRack circa 1995, photo Arri GB Ltd.

Fig 31: ADB Eurorack circa 1996, photo: ADB-TTV Technologies SA.

Fig 32: Anytronics Contractor Dimmer Cabinet circa 2004, photo: Anytronics Ltd.

in some depth in Chapter 8, and removes all the frills to deliver a neat low cost solution that removes all of the potential cable tangling of a 6 pack solution.

With prices of this type of cabinet at around £70 ($125) per channel, dimming has now become a commodity product enabling almost any venue to be able to afford a reliable dimmer that can be safely installed in an electrical room giving years of trouble free service.

The final area where major changes have been seen is within the high density dimmer racks. These are cabinets where a large number of dimmers can be situated in floor mounting racks allowing up to 108 channels of 3 or 5kW dimming to be housed in a space no bigger than 900mm wide x 750mm deep by up to 2250 mm high.

High density dimmers have now become the standard solution for the medium to large scale venues, enabling large channels numbers to be accommodated in dimmer rooms that previously only housed perhaps 120 or 180 channels of the Strand JTM or STM dimmers. These cabinets are completely digital, contain similar facilities to those described for the new 24 channel racks and have the advantage that they can accommodate a variety of different dimmer and non-dim ratings at a typical price level of around £150 per 3kW dimmer. This is not dissimilar to the price per channel for a 24 channel cabinet. Some of the latest cabinets are able to accept Ethernet directly, allowing them to be connected onto the lighting network without having to convert to DMX. These cabinets also benefit from diagnostic systems that can feed data back to a lighting console or to a stand alone PC. This helps technicians fault find when large numbers of dimmers are in use. High density cabinets are produced by ADB (Eurodim 3), Colortran (ENR), ETC (Sensor), Strand

(SLD and recently EC21) and Transtechnik (FDX90). All of these tend to be produced with different rise times to suit theatre, concert, opera and television applications.

Probably the best known high density dimming system that was responsible for lowering the price whilst delivering high customer facilities was Strand's CD80 and the later digital CD90 range. Produced by Strand America this product saw high volume sales across the States, Far East and other territories. It never reached Europe due to different electrical and other standards requirements. *Fig 34* shows such a cabinet taken from the 1995 Strand USA brochure. CD90 never achieved the phenomenal success of the CD80 range. Indeed Johnson Controls from Canada still offers upgrade processing kits for CD80 to bring them into the digital world.

Finally, the early part of the 21st century has seen a new development in dimmer technology using the power of transistors to actually control the sine wave. These have the significant advantage that they do not disturb the waveform like triac and thyristor based dimmers ensuring a much smoother fade, less lost power and produce an acoustically quiet solution. These dimmers are now being produced in modular format to plug into the cabinets mentioned previously. *Fig 36* and the front cover, shows the very latest high density rack launched in September 2005 from IES in Holland. IES have always been innovators in terms of different dimmer designs, being the first to launch distributed bar mountable packs and here yet again we have a rack that can accept many different types of modules from triac to thyristor to sine wave. In 2003 IES became part of the ETC Group as did another dimmer innovator, Lighting Methods, in 1993. The whole concept

Fig 33: ETC Sensor CE 2005 photo: ETC Europe Ltd.

Fig 34: Strand CD90 High Density economically priced digital dimmer rack photo: Strand Lighting, Inc.

of the latest generation of sine wave dimmer is discussed in much more detail later in the book.

It is interesting to see how in relative terms the cost per dimmer channel has not really changed over the past 30 years once inflationary issues have been considered. If anything, the digital revolution has resulted in better dimmer value for money.

2.4 Further Historic Information

Useful Sources for further historic information are shown below:

The Strand Archive, Exeter University UK
www.strandarchive.co.uk

The STLD Archive UK
www.lightingsolution.org

Kliegl Collection USA
www.klieglbros.com

Johnson Controls Canada
www.johnsoncontrols.com

Theodore Fuchs Collection on Theatre Technology located in the Lee Library at the Brigham Young University in Provo, Utah, USA.

Larry Wild at the Northern State University, Aberdeen, South Dakota, USA, email wildl@northern.edu. Larry maintains a web site with a history of stage lighting.

The Strand Century USA archives are held at The Pennsylvania State University, Stage Lighting Archives, and they can be found on www.theatre.psu.edu. The director of the archive is William Kenyon.

Fig 35: ETC Matrix II High Density Dimmer Cabinet circa 2006 photo: ETC bV.

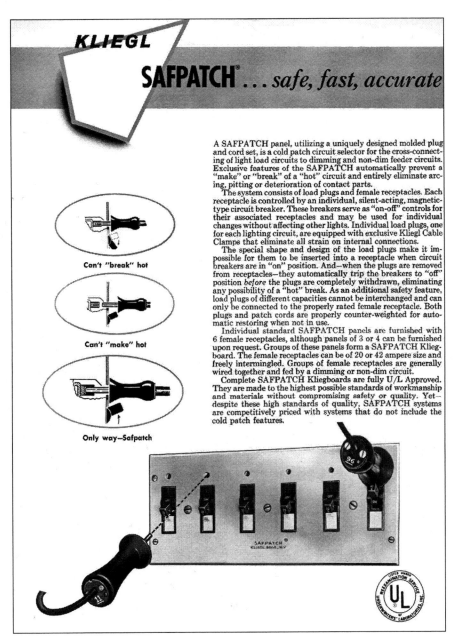

KLIEGL

SAFPATCH ... safe, fast, accurate

A SAFPATCH panel, utilizing a uniquely designed molded plug and cord set, is a cold patch circuit selector for the cross-connecting of light load circuits to dimming and non-dim feeder circuits. Exclusive features of the SAFPATCH automatically prevent a "make" or "break" of a "hot" circuit and entirely eliminate arcing, pitting or deterioration of contact parts.

The system consists of load plugs and female receptacles. Each receptacle is controlled by an individual, silent-acting, magnetic-type circuit breaker. These breakers serve as "on-off" controls for their associated receptacles and may be used for individual changes without affecting other lights. Individual load plugs, one for each lighting circuit, are equipped with exclusive Kliegl Cable Clamps that eliminate all strain on internal connections.

The special shape and design of the load plugs make it impossible for them to be inserted into a receptacle when circuit breakers are in "on" position. And—when the plugs are removed from receptacles—they automatically trip the breakers to "off" position *before* the plugs are completely withdrawn, eliminating any possibility of a "hot" break. As an additional safety feature, load plugs of different capacities cannot be interchanged and can only be connected to the properly rated female receptacle. Both plugs and patch cords are properly counter-weighted for automatic restoring when not in use.

Individual standard SAFPATCH panels are furnished with 6 female receptacles, although panels of 3 or 4 can be furnished upon request. Groups of these panels form a SAFPATCH Kliegboard. The female receptacles can be of 20 or 42 ampere size and freely intermingled. Groups of female receptacles are generally wired together and fed by a dimming or non-dim circuit.

Complete SAFPATCH Kliegboards are fully U/L Approved. They are made to the highest possible standards of workmanship and materials without compromising safety or quality. Yet—despite these high standards of quality, SAFPATCH systems are competitively priced with systems that do not include the cold patch features.

Can't "break" hot

Can't "make" hot

Only way—Safpatch

Fig 36: Kliegl Safpatch System circa 1961-1970, photo: McGraw Collection, USA.

THEATRE DIMMERS

Figs. 533, 536 and 539 show our Round Type Dimmers for either Direct or Alternating Current, for use in churches, town halls, lodge rooms, motion picture theatres, etc. This type can be mounted flat on the wall or switchboard. Each dimmer consists of a circular base of soapstone on which are mounted the successive steps of resistance, the copper contact segments and the terminals. The resistance material is completely covered by a cement composition, rendering the dimmer moisture proof, and fire proof. The soapstone base is encased in (and insulated from) an enameled cast iron cover which, when adjusted over the base plate, covers the whole face of it except the central portion, or part on which the copper contact segments are mounted.

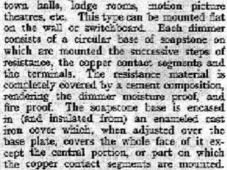

The cover is fastened to the base by four insulated bolts and is provided with lugs through which pass the screws that secure the dimmer plates to the frame in which they are assembled. The contact segments are arranged in a circle, and over them rides a double-ended contact lever carrying a contact shoe at each extremity. All current carrying parts are thoroughly insulated from the framework and operating mechanism and in assembling the plates sufficient allowance is made to permit of easy access to any part of the installation.

ROUND TYPE DIMMERS

FOR 2 WIRE, 110 VOLT CIRCUIT

FOR 2 WIRE, 220 VOLT CIRCUIT

| No. of Metal Ic Filament Lamps | | No. of Carbon Lamps | No. & Size of Plates | Code No. | List Prices | No. of Metal Ic Filament Lamps | | No. of Carbon Lamps | No. & Size of Plates | Code No. | List Price |
60 watts	40 watts	55 watts				80 watts	40 watts	55 watts			
3	7	3	1-6"	532	$2.30	2	4	3	1-6"	530A	$9.30
4	9	4	1-6"	530	8.50	4	9	4	1-10"	1530	12.00
5	8	5	1-9"	531	8.50	5	8	5	1-10"	1531	12.00
9	14	14	1-9"	532	8.30	9	14	10	1-11"	1532	12.00
11	17	12	1-9"	533	8.50	11	17	13	1-11"	1533	12.00
14	21	15	1-11"	534	12.00	14	21	15	1-11"	1534	12.00
18	27	16	1-11"	535	12.00	18	27	16	1-11"	1535	12.00
		17	1-11"	536	12.00			21	1-11"	1536	12.00
23	34		1-14"	537	17.00	43	34		1-20"	1537	17.00
27	41	30	1-16"	538	17.00	37	41	30	1-20"	1538	17.00
30	55	40	1-16"	539	17.00	38	55	40	1-20"	1539	17.00
		50	1-16"	540	17.00			50	2-10"	1540	17.00
46	80	50	2-13"	541	36.00	46	70	60	2-15"	1541	39.00
55	82	80	2-13"	542	36.00	55	82	60	2-15"	1542	39.00
73	110		2-13"	543	36.00	74	110	80	2-15"	1543	39.00
		100	2-13"	544	36.00			100	2-15"	1544	39.00

Fig 37: Kliegl rheostat dimmers from their 1914 catalogue, photo McGraw Collection USA

3

UNDERSTANDING DIMMERS

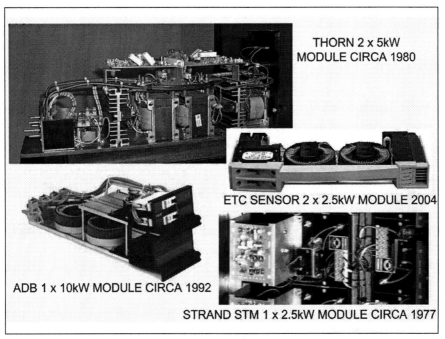

THORN 2 x 5kW
MODULE CIRCA 1980

ETC SENSOR 2 x 2.5kW MODULE 2004

ADB 1 x 10kW MODULE CIRCA 1992

STRAND STM 1 x 2.5kW MODULE CIRCA 1977

Selection of dimmer module from 1970s, 1980s, 1990s and 21st Century
photos ADB Technologies SA., ETC Europe Ltd., the STLD Archive and the author.

Contents:
- **General Dimmer Considerations**
- **Power Control**
- **Interference Suppression**
- **Acoustic Noise**
- **Dimmer Law**
- **Dimmer Ratings**
- **Heat Dissipation**
- **Conclusions**

3.1 General Dimmer Considerations

A dimmer is defined as an electrical device used to control the intensity of a light bulb by the action of a control lever or remote control input. This is achieved by some form of power control device being controlled via an electronic circuit. Dimmers dissipate heat through the action of the power control device and associated filtering circuits. Equally, no dimmer is 100% efficient, so these inefficiencies tend to appear as generated waste heat. Better dimmers show up as being more efficient and typical figures show efficiencies of higher than 98%. It is important here to define what constitutes an entertainment dimmer and might be used in an architectural or residential application.

In the residential world the dimmer has made similar advances to those seen for theatre and television. The original rotary controlled dimmer on the lounge wall has long since been replaced with push button multi-preset wall-box dimmers. These have to be small enough to be mounted directly into a wall, contain the power control and interference reduction circuit, be wired into a switch line and ideally make no noise! One significant advantage that a wall box dimmer has over an entertainment dimmer is that of having to produce the same output, channel by channel. With a unit wall box dimmer inconsistencies are not a problem.

As heat is generated it has to be removed from the dimmer cabinets or racks and dispersed into the dimmer room – otherwise the sensitive electronics within the cabinet, or the power control devices could overheat. Where large numbers of dimmers are housed in one cabinet this often requires forced cooling fans to be fitted in the cabinets. Whilst these remove the unwanted heat they generate another unwanted side effect: acoustic noise. Some smaller dimmer cabinets can disperse heat produced by the action of natural air convection and therefore do not require fans.

The dimmers must be connected to a reasonably large electrical power supply and thus must be considered a higher risk item in terms of any fire or electrical risk assessment when planning a venue. Remember that whilst the number of dimmer channels may be high, not all of these dimmers may be in use at one time. Therefore the size of a supply can be based on anticipated light levels rather than total quantity of dimmers connected to the electrical supply.

Due to the amount of light used in a venue the dimmer capacities per channel can be quite high with 2.5, 3 and 5kW being typical. This results in some types of dimmer being housed in large floor or wall mounted cabinets. With the size of the electrical power distribution system, these make for a relatively large amount of equipment to locate within the venue. This necessitates careful choice of the location as the dimmers will have to be moved to this location, will generate a fair degree of heat, will need a large power source to feed them and some will generate a high degree of acoustic noise.

All thyristor and triac dimmers 'chop up' and distort the AC (alternating current) power waveform, and during this process they create large amounts of electrical interference. Accordingly, these types of dimmer add filtering circuits to reduce these interfering emissions by means of wound inductive components. These can be quite heavy and have an unfortunate characteristic in that they emit an audible dimmer 'buzz'. Accordingly, dimmer locations should take these acoustic emissions into consideration. Good dimmers use acoustic noise damping mountings to reduce transmission from the choke to the module or dimmer casing and from the cabinet to the structure of the building. This may consist of a neoprene type gasket mounted under the choke or the base of the cabinet or between the rear of a cabinet and a wall.

3.2 Power Control Section

It is not my intention to describe in great depth how a dimmer is designed but I do believe it is worthwhile to understand a little of how they work as it will help to clarify points raised within this chapter.

Most modern professional dimmers are based around thyristors as the power control device. These are uni-directional devices requiring two thyristors to control an alternating waveform, one for the positive half cycle and one for the negative. Lower cost dimmers use triac devices which are bi-directional. Therefore only one device is required per dimmer, and these tend to cost less than a thyristor based equivalent dimmer.

These semiconductor devices are highly efficient with very low losses across the device. The loss is defined as the difference in voltage from the input to the output of the dimmer. They are also very good at managing the connected load with, typically, one 3kW dimmer being able to correctly dim loads from around 60 Watts to 3000 Watts without the necessity of adding load lamps.

A modern dimmer is based around a power control section, an interference reduction section, a synchronisation section and an electronic control section. The power control section in a dimmer will usually consist of a pair of thyristors, these being a controllable semiconductor electronic switching device. With the advent of microprocessor technology some dimmers combine a number of these elements to further reduce the overall size of the dimmer.

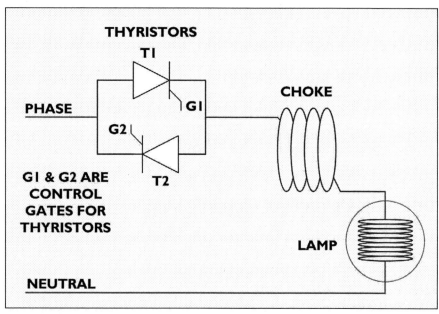

Fig 1: *Typical Thyristor Dimmer Power Control Circuit.*

Fig 1 shows a typical thyristor dimmer circuit. The drawing shows thyristor 1 as T1 and thyristor 2 as T2. The thyristors are controlled by the action of electronically generated hard fired pulses being fed into gates G1 and G2.

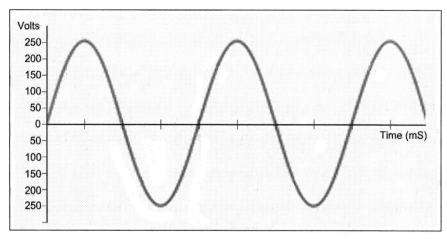

Fig 2: *Supply sinusoidal waveform feeding into the power section of the dimmer.*

Until control pulses are sent into the thyristors they will not conduct and thus there is no current flow – the lamp is off. These pulses are synchronised to the 50 or 60 Hertz mains frequency shown in *Fig 2*. The duration of the pulse governs the on time of the thyristor and thus the total current through the lamp. *Fig 4* shows typical pulses being fed into Gates G1 and G2. *Fig 3* shows

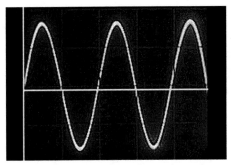

Fig 3: Mains Sine Wave, photo: the author.

an actual trace of such a mains waveform as displayed on an oscilloscope.

The thyristors will therefore switch on for a time period equal to the gate pulses. For example, if we have a control desk set at 50% intensity with a linear performance from the dimmer the output power should be 50%, i.e. approximately half the RMS electrical supply voltage. The thyristors would conduct at the 90° point halfway between the start of the half cycle and the end of the half cycle. The resulting waveform reaching the lamp is shown in *Fig 5*.

As can been seen, the waveform has been chopped from the original

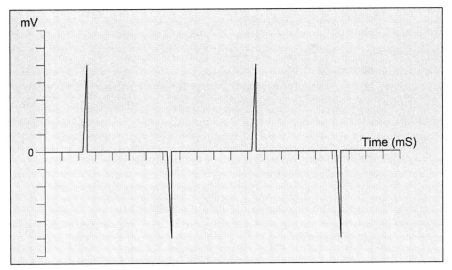

Fig 4: Typical control gate pulses into the Thyristors.

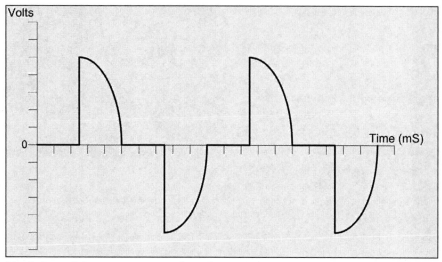

Fig 5: Typical dimmer output waveform that might be seen at the Lamp.

Fig 2 form and it is this chopping action which gives rise to the interference and harmonic distortion. *Fig 5* shows a typical output waveform that might be seen at the lamp.

3.3   Interference Suppression

Whilst the thyristors are being switched on and off they generate a lot of electrical interference, similar to rapidly switching a light switch on and off with a radio nearby. This interference is very harmful in any environment and particularly an entertainment venue as it may upset audio and video systems. Accordingly, all triac and thyristor dimmers add interference reduction circuitry, which is usually a wound inductive choke. The choke reduces the rate of rise of current in the output of the dimmer, reducing the very spiky output waveform to a smoother curve and reducing the interference.

One method employed by some manufacturers and consultants to determine the quality of a dimmer is 'rise time'. This is explained technically as the slowing down of the rise time of the leading edge (switching point) of the dimmer waveform when measured between 10% and 90% conduction angle with the dimmer loaded to its full rated load. In more understandable terms this really means how large is the choke connected between the power control device and the load, and how much slowing down of the rate of current rise is produced. A typical thyristor dimmer can switch on within 2 or 3 microseconds; with the choke is applied this may be slowed to between 50 and 600 microseconds (μS). Generally the longer (higher) the rise time the larger the choke and the lower the generated interference. However, the larger the choke the greater its physical size and the greater the loss in voltage efficiency due to losses created within or across the choke.

In venues that are particularly sensitive to dimmer interference or filament noise, high grade dimmers are specified. If these are based around thyristor power control devices a means is required to test their performance and likely noise generation. The BBC produced a dimmer specification measurement system for such dimmers. This is called the BBC PID Dimmer Specification. This does not define an acceptable rise time but stipulates the amount of interference measured in a simple passive circuit connected across the output of the dimmer with a fully rated load connected - see *Fig 6*. This method was employed because whilst permanently installed cables can be well separated from audio and video cables this procedure fails immediately when loose extension cables are considered and used. Generally, audio systems are more susceptible to noise than video systems and thus other organisations have developed similar techniques of using microphones or measured lengths of cables wrapped around dimmer load lines. The BBC method is explained briefly as it helps to clarify points made in this chapter:

a) r.m.s. measurement techniques are required as any generated noise is proportional to its energy content.

b) The test has to be weighted, as it considers electrical interference that becomes audible and therefore requires weighting due to the human ear response.

To use the test circuit true r.m.s. measuring meters are required and these are readily available from many manufacturers. The circuit is designed to give a similar response to the human ear and thus additional weighting is not required. The test circuit must be encased in a proper metal enclosure to ensure that no stray electromagnetic fields can affect the measurements. The electrical supply should be as low impedance as possible as high impedance supplies will affect the test results.

The correct test procedure is to connect the dimmer to the electrical supply; connect a fully rated load as shown. The dimmer should then be faded from 0 to 10 in steps of 1 on the control system and the millivolt meter readings recorded. Typically the greatest noise generation will occur at a 90^0 firing angle.

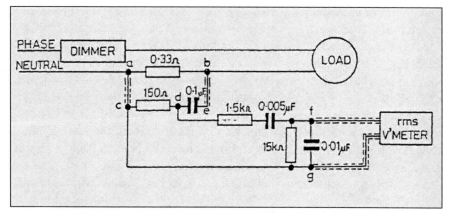

Fig 6: BBC PID /171 Draft Edition 6, March 1992 Dimmer Noise Measuring Circuit.

To meet the BBC requirements the true r.m.s. readings must not exceed 15 millivolts r.m.s. for 3kW or 5kW dimmers and must not exceed 30 millivolts for larger 6kW and 10kW dimmers. My experience is that these 15 mV levels can be exceeded for theatre and other performance venues without a problem, always assuming that a high quality audio system has been correctly installed.

As a guide, when dimmer load cables are being installed good practice recommends they should be installed within their own electrical containment. If this is not possible it is acceptable to run them with general power, house light, working light and general services power. On no account should they be run with audio and video cables - nor should they be run parallel to these even if each system is run in separate containment, due to induction of noise and interference into the audio and video system cabling. If cables must cross, always cross them at 90 degrees but avoid crossing if at all possible.

These tests have shown that dimmers behave in many different ways and some so called 'high rise time dimmers' fail the above tests whilst well-made medium grade dimmers with lower rise times will pass. Experience suggests that wise practice is to look at the manufactured quality of the dimmer, the size of the chokes, construction of the cabinets and the size of the thyristors and heat sinks. Quality dimmers are well engineered and manufactured products adhering to good practice are easily visible to the enquiring individual!

Listed below are typical rise times offered by currently available dimmers and the rise time applications that should be considered for different applications:

50 - 80 microseconds:	Schools, Colleges and Small Theatres and Clubs
200 microseconds:	Theatres, Conference Centres and Hotel Ballrooms
450 microseconds:	Broadcast TV Studios, Large Theatres and Opera Houses
800 microseconds:	Concert Halls and Recording Studios and distributed based dimming solutions

Lower cost dimmers tend to use triacs as the power control device. These types of dimmer tend to offer units with less performance than the equivalent thyristor based solution. They are highly suitable for school, retail, college, small theatre, hotel and general dimming applications but should be avoided in all medium to large scale venues due to their reduced performance and increased interference generation. Perhaps, if manufacturers offered high rise time versions of their triac dimmers they could then be considered for professional venues. Furthermore, these dimmers can often work well with electronic transformers used to power low wattage lighting fixtures, due to their higher electrical losses.

3.4 Acoustic Noise

During the dimming process a complex structure of waveform distortion and harmonics are generated, as explained previously. This includes both high and low frequencies; the low frequencies can set up vibrations within the connected lamp filaments. If these happen to match the natural resonant frequency of the lamp filament an audible buzz or 'lamp sing' may be heard. This effect tends to be most noticeable in luminaires that use lamps with a long filament such as a groundrow or cyclorama flood, or in a sealed beam Parcan. Lamps with more compact light sources such as Fresnels and profiles do not tend to exhibit the problem to the same degree. Again, the audible lamp 'buzz' can be reduced by using a dimmer with a greater degree of interference reduction or a higher rise time.

3.5 Dimmer Law

It is important that a relationship is established between the fader level setting and the output voltage reaching the lamp. This must be consistent dimmer by dimmer and channel by channel to ensure high levels of repeatability. From the lighting designer's point of view, control console fader settings define the dimmer output voltage which defines light levels seen at the luminaire.

One of the dimmer designer's problems is that the human eye only really notices large changes in brightness, and these often need changes in the order of 40 to 50% to register. Equally, the effect of the dimming also depends on the colour, the depth of field the eye can see and the interaction between light sources if multiple spotlights are illuminating the same area. How can a dimmer cope with these requirements and produce a natural change for the eye? The answer lies in the 'dimmer law'. This balances the non linear relationship of the power input to the lamp and light output and the way the eye perceives intensity changes.

Fig 7 shows the relationship between control console settings to light output using a square law commonly used within a theatre dimmer. This is the lighter line on the graph. The darker line shows the current through a tungsten theatre lamp relative to the control console setting.

With a lighting console the fader action needs to be linear for the operator to be able to easily gauge the changes in intensity. The natural electronic circuit behaviour of a thyristor dimmer produces an S characteristic for light output providing there is a linear change in firing angle. To correct this, the dimmer needs to be provided with a conversion programme that artificially changes the control input to light output relationship. With modern digital dimmers this is achieved by providing a 'look up table'. Here, for every control input software is provided to dictate what the output voltage should be. As this is simply a number that is stored, a number of different laws can be calculated and then stored within the dimmer processor and be re-called at will. As this function is now software driven rather than being reliant on electronic components and their tolerances it is possible to make the dimmers highly consistent as well as removing the regular dimmer trim requirements.

For every control signal input from 0 to 100% a table is created that produces a firing angle within the dimmer to produce whatever curve is required. A number of typical curves are in use today. One

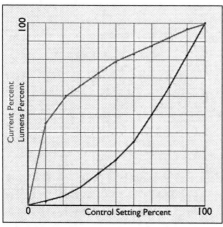

Fig 7: Graph of Control Setting to Light and Current Variations.

is Pre-Heat where the dimmer is requested to produce a small output voltage to increase the speed of response and to slug the effects of thermal shock when the lamp is turned on, this significantly prolonging lamp life. Another is to produce a 120 volt output from a 230 volt input allowing 110/120 volt lamps to be used without series wiring or use of a transformer. For television a special TV law is created that allows most of the control at the top of the curve. A special curve also exists for theatre and other curves provide switching functions to allow non-dim operation where a separate switch on and switch off point are provided. *Fig 8* has been taken from a dimmer sales brochure from 1965 and actually shows the trace on the oscilloscope at different points on the curve and also shows what happens when voltage regulation and current limiting are applied. In the early days of TV and in parts of the world where the supply voltage was often not stable voltage stabilisation was added to dimmers. Basically an element of the output was monitored and used to control the output of the dimmer. Like all things in life, you only can get out what you put in. Therefore if the supply voltage drops the output voltage will drop unless you set a threshold of say 100 or 220 volts where minor voltage swings can be handled.

One other important consideration is that when a lamp is dimmed the colour temperature of the lamp changes. *Fig 9* shows the results of applying a TV dimmer law onto a dimmer connected to a 240 and a 120 volt AC supply. The actual numeric values are taken from the curve and are important because the percentages of light, power and colour temperature are the same on both electrical supply systems. Each volt of a 120 volt system produces a 10 degree Kelvin change in colour temperature, a 240 volt system produces a 5 degree change. This is due to the relationship between degrees of Kelvin and the current.

If the same wattage lamp is used the 120 volt system will require twice the current of a 240 volt system. Colour temperature is highly critical in TV venues but is equally important in theatre as the lower the output voltage the more yellow the lamp becomes and if colour filter is in use this can change completely the projected colour.

Many early electronic dimmers required the minimum and maximum voltages to be set for a fixed dimming curve. This was a laborious process and therefore many dimmers were left to 'drift'. This was often visible to the audience or visiting companies as some of the rig was gently 'bleeding' or sometimes pulsing without any control. Alternatively there was the violent

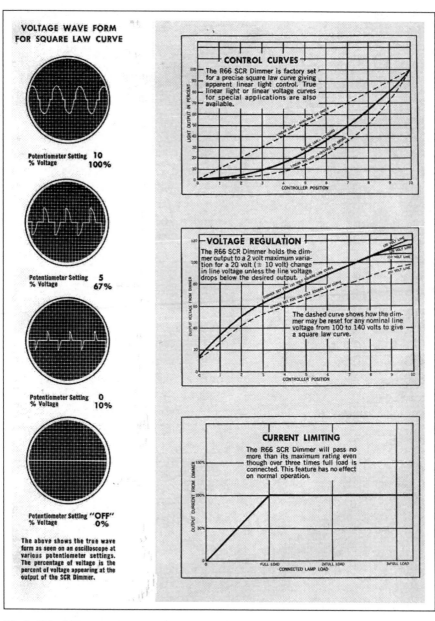

Fig 8: Kliegl Thyristor Dimmer Curve Data from 1965 – note the Off and the 0 control intensity settings, photo McGraw Collection, USA.

FADER SETTING	% LIGHT OUTPUT	COLOUR TEMP (deg K)	% OF COLOUR TEMP	OUTPUT VOLTS @ 240V	OUTPUT VOLTS @ 120V	CURRENT %	POWER %
10	100	3200	100	240	120	100	100
9	81	3120	93	224	112	96	89
8	64	3040	88	211	106	93	82
7	49	2960	81	194	97	88	72
6	36	2860	74	178	89	85	63
5	25	2750	66	158	79	78	52
4	16	2600	59	142	71	73	43
3	9	2400	51	122	61	67	34
2	4	2200	39	94	47	59	23
1	1	-	23	55	27	46	11
0	0	-	0	0	0	0	0

Fig 9: Numeric Values from Square Law Curve.

switching off (inversion of the control signal) of the dimmer when the fader reached 100% - and yet it had been okay at 98%!

Whilst many control consoles now offer a wide variety of dimmer laws I suggest that it is advisable to maintain the defined law within the dimmers for the conventional lighting installation. Laws offering switch functions or specific curves to match luminaire characteristics such as fluorescent can be useful. However an important issue to remember is that the console set laws *will only operate* when the console is powered up. If circuits are being tested locally then the dimmer will behave as locally programmed. This could result in over voltage reaching the connected lamp if, for instance, a 120 volt law had been set from the console. I believe that dimmer laws, DMX address, response speed, upper and lower limits all belong within the dimmer and dimmer programme leaving all the console to handle the 'artistic control'.

3.6 Dimmer Sizes

Historically dimmers were available in capacities to match the different lamp types available. In Europe it was common to find 1kW (5 Amp), 2.5kW (10A), 5kW (25A) and 10kW (50A) types. With some harmonisation of the European electrical standards and connectors the power capacities today tend to be set by the ratings of the connectors used with 600/750/1.2kW, 2.5/3kW, 5/6kW and 10/12kW being typical in theatre, television and film applications. Smaller ratings are still provided for school and architectural applications and more recently to operate directly with the lower wattage cool generation of profile instruments. As explained before, dimmers will operate correctly with loads substantially smaller than their total capacity, so never worry about using a modern 5kW dimmer with a 500W load.

In the USA and 120 volt markets the current flow is always twice that of the 230/240 volt markets. Consequently if we look back to the electro-mechanical period common dimmer ratings these were 2, 2.5, 6, 6.6 and 8kW. When electronic dimmers were launched the current ratings generally became 3, 6 and 12kW. The current trend is for 1.2, 1.8, 2.4, 6, 12 and some 24kW units.

3.7 Heat Dissipation Considerations

The action of the dimmer during the control of the light intensity generates heat. In a way this is no different to what happens if you were to continuously switch on and off a lamp at home. After a little while the switch will get hot and eventually burn out. In a dimmer all of the major components have a degree of resistance (R), and or inductance (L), and or capacitance (C). Each of these L, C and R components introduce small effects on the output waveform. The resistive component creates a voltage loss across the device which has to show up somewhere. In this case the only option to disperse the energy is to produce heat. The exact amount of heat will primarily depend on the type of power control device, the size of the choke and its winding and the size of the internal dimmer cabinet wiring. To assist with this calculation, listed below are typical average dissipations. These are shown in watts of heat dissipated, and they can be converted to kcal/hour by multiplying the watt figures by 0.86 (1 Watt = 0.86 kcal/hour):

Portable triac based dimmer Dissipation rate 2% of connected load

Per 2.5kW dimmer channel this typically equates to 2500 x 0.02 = 50 watts of heat dissipation. In other words the dimmer can be stated as being 98% efficient.

Thyristor Based dimmer Dissipation rate 2.5% of connected load

For a 3kW dimmer channel this equates to a heat dissipation of typically 3000 x 0.025 = 75 watts of heat dissipation. Here the dimmer can be confirmed as being 97.5% efficient.

IGBT or sine wave based dimmer Dissipation rate 3% of connected load.

For a 3kW dimmer channel this equates to a typical heat dissipation of 3000 x 0.03 = 90 Watts. Here the dimmer is only 97% efficient.

If we look at medium and high density modern dimmer cabinets we can see how quickly the heat dissipation can build up. If we consider a dimmer cabinet with 96 x 2.5kW triac dimmers then the total dissipation becomes 96 x 2500 x 0.02 = 4800 Watts or 4.80kWs.

A cabinet with 48 x 5kW thyristor dimmers would dissipate 48 x 5000 x 0.025% = 6000 Watts or 6kW's. In a big venue with hundreds of dimmer channels this can easily build up into considerable quantities of kilowatts and thus any dimmer location will require good ventilation, even air conditioning, to adequately dispose of the generated 'dimmer heat'.

It should be remembered that different countries have different climatic conditions, with most currently manufactured dimmers designed to operate safely in temperatures up to 35 degrees Celsius. If the ambient temperature is 20 or 25 degrees air conditioning is an absolute necessity as the rate of temperature rise in the dimmer cabinets and the dimmer room will quickly exceed this figure. In cooler climates, like the UK, a forced cooling system in a well ventilated dimmer room may be sufficient. Good practice recommends calculation of the heat dissipation during the design phase of any dimmer system and dimmer room design. Local regulations may also affect the heat extraction system. As the dimmers can be considered as a potential electrical fire risk any smoke generated should not be extracted into the general building system. Accordingly, good practise recommends that any extracted air from the dimmer room should be separately vented to the outside world to avoid spreading smoke throughout the building. Dimmer rooms may need to be classified as a 1 hour fire room under some countries' fire regulations. This will require proper fire rated doors to be fitted with self-closers. In some countries automatic fire extinguishing systems may be specified as mandatory.

A point to remember is that any dimming system capacity is not necessarily the total rating of all of the dimmers added together. It may be that the size of the electrical supply does not allow all the dimmers to be used simultaneously. Whatever diversity factor has been applied to the electrical supply can also be applied to the heat dissipation. Diversity and other electrical issues are more fully explained in Chapter 8.

For example, if we consider a venue where 240 x 3kW 230 volt dimmers are to be installed this would require a theoretical electrical supply size of 240 dimmers x 3kW x 4.35 Amps per kilowatt (calculated by Amps =

kilowatt/230 volts) = 3132 Amps single phase or 1044 Amps per phase for a 3 phase supply.

This results in a theoretical dimmer heat dissipation of

240 x 3000 x 0.025 = 18.00kW's or 15.48 kcal/hour.

However, if it is decided during the planning stage that only 70% of the dimmers will ever be required at the same time, an electrical diversity factor (utility factor) of 70% can be applied. The total electrical supply size is then reduced to 3132 x 0.7 = 2192 Amps single phase or 730 Amps three phase. As the total supply is restricted, by the same argument the dimmers can never generate more heat per channel than the total number of dimmers that can be powered at one time by the electrical supply. We can therefore reduce the heat dissipation by the same diversity factor. Accordingly the total heat dissipation would be reduced to 0.7 x 18.00kW = 12.60kW's or 10.836 kcal/hour.

3.8 Ratings of Dimmers

Dimming technology has moved forward rapidly during the past 30 years; what has not really changed in the rating of dimmers used in the performance venue. This is primarily due to the fact that lamp ratings have not really changed in this period. Whilst different gasses now fill the lamp envelope, light sources are more compact but still the 500, 650, 1000, 2000 and 5000 watt lamp are widely used. In the past 10 to 15 years other lamps have emerged that offer improved lumen per watt ratios such as the 1200 watt T class and the 575/600/800 watt lamps for dichroic profiles.

From the outset of electronic dimming ratings of 5 Amp, 10 Amp, 20 Amp and 40 Amp were commonplace, 5 Amp being the rating widely used in schools in the UK as an appropriate 5 Amp 3 pin round plugtop was available. In the UK theatre market an historic 15 Amp connector was adopted as this allowed up to 2kW lamps to be used. In Europe the standard has been the 2 pin with or without earth Shuko, although this has varied country by country. In the USA the Edison, the Grounded Stage Pin and the Twistlock connectors were and still are the standard theatre connector.

The connectors governed the dimmer ratings, so the norms were historically 5 Amp (1kW), 10 Amp (2.5kW) and 20 Amp (5kW), in film and television applications the 40 Amp (10kW) dimmer was also produced. In Europe the 2.5kW and 5kW dimmer were the norm, again based around the connectors. In the USA, where the 110 volt voltage produces twice the current, ratings of 20 Amp and 40 Amp were the norm. In the present day most of these connectors remain and the historic ratings have been slightly amended to take account of some European harmonisation and some standards within the industry. European ratings of connectors for professional applications remain with the 10 Amp Shuko but now include the CEE 17 (BS4343) 16, 32 and 63 Amp connectors with equivalent power ratings of 16, 25 and 45 Amps. The result is each country and each of the performance industries maintain their own standards and therefore the dimmer manufacturers produce dimmers that meet the biggest number of market opportunities. In Europe this means that in 2005 products for performance are 2.5, 3, 5, 6, 10, 12 and 24kW rated.

Fig 10 shows examples of these connectors via front panel views of the Pulsar Rakpack portable 6 channel 10 Amp dimmer that is produced in the UK, but is sold around the world. Europe will ultimately have to harmonise into standard solutions; the electrical protection industry is driving this forward by forcing the issues with circuit breaker ratings.

The CEE 17 (Ceeform/BS4343) range of connectors is receiving an ever greater uptake from all realms of the performance industry whether they are in the installation, touring, TV, film, theatre or rental sectors. Almost all European

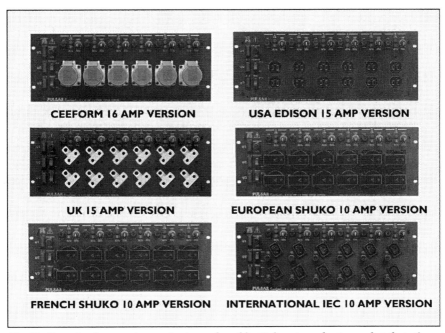

Fig 10: Sample of connector variants produced by Pulsar in order to market their 6 channel Rakpack around the world, photos: Pulsar Ltd.

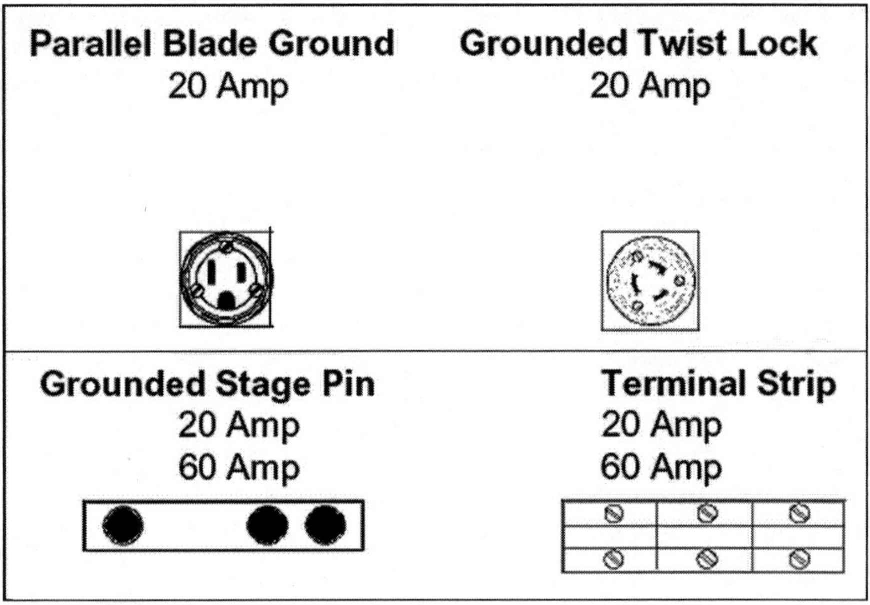

Parallel Blade Ground 20 Amp	Grounded Twist Lock 20 Amp
Grounded Stage Pin 20 Amp 60 Amp	Terminal Strip 20 Amp 60 Amp

Fig 11: Connectors fitted in USA by Electronics Diversified to their Scrimmer II Power Packs, drawing: Electronics Diversified, Inc.

manufacturers now produce 230 volt dimmers with 3kW ratings and a 16 Amp Ceeform outlet. In the USA the connectors are equally numerous although some common versions within Europe are appearing such as the Powercon connector. *Fig 11* shows the connectors Electronics Diversified offer on their Scrimmer II Power Pack.

When designing a dimming system a point will be arrived at where specifying the ratings of the dimmers will become an issue. In small scale lighting projects such as a school stage, college, amateur theatre, studio theatre, hotel ballroom, shopping mall or a small arena almost always 20A (USA) and 2.5 or 3kW dimmers in 230 volt countries would be used. 5 or 6kW dimmers in Europe are usually associated with larger scale buildings or where television companies might want to come into a venue to film something for TV. In the USA the 40A or 10/12kW dimmer is the norm for these applications. Because cameras are not as efficient as the human eye, higher levels of lighting are required when filming a theatre performance. It is sensible to provide some 5kW outlets in Europe and 40A or 12kW in USA around the front of house and stage areas into which TV lights can be connected. Larger venues will also use 5kW rated luminaires to provide adequate stage coverage or colour washes, to connect projection equipment or other special effects. In opera houses a much larger quantity of 5kW dimmers will be used than in a repertory theatre. In an arena used for a wide variety of events, where long throw distances are involved, a greater quantity of 5kW in 230 volt or 40A/12kW in 115 volt dimmers would again be required.

With small to medium sized TV studios with limited headroom, typically less than 3.5 metres, 2.4 to 3kW rated dimmers in 230 volt countries and 1.2 or 2.4kW in 115 volt countries are more than adequate as the largest light source will now usually be no greater than 1.2kW. In studios with a higher grid and of a greater size then using dimmers of 5kW in 230 volt and 10/12kW in 115 volt countries is a sensible solution. In all cases one must consider: does the luminaire stock already exist or are new units going to be purchased? If existing stock is to be re-used, certainly 2 and 5kW instruments will be present and then suitably rated 5kW dimmers are essential. If new stock is being considered then a higher proportion of 1 and 2kW units will be purchased and 3kW dimmers may suffice.

Remember that all the different types of packs, flight cased dimmers, medium density hard wired and modular plug-in dimmers are all available in 230 volt markets in 10A, 3 and 5kW ratings. 10kW ratings are almost never included in modern venue design as the luminaires are highly inefficient and are no longer required for deep saturated colour washes. In the 115 volt countries we see 1.2 and 2.4kW, 20 and 40 Amp and 10 and 12kW.

3.9   Design Considerations for Building a Dimmer Room

As previously stated, dimmers generate a lot of waste heat, generate a degree of acoustic noise, require reasonable amounts of electrical power and need access and space for maintenance. Historically, rooms were dedicated to house dimmers but recent developments of packaging dimmers into smaller cabinets allows them to be housed almost anywhere. However, wherever fixed dimming is installed there are some important considerations.

If designing a venue from scratch the best solution is to allocate a space into which the dimmers and associated electrical switchgear can be accommodated. Try to keep this room away from the stage or the auditorium and also away from any structural walls as these may allow mechanical and acoustic noise to be transmitted into the venue. Remember some dimmer cabinets can be physically large and heavy and thus access to the dimmer room for these items must always be considered, not only at the initial building stage but also when the equipment is replaced some twenty years later on! As a designer it is your responsibility to consider the removal of equipment that you are now specifying to be installed, as part of a 'designers risk assessment'.

One should remember that a large amount of electrical cabling will be required from the dimmer cabinets to deliver the dimmed output to the luminaire socket outlets. If these cables can be restricted in length, smaller diameter cables may be used, with smaller electrical containment and thus a reduced installation cost. This always assumes that the installation is fully compliant with current electrical regulations. This has often resulted in dimmer rooms being located on the upper floors of theatre or in a plant room of a conference centre, close to the lighting grid. In smaller venues with limited height – 3 to 5 metres – there is no such advantage and ground floor level dimmer rooms are acceptable. *Figs 12 and 13* show a relatively small scale installation in Scandinavia where high density dimmer cabinets were used and 3 core type load cables for every circuit.

Fig 12: Cables as they dropped into the dimmer room before termination
photo: Andy Pike.

Fig 13: Completed Dimmer Room with cables terminated into high density dimmer cabinets with power metering and DMX patch rack, photo: Andy Pike.

With all types of room the removal of waste heat is very important. Again, good practice offers the best design guide. As the dimmers contain large amounts of electrical power there is a risk of an electrical fire. When such a fire develops any resulting smoke should be evacuated away from public areas such as the auditorium, the stage, offices and technical areas. Accordingly a separate exhaust from the dimmer room to the outside air is highly recommended. This could consist of a simple 'Vent Axia' type wall or window extractor fan to a full air conditioning system with an external extraction duct. It is also good practice to use fire type doors into dimmer rooms with self closers to ensure adequate fire protection is provided. Consideration should also be given to fire extinguishing systems and adherence to local fire officer regulations. Before embarking on designing a dimmer room I strongly recommend that the local fire officer or civil defence department are contacted and these issues discussed as different regulations exist in almost every country. In some countries even regional variations have been witnessed.

In rooms containing large amounts of dimmers automatic gas type extinguishing systems may be allowed and can offer excellent levels of fire protection. These protection systems can be dangerous to personnel so adequate safety precautions must be adhered to. If such systems are required then it is wise to contact specialists in this field as they will have provided similar solutions within other venues. Remember, in all dimmer rooms, small or large, fire is a serious issue which should always be addressed, considered and the appropriate levels of protection provided. Once again my experience teaches me that country by country the requirements and regulations are so widely different so always contact the local fire department. Do not assume that because you did it this way last time it will work the same way this time. In the UK gas systems are no longer acceptable and standard formats of fire extinguishers are preferred.

Electrical switchgear will be required to provide the required electrical supplies to the dimmer cabinets. At first glance one might provide one large isolation device feeding a number of cabinets. Whilst this may be acceptable, will be low in cost and easy to install, it is not good practice. Allow sufficient space in the dimmer room for an electrical switchboard where a main incoming protective device is fitted and separate outgoing protection for each and every dimmer cabinet. This has the advantage that if an overload occurs in one cabinet the protective device will trip without affecting all other cabinets. Switchgear can be quite bulky, so always allow sufficient space. Again, access is important as the switchgear may need to be replaced or maintained during the life of the venue. Allow space for the load cables; containment is bulky and will often need to be fixed to the ceiling or walls as many cabinets have cable access at the top. In larger dimmer rooms the application of a false floor (computer type floor) can provide a means of hiding these cables and can include the necessary fire protection detectors.

Another consideration is the access required to the dimmer cabinets. Some will require front access only, others will require rear and front or rear and side, thus the layout of the cabinets within the room is important.

With smaller venues, using portable packs or flight cased dimmers, these could be located in one area of the dimmer room – each pack fed with a separate isolator, all resulting is a small room with a simple heat extraction fan being required. Space should be provided around the packs for air movement and for maintenance.

Venues using the medium density type hard wired dimmers tend to require wall space onto which the dimmers can be mounted. Remember to apply acoustic damping materials between the cabinets and the supporting wall. Where dimmer room walls are of limited strength, application of metal supporting structures, such as Unistrut, can help to spread the resulting weight load. When laying out these dimmers remember to allow space for maintenance access and space between cabinets to allow for an adequate air flow. Ideally the electrical protective device should be sited close to the cabinet allowing it to be quickly isolated if problems occur or for maintenance purposes. Again, consider the electrical containment; this will need to run under or above the dimmer cabinets and will need to exit the dimmer room into the venue at a convenient point.

With high density cabinets, where a large number of dimmers are enclosed in one cabinet, this results in considerable weight that can reach, with some types of cabinet, 300 to 400kg when loaded with 96 dimmers. Therefore the dimmer room floor must be designed to accommodate such weights and care with computer type flooring is needed to accommodate these floor loads. With a large venue this may equate to a number of metric tonnes so the structure of the dimmer room will need to be designed accordingly. Again, try to locate the dimmer room away from the structure of the venue; if this is not possible use acoustic damping materials between the base of the cabinet and the floor.

With modern lighting data networks of DMX and Ethernet there is absolutely no reason why all the dimmers have to be located in one room. In a recent hotel project the author was involved with, the most economic solution was to locate dimmers in the electrical riser cupboards on each floor of the building. This maintained short cable runs from the dimmers to the loads, producing an economic solution.

Finally, do not be afraid to consider distributing the dimmers around the lighting installation itself, using portable dimmable bars and packs. This can make for a very flexible solution, and reduce significantly the amount of cabling travelling to a lighting bar, particularly if this is a flown bar and cables have to be managed to rise and fall as the bar moves. This removes completely the requirement for a dimmer room leaving only a requirement for a distribution board, with protection for power outlets, to be located somewhere in the building. More of this is explained in the new technology dimmers covered in Chapter 7.

3.10 Dimmer Diagnostics and Fault Reporting

With large numbers of dimmers it is difficult for the venue electricians to keep a watchful eye on every dimmer. For this reason some of dimmer manufacturers have added diagnostic systems that look at the dimmer status and report problems such as circuit breaker tripped, fan failure, loss of DMX, short circuit on thyristor, output current and dimmer output voltage, etc. The systems basically break down into two types, namely those that constantly monitor on line the dimmer parameters and report these to a PC or a lighting desk or network. The second type provide off line monitoring systems that test the dimmers when they are not in operation by use of a sequential testing system.

The sequential systems are low cost and yet provide useful amounts of information but only when the dimmers are not in use. This ensures that electricians can check a dimmer installation prior to a show being recorded. Whilst not updating the status during operation it can save considerable testing time as each dimmer will be turned on and off, reporting data about each dimmer. During this process the load can be measured and stored on the system. When the user defines that the dimmers and luminaires are working correctly for a show, the diagnostic system can be requested to store this as the master data. When the diagnostics are run at a later time the system will automatically compare the new data with the master and then flag the differences. The systems are accurate enough to be able to detect, due to the change in electrical current values, that one lamp of a pair is not working.

The on-line systems are more expensive because separate voltage and current transducers are fitted to each dimmer channel and to each cabinet. The on-line diagnostics operate by sending a request for data signal to the diagnostic processing equipment. This scans the processors in all the connected cabinets picking up information and then transmits this back to the requesting PC or lighting console.

During this scanning process every dimmer channel being turned on at that moment by the lighting desk can be checked for voltage and current. If a channel is being turned on and there is output voltage the system knows the dimmer has fired and the output protective device is okay. If no output voltage is measured we know that the protection device may have tripped or the dimmer is not firing. The same applies to current, if we measure a current and display the real value we know that on a 240 volt system 4.167 Amps = 1kW lamp, 8.334 Amps = 2kW lamp, etc. If there is no current flow there is no lamp connected or the lamp has failed.

Similarly we can check that the processor is working correctly, and that DMX is being received, and examine the local programming that has been set at the dimmer. Critical factors like temperature can be measured and over-heat problems reported.

The user can programme these systems to issue flag warning messages when a new error is detected. These can immediately be reported by the lighting director and electricians dispatched to investigate the problem saving valuable fault finding time. Systems are available from ADB, Colortran (USA), Compulite, Electronic Theatre Controls, ETC Europe, Entertainment Technology (USA), IES, Strand Lighting and Transtechnik.

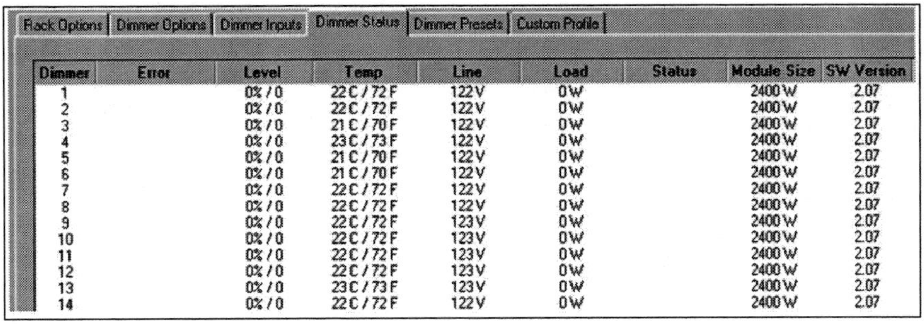

Rack Options	Dimmer Options	Dimmer Inputs	Dimmer Status	Dimmer Presets	Custom Profile				
Dimmer	Error	Level	Temp	Line	Load	Status	Module Size	SW Version	
1		0% / 0	22 C / 72 F	122 V	0 W		2400 W	2.07	
2		0% / 0	22 C / 72 F	122 V	0 W		2400 W	2.07	
3		0% / 0	21 C / 70 F	122 V	0 W		2400 W	2.07	
4		0% / 0	23 C / 73 F	122 V	0 W		2400 W	2.07	
5		0% / 0	21 C / 70 F	122 V	0 W		2400 W	2.07	
6		0% / 0	21 C / 70 F	122 V	0 W		2400 W	2.07	
7		0% / 0	22 C / 72 F	122 V	0 W		2400 W	2.07	
8		0% / 0	22 C / 72 F	122 V	0 W		2400 W	2.07	
9		0% / 0	22 C / 72 F	123 V	0 W		2400 W	2.07	
10		0% / 0	22 C / 72 F	123 V	0 W		2400 W	2.07	
11		0% / 0	22 C / 72 F	123 V	0 W		2400 W	2.07	
12		0% / 0	22 C / 72 F	123 V	0 W		2400 W	2.07	
13		0% / 0	23 C / 73 F	123 V	0 W		2400 W	2.07	
14		0% / 0	22 C / 72 F	122 V	0 W		2400 W	2.07	

Fig 14: Screen Display from Entertainment Technology Capio Plus dimmer rack using Horizon Talkback software, photo: Entertainment Technology, Inc.

3.11 Non-dims, Switches and Relays

One final subject that should be considered in this chapter is that of switched circuits. With modern installations and the types of instruments needing to be controlled we are fast approaching the time when more and more switched circuits are being demanded. Historically these circuits comprised of a mains operated switch located on a large panel in the control room. When sound systems appeared everyone got fed up with the clicks and bangs when the smoke machine was turned on. The next phase saw applications of relays and contactors with possibly some low voltage control, allowing the control panels to get smaller and to be used remotely in the auditorium for plotting sessions.

In recent years we have seen the application of electronic technology and switches activated by DMX have become widespread. There is a universal requirement for these devices in any lighting system whether it is a retail outlet, night club, exhibition, theatre or TV - in fact anywhere where lighting needs to be switched on and off or where items need to be centrally controlled from the lighting control system.

The next chapter looks at the different types of dimmer formats; in most of these formats switching versions are available. The power control device is sometimes a triac, some times solid state relays. The use of these needs some care as when inductive loads are applied some of the lower cost units cannot handle the inrush current, resulting in device failure. The versions which include physical electrical contactors fired by DMX can handle all types of load reliably.

3.12 Conclusions

This chapter has looked at the way conventional electronic dimmers operate, the potential acoustic and electrical noise produced and how this can be reduced. We looked at the way a dimmer curve can help to improve the performance and produce a better linear performance between intensity and fader settings. We looked at the different types of curve and explained why there is a difference between a theatre dimmer and one used for television.

Time was spent looking at the different dimmer ratings and what must be considered in terms of the amount of heat that the dimmer will dissipate. We then looked at the important design issues that should be considered when planning a dimmer room, where to locate it and what cooling might be required. The opportunities offered by adding diagnostic and reporting systems were considered and some brief notes on switches and non-dims were provided. The next chapter looks at ways of calculating the number of dimmers needed for performance venues and TV studios.

Fig 15: Strand EC90 high density modular dimming system circa 1996, photo: Martin Tyrer

STRAND CONTROL

COMBINED SWITCH and DIMMER BOARDS

The above are two types of dead-front switch and dimmer boards. The one on the left is a 3-colour board, with 15 ampere tumbler switches, back of board colour master switches, bracket type dimmer handles, quick motion master wheels, and slow motion worm drive.

That on the right is a 4-colour board, with 30 ampere back of board type knife switches, back of board colour masters, and master blackout switches, bracket type dimmer handles, quick motion master wheels.

Similar boards have been installed in—

Westminster Theatre	Arts Theatre, Cambridge
A.D.C., Cambridge	Regal, Wimbledon
Pavilion, Maidstone	Regal, Rotherham
Regal, Margate	Festival Theatre, Edinburgh
R.M.S. "Queen Mary"	Cork City Hall
Winter Gardens, Llandudno	&c., &c.
Holborn Empire	

STRAND ELECTRIC

AND ENGINEERING CO., LTD.

FLORAL STREET, COVENT GARDEN, W.C.2

Telephone :
Temple Bar 7464 (6 lines).

Telegraphic Address :
Spotlite, Rand, London.

Fig 16: Excerpt from the Strand 1936 catalogue showing dead front switch and dimmer boards.

4 DIMMING SYSTEM DESIGN

It's amazing what you find at a car exhibition! PRG Europe Avolites flight case at MPH Car Show Earls Court Exhibition Centre 20th November 2005, photo: the author.

Contents:
- Electrical Power Requirements
- How to Calculate Size of Electrical Supply
- Example of Medium Size School Hall System
- Example of Multi-purpose College Hall
- Example of Medium Size City Theatre
- Example of High Grade Conference Centre
- Example of News and Current Affairs TV Studio
- Conclusions

4.1 Introduction

This chapter looks at the electrical requirements for a given dimming system and considers how the size of the electrical supply might be calculated as well as looking at the number of dimmer channels that should be provided for a venue. The ideas put forward in this chapter are the guidelines that I use when designing solutions. They pick up some of the theory proposed by others but may be different from other ideas and teachings. So please use these as rule of thumb guides. They have served me well so far but as lighting becomes ever more complex with different instruments requiring different electrical connections all of us get asked to advise or plan or use these systems. I hope in the coming sections of this chapter that I have picked some examples that will help give some thoughts and ideas, but do not be afraid to change the rules of thumb. They are guides only and will need to be altered as technology advances or as different shapes and sizes of performance venue have to be considered. I have tried to make these examples international, but I am no expert on the ideologies of different countries and their styles of production. So forgive my inexperience here.

4.2 Electrical Power Requirements and Venue Design Light Levels

Electrical power is a large item within any performance venue's running costs, so it is therefore sensible to ensure that an adequately sized supply is provided rather than a high capacity supply which is never used to its maximum. Remember that most electrical authorities make charges for standing electrical services whilst others impose peak demand charges when predicted levels of power are exceeded.

4.3 How to Calculate the Size of Supply Required

Firstly it is important to consider the area to be illuminated, the overall size of the venue, the lighting requirements, and whether the lighting is for performance, exhibition, events, architectural, night club, concert, recital or other applications. The latter need careful analysis as each type of function has very different lighting requirements. For example, in a concert hall the lighting may well need to be relatively static, be directly overhead and require a uniform lighting level of perhaps 1200 lux. However in a theatre staging different performances nightly the lighting requirements are to provide a scheme that must allow lighting designers to create different solutions for each show. In a television studio different methods are employed based on the lighting levels needed for the camera to operate properly and be able to use the cameras depth of field when framing a picture. Here calculations are based on providing around 400 to 700 lux per square metre of studio floor space.

Lighting is not only about the area to be lit; as previously explained natural lighting is as much about the lighting angle and position relative to the subject. Of course space needs to be found to fix the luminaires in positions that create the lighting designers' angular opportunities. This is always a battle as the architect wants the venue to work properly but, perhaps, does not want to see the light sources! When designing a venue the available lighting positions must be considered first. This governs how many luminaires might be rigged and therefore how many dimmers are required and at what capacity.

Classical teaching considers the lighting requirement, the area to be illuminated, the potential luminaire hanging positions, the operational requirements of the venue – fixed rig or fully flexible – and finally then splits the area to be illuminated into lighting areas or zones. Once the total number of zones is added up then other considerations must be thought through – is this to be illuminated in one or more colours, are special effects required, are additional side lighting or back lighting included?

One of the best ways of trying to work out roughly how to light a venue is to divide the area to be illuminated into 2 metre x 2 metre (or 6 feet x 6 feet) squares, then add up the squares – this equating to the total number of luminaires needed to light the area under design in one direction and one colour. If two or more colours are required then multiply the one colour total by the number of additional colours. Then add in side lighting or back lighting on a similar 2 metre x 2 metre (6 feet x 6 feet) basis. If a cyclorama cloth is involved, then divide the cloth into 2 metre widths and add a luminaire per colour per area. If a very high cloth is involved than add a similar quantity for the groundrow (bottom lighting). I then usually add 20% of this total to then cover special effects and other specific lighting functions.

Experience teaches us that the size of the 'lighting division' areas must vary depending on the height that the luminaire is suspended at. In a low height space such as a school stage with bars at 3.5 to 4.5 metres we may do better to use areas sized at 1.5 x 1.5 metres (5 feet x 5 feet). In a professional theatre with bars fixed at 8 metres high, 2 to 3 metre (6 to 10 feet) squares are okay. In larger opera stages or areas with high lighting bars the areas may extend to as large as 4 metres x 4 metres (13 x 13 feet). This larger format works well in concert halls, exhibition centres and museums where relatively fixed lighting in one colour is required.

As an example of all of these complicated issues a number of typical venues have been considered. These are intended as guides and therefore sizes have been given allowing readers to scale upwards or downwards from the figures given. Basic schemes only are shown for each type of venue to avoid making the layouts in A5 size difficult to read. Where optional luminaire hanging positions should be considered these have been identified and the affects of adding them to the circuit totals have been shown.

However, before any of this can be considered there is one vital part which must be undertaken first. This is to sketch out the layout of the room, mark on obstacles or existing lighting locations, use graph paper to make the scaling easier and then remember the guide rules of trying to create a 45 degree lighting angle. *Fig 1* shows such a simple layout drawing for the first example a medium sized school hall.

4.4 Example 1: Typical Medium Size School Hall Stage

This hall is typical of the average school stage. It has a standard stage curtain behind the proscenium, a mid stage curtain and a rear cyclorama or painted wall. The area to be illuminated on stage is around 8 metres (26 feet) wide x 5 metres (16 feet) deep. A forestage area is provided for morning assembly and parents days with access stairs from the hall floor. The over stage bar height is assumed to be 5 metres (16 feet).

With this small stage 1.5 x 1.5 metre (5 x 5 feet) squares have been used. Using only the squares that require illumination we have 5 wide x 3 deep producing 12 lighting areas over the stage plus a further 4 areas for the forestage and the area under the proscenium that the over stage No 1 bar cannot reach. So there are 16 areas in total to light this school stage correctly in one colour. If the front of house side bars were included we could add another 4 areas producing 20 in total.

Hence for the school stage we need 20 dimmer channels and 20 spotlights in the simplest form. As stages tend to be lit in warm and cool colours we end up with 40 channels and 40 spotlights. Some further circuits could be added if a rear cyclorama cloth or painted wall is included. Typical for this venue's cyclorama width adding 4 circuits per colour would be fine, so with 2 colours this would add another 8 circuits.

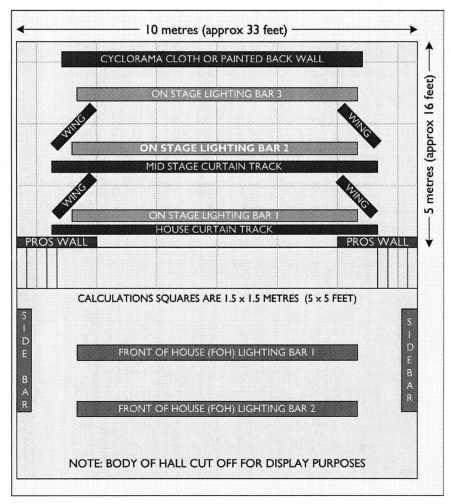

Fig 1: Example of School Hall Lighting Layout using a 1.5 metre (5 feet) rule.

For this medium size school hall the analysis of the circuit and dimmer requirements are shown laid out in *Fig 1* and detailed as follows:

Over Stage Total of 28 circuits are required, this could be split up as:

On Stage Bar 1:   8 sockets

On Stage Bar 2:   8 sockets

On Stage Bar 3:   12 sockets – 3 colours of cyclorama wash

Front of House Total of 20 circuits are required, this could be split up as:

Front of House Bar 1:   8 sockets
Front of House Bar 2:   8 sockets
Front of House Side 1:   2 sockets
Front of House Side 2:   2 sockets
Total Circuits for the School: 48 sockets

This could be reduced to 44 if no front side lighting is used, reduced further to 40 if only 2 colours are used on the cyclorama.

Earlier in this book the historic use of cord patch panels was mentioned. In such a school it would be beneficial to cable more circuits back to a patch panel and then provide 36, 42 or 48 dimmers with twin socket outlets if 6 channel packs are used or 48 channels of installed dimmers. This creates the maximum lighting flexibility and also allows the school to start with a limited amount

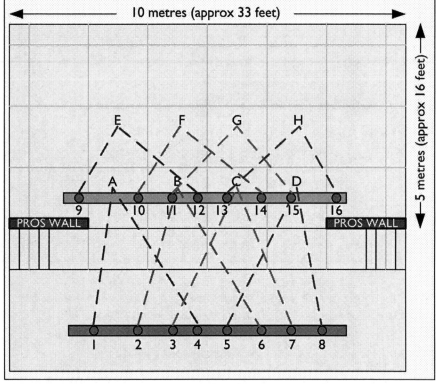

Fig 2: School Hall Luminaire Positioning using the 1.5 metre rule.

of equipment and then add more dimmers and luminaires as funds become available. This aspect of designing with future expansion in mind can be a sensible precaution with some types of venues such as schools, universities, museums and amateur theatres. Budgets are always a major restriction to designers but these types of venue are usually able to raise funds or need to make changes during the lifetime of the equipment. *Fig 2* provides a sketch of how the 1.5 or 2 metre luminaire rule was constructed for this example.

Bar No 1 is suspended in the auditorium and provides the front light for the performers. Bar No 2 is over the stage and is also used to light the performer adding some contrast with slightly different angles or colour.

The positions of the lights cross to add some realism to the lighting. In terms of system design the 8 outlets allow the required 4 zones to be lit in 2 colours and to create some 'focusing flexibility' as luminaires can be angled as required crossing into areas or being focused directly forward.

4.5 Example 2: Multi-Purpose Large School or College Hall Stage

This hall is truly multi-purpose in so far as a conventional stage is provided at one end of the hall with a 'theatre in the round' style space in the centre of the main body of the hall. The conventional stage has already been dealt with in Example 1. The theatre in the round area needs to be lit from more than one side at all times as the each member of the audience can always see each performer no matter where they sit. This is unlike a conventional 'proscenium' stage where all of the action is located in one location and the audience is looking in one direction only. This requires the lighting to come from all 4 sides or from 3 sides if the 120 degree rule is used. For the purposes of this analysis let's work with the 120 degree rule and let's assume that each position needs to be lit from 3 positions each at 120 degrees to one another. Extracting the main body of the hall from *Fig 3* we have *Fig 4*.

This shows that once again the performance area is divided into 4 areas wide x 2 areas deep. This produces a total of 8 lighting areas. However this time each area has to be lit from 3 positions each at 120 degrees to one another or from 4 positions each at 90 degrees to one another. The latter solution is expensive on instruments and dimmers; whilst producing the best quality, this takes time to focus and relies on good focusing to set up properly. With 8 zones each lit from 4 positions we would need 32 lights in one colour or 64 if two colours are needed. If we adopt the 120 degree rule with 3 lamps for 8

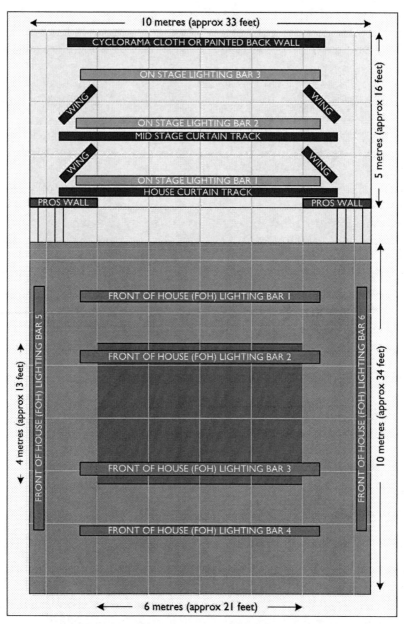

Fig 3: Large Multi-purpose Hall Luminaire Positioning using a '1.5 metre (5 feet) rule'.

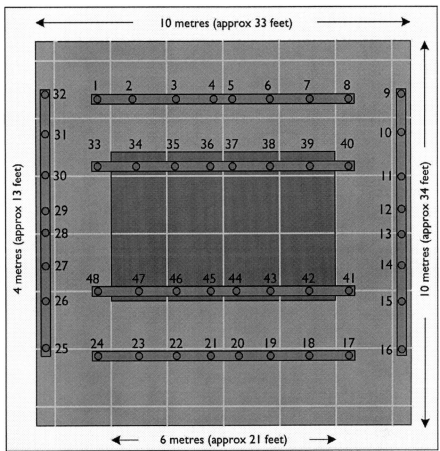

Fig 4: 'Theatre in the Round' layout for Multi-purpose Hall.

zones we have 24 lamps for 1 colour or 48 for 2 colours. With such a small area colour wash can be spread out to cover a wider area.

An example of this would be to use 2 metre (6 feet) zones. Here the lighting areas would have been reduced to 6 rather than 8 resulting in 24 lamps per colour with 90 degree illumination or 18 with 120 degrees per colour leaving some spare dimmers and positions for specials.

We now begin to see a trend that if we work out the area to be illuminated and then calculate the number of zones, decide on the number of washes of light we need, and again some percentage for special lighting or effects, we can quickly work out the number of positions needed for lighting an area from a potential lighting position. I use the following guide at the design stage for a conventional stage lighting system:

Assuming that the lighting throw distance works with a 500/650W (2 to 5 metres – 6 to 16 feet) or 1/1.2kW (4 to 8 metres – 13 to 26 feet) or 2kW (5 to 9 metres – 16 to 30 feet) lamp the following can be applied.

Number of lighting zones in area to be illuminated	= A
Number of required colour washes	= B
Number of special or effects lights	= (A x B) x 0.2 (round-up)
Number of cyclorama zones*	= C
Number of cyclorama colour washes*	= W
* = Where applicable (if cyclorama lighting is included)	
Number of required dimmers, sockets and luminaires in general zones	= A x B + (A x B) x 0.2

So applying this guide to an area with 10 lighting zones over the width of a stage, needing a 2 colour wash, with some specials we would then have: (10 x 2) + (10 x 2) x 0.2 = 24 outlets.

This would be a typical number for a large size of theatre stage where we have a proscenium opening of 20 metres per lighting bar over the stage area.

Number of required dimmers, sockets and cyclorama lights in cyclorama zone = (C x W)

So if we have a cyc 20 metres wide we would have 10 x 2 metre zones washed in 3 colours we would need: (10 x 3) = 30 outlets.

Here another aspect needs to be considered – that of the rating of the dimmer. With a cyclorama we probably always want to use the same colour evenly across the cyclorama so we can consider grouping the luminaires or sockets together on a larger capacity dimmer if a large width cyclorama cloth over 4 to 5 metres high is being used. The 30 outlets basically represent 10 circuits of 3 colours. With this height of cyclorama a lamp of 1000 or 1250 watts will be used in a cyclorama light. This means that we could group 2 of these together on a 2.5 or 3kW dimmer or we could group 4 of them together on a 5 or 6kW rated dimmer. In this way the number of dimmer channels can be reduced and potentially the number of dimmer cabinets and thus space required in a dimmer room.

Using the same rule for our first average school stage we would end up with

15 zones. This would result in 36 dimmers excluding the cyclorama or 51 if a 3 colour cyclorama wash is included. This is 3 more than before because we have added some circuits for special or effects lighting. Remember that these are guides only to estimate circuit numbers to allow the quantity of dimmers, sockets outlets and later luminaires to be specified and costs calculated.

4.6   Example 3: Medium Sized City or Civic Theatre

At some point an architect or a lighting system designer will face the prospect of working on a city theatre. Many of these have been built around the world over the past 30 years. Many suffer from the fact that the architect and designers are local to the city and lack the experience of building such a venue unless experienced designers and architects are brought into the project. They are often the pride and joy of the local community, having taken many years to fund and develop through all the planning stages.

Theatres of this type have no resident company and tend to be on 'the touring circuit', accepting shows on a weekly basis of many different types from drama, musical, opera and ballet as well as infilling the programme with conferences and other civic events. This requires the lighting system to be acceptable to professional touring companies as well as being highly flexible as to what types of local productions can be lit.

Fig 5 shows a simplified plan view of the stage and the auditorium. The theatre has a conventional stage area equipped with counter-weighted flying facilities, a forestage elevator and three front of house bridges as the depth of the auditorium is short, with an adjustable ground floor seating block that can be set flat or set to rake. A second level of seating is provided with a relatively steep rake. The stage area, shown shaded, is 25 metres (82 feet) wide x 20 metres (66 feet) deep with a proscenium opening of 16 metres (53 feet) wide x 5.5 metres (18 feet) high. Over the stage area a proper theatre grid is provided at a height of 14 metres (46 feet), allowing full scenery height flying. The stage is equipped with a full house curtain, two sets of travellers (cross stage) curtains together with five sets of masking legs.

To light the stage and forestage area the architect has decided that three front of house lighting bridges are required; three being provided so that when the ground floor is level a forestage extension can be added for fashion shows and similar presentations.

The stage area to be illuminated measures 18 metres wide x 16 metres deep. Dividing this into illumination squares of 2 metres by 2 metres we end up with 72 areas.

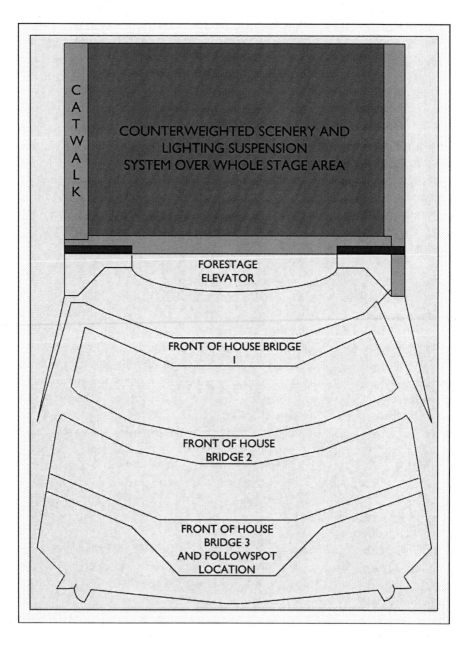

Fig 5: City Theatre Basic Building and Stage Layout

Adding in the forestage area adds a further 16 areas. This produces a total excluding any cyclorama or special requirements of 88 areas. If these areas are split down into individual zones, like the first example of the school hall, then this results in a stage illumination width of 18 metres producing a total of 9 zones or 18 lamps if a 2 colour wash is required or 27 if a 3 colour wash is needed. If we use the formula and add in the specials this results in the following:

If number of lighting zones in area to be illuminated	= 9
Number of required colour washes	= 3
Number of special or effects lights	= (9 x 3) x 0.2 = 6
Number of required dimmers/sockets in general zones	**= (9 x 3) + (9 x 3) x 0.2 = 33**

The front of house positions would be structured so that light from the first bridge reaches under the proscenium and onto the stage area. The second FOH bridge covers from the front of the forestage to under the edge of the proscenium. The third bridge provides locations for followspots and positions for instruments to light the front of the forestage and coverage of any stage extension. As the stage extension will be seen from three sides this indicates that side lighting positions, not shown on *Fig 5*, will also be required. As the width of the forestage is 16 metres x 2 metres deep we have eight areas to light. The third bridge has less areas to light so we can take a view that we should allow 50% of the sockets on the other two bridges.

Using the same formulae we have the following:

If number of lighting zones in area to be illuminated	= 8
Number of required colour washes	= 3
Number of special or effects lights	= (8 x 3) x 0.2 = 5
Number of required dimmers/sockets in general zones	**= (8 x 3) + (8 x 3) x 0.2 = 29**

As far as the final stage bar is concerned this is used to light the cyclorama. This cyclorama cloth will need to be 18 metres (60 feet) wide by 6.5 metres (21 feet) high to ensure that the stage set out can work correctly. At this height both top cyclorama and bottom groundrow lighting will be required in order to achieve an even wash across the whole cloth. Therefore the formula used previously will need to be multiplied by two to take into account the groundrow circuits. So applying the formulae we have:

Number of top cyclorama zones	= 8
(number of zones within cyc)	
Number of top cyclorama colour washes	= 4
Number of groundrow cyclorama zones	= 8
(number of zones within cyc)	
Number of groundrow cyclorama colour washes	= 4
Total number of circuits at top	= 64

This solution represents a large number of 2.4/2.5 or 3kW circuits. As stated previously, a more economic solution would be to use 5/6kW dimmers. As each cell within a cyclorama is rated at 1 or 1.25kW we can put 4 of these safely onto a 5/6kW dimmer. Accordingly we could replace the 64 sockets with 32 x 3kW dimmers by pairing circuits on the bar – 16 at the top and 16 at the bottom or we could reduce this still further by using 16 x 5 or 6kW dimmers, 8 at the top and 8 at the bottom. This will require the appropriate cabling system to deliver 5 or 6kW circuits to the bar where these will have to be safely split into 1 or 1.25kW feeds to each cell of a cyclorama luminaire.

Another note here. Always try and use an even number of sockets as luminaires always tend to rigged as pairs as shown in *Fig 2*. Consequently, in the summary below, figures have been amended to reflect an even number requirement.

In summary then we have the following lighting areas and sockets:

FOH Bridge 1	= 30 circuits rated at 2.5 or 3kW
FOH Bridge 2	= 30 circuits rated at 2.5 or 3kW
FOH Bridge 3	= 14 circuits rated at 2.5 or 3kW
On Stage Bar 1	= 34 circuits rated at 2.5 or 3kW
On Stage Bar 2	= 34 circuits rated at 2.5 or 3kW
On Stage Bar 3	= 34 circuits rated at 2.5 or 3kW
On Stage Bar 4	= 8 circuits rated at 5kW
Groundrow	= 8 circuits rated at 5kW

So far this totals 176 x 2.4/2.5 or 3kW and 16 x 5 or 6kW circuits.

What has been forgotten? Currently no circuits have been allocated to the stage floor area, no circuits have been added for side light across the stage, and none have been allocated in the auditorium for side lighting and coverage of the stage extension. Also what happens if a TV company turns up and wants to plug in their lights? Also, how do we install devices that need direct rather than dimmed power? We will review each of these questions in turn.

For stage floor circuits experience shows that wherever these are located cables have to emerge across the stage to feed the units. These are always problematic to hide and make safe from being tripped over. One historic solution was to mount 'dip traps' into the stage floor. These comprised a recessed socket accessed via a lift up flap with cable entry points cut out of the hinged lid. These tended to be located off stage in the wings allowing stands to be powered together with other specialist lighting without cables encroaching into the acting area.

Modern stage design tends to move these to the proscenium, rear and side walls of the stage. These are mounted in surface mounted socket boxes allowing any item of equipment to be plugged in as required. Where cables have to run to sections of the acting area for scenery they can be dropped down from above or wired through the scenery to plug into a stage level socket box. How many sockets should be located at stage level? Firstly the groundrow cyclorama lighting circuits have already been addressed, and this leaves only the other usages to be considered. This might be to connect 'practicals', lights on stands to shine through windows, effects or for 'specials'.

In terms of the number of outlets there is no really hard and fast rule. I suggest that 10 to 20% of the over-stage circuits is as good a way of estimating the floor level circuits. This would result in 20 circuits being provided at stage level.

In terms of side lighting positions the sensible solution is to consider that a side lighting position should be provided on the stage left and right sides corresponding to each over stage lighting bar. As each side lighting bar would need to be able to create the same colour washes as the over-stage bars plus be able to provide special side lighting it is sensible to use modules of 3 or 4 channels. Accordingly I would advise that for small stages 4 channels is adequate, for the larger stage 24 channels is preferable increasing to 36 or 48 channels for large ballet or music related venues. As these may require colour scrollers or moving lights also to be powered on the ladder it is sensible to provide a minimum of 1 non-dim per ladder per 12 dimmed circuits.

For this application the front of house side lighting is to provide lighting primarily for a stage extension. Once again this can be viewed as a number of 2 metre x 2 metre (6 x 6 feet) lighting zones. As this will need to be washed in the same colours, the same formulae can be applied as was used for the main stage.

Fig 6: Vertex Solid Stage Relay
photo: QIS Ltd.

Accordingly if we assume the stage extension is 6 metres (20 feet) long and 4 metres (13 feet) wide this gives another 12 lighting areas. Remember that this must be lit from 2 sides so we need to replicate the lighting from the left on to the right hand side.

Another issue concerns additional 5kW or 6kW outlets that can be used for TV lighting as well as for other larger luminaires. If the venue expects to be used for TV recording it is a wise precaution to add some 5kW or 6kW outlets on to each of the lighting bars. As a guide TV companies will need to not only increase the light level on stage but also will want to add lighting to illuminate the audience. Therefore a wise precaution is to add at least 2 x 5kW or 6kW outlets to each front of house location and to each of the over stage bars.

The final question is how to power items that need direct rather than dimmed power. The historic method was to provide power outlets around the theatre that were then wired back to a mains rated switch panel. These had the unfortunate effect of creating clicks and bangs on sound systems when they were switched on and off. Later on, low voltage relays or contactors were added that were rated to switch the required mains voltages but were operated by low voltage panels. These were fine but could not be plotted into lighting cues or memories and relied on the lighting technician remembering to turn on the circuit at the required time. A better method is to add 'non-dim' direct power circuits that can be controlled by the lighting console and are therefore part of the lighting control network. To this end most dimmer manufacturers now produce non-dim cabinets or plug in modules that perform under DMX control as a 'switch on and off' device. This can be contactor controlled or can utilise a solid state relay. These are high speed semi-conductor load switching relays which are turned on at the zero crossing point thus reducing inrush currents and are turned off when the current is at its lowest reducing unwanted electromagnetic interference.

For most performance venues non-dim outlets are becoming as important as dimmed outlets. This is because the heavy usage of motorised luminaires, motorised wash and profile lights, discharge sources, colour scrollers and effects

OUTLET LOCATION	2.4/2.5/3kW DIMMED	2.4/2.5/3kW NON DIM	5 or 6kW DIMMED
FOH BRIDGE 1	30	4	2
FOH BRIDGE 2	30	4	2
FOH BRIDGE 3	14	4	2
ON STAGE BAR 1	34	4	2
ON STAGE BAR 2	34	4	2
ON STAGE BAR 3	34	4	2
ON STAGE BAR 4			8
GROUNDROW			8
STAGE FLOOR	20	8	
FOH SIDE LEFT	12	2	2
FOH SIDE RIGHT	12	2	2
STAGE LADDERS	24	2	
TOTALS	244	38	32

Fig 7: Summary of City Theatre Dimmed and non-dimmed circuit allocation.

equipment is becoming commonplace. In some venues such as a night club the moving light usage is much greater than the generic luminaire load with dimmers. For our current example of a City Theatre that accepts incoming touring shows we can be sure these supplies will be required. As direct powered equipment will need to be used anywhere that generic luminaires will be used we must distribute non-dims in the same locations as the dimmed circuits. In a theatre or conference centre I would recommend that a minimum of four non-dim outlets are provided on each Front of House Lighting Bridge and Over Stage Bar. With on stage side lighting ladders or booms at least one non-dim per ladder should be provided. Each stage level socket box should be equipped with two non-dims as these could be used to power smoke and dry ice machines, projectors, floor mounted moving lights and other effects equipment.

Fig 7 summarises my recommendation of the lighting dimmed and non-dimmed circuits for such a City (Council) Theatre. With such an installation it would make sense to use the modular plug-in high density dimmer solution as this allows dimmers and non-dims to be housed within 3 x 96 and 1 x 48 channel cabinets occupying a minimum of space allowing use of a small dimmer room.

4.7 Example 4: High Grade Conference Centre

Across the world major cities are building conference and convention centres that tend to really be a multi-purpose theatre! Any multi-purpose venue has by its very nature to be a compromise as often the prime role gets lost during the design phase. This can result in a finished solution that is so much of a compromise it fails to work in any mode.

Before planning a lighting solution make sure that a clear brief has been identified. If the prime role is conference then the stage area can be relatively simply lit. If product launches are to be staged then better facilities are required. If occasional musical recitals are to be staged then concert lighting will become important. Each type of event requires a slightly different lighting solution. If no clear brief can be provided then think of a more theatrical solution as this is the most flexible and will cater for most eventualities.

The auditorium is relatively intimate with almost a horseshoe shape with side seats able to see well into the stage wings. The stage area is 32 metres (105 feet) wide x 15 metres (50 feet) deep with a proscenium opening of 17 metres (56 feet). The floor to underside of proscenium height is 9 metres with an adjustable proscenium header than can reduce this to 6 metres (20 feet). The stage area is equipped with 58 conventional counter-weighted bars each rated to carry loads of 500 kg. A forestage elevator is provided more for production launches and conferences than for use with an orchestra – this measures approximately 17 metres (56 feet) wide x 3.5 metres (12 feet). To assist in this design the architects have been advised by a consultant about possible lighting locations. Looking from the projection room to the rear of the stage these have been defined as:

Auditorium	Stage Area
2 x Followspot Positions	On Stage Lighting Bar 1
Auditorium Side Lighting Slot Aud. Left Rear	On Stage Lighting Bar 2
Auditorium Side Lighting Slot Aud. Right Rear	On Stage Lighting Bar 3
Auditorium Side Lighting Slot Aud. Left Front	On Stage Lighting Bar 4
Auditorium Side Lighting Slot Aud. Right Front	On Stage Cyclorama Bar
Front of House Lighting Bridge No 1	On Stage Sockets Stage Left
Front of House Lighting Bridge No 2	On Stage Sockets Stage Right
Forestage Lighting Grid	Under the forestage lift

This building has to cater and attract major conferences and product launches, compete for these events with other world class venues, and the local authority want to use the venue to attract people and business to the city. Accordingly the venue has to be equipped to a high standard and offer the event and conferences organisers the opportunity to create a real 'razzle dazzle' show with that extra sparkle.

Dividing the working area of the stage 20 metres (66 feet) wide x 14 metres (46 feet) deep into 2 metre (6½ feet) squares this produces 70 squares. The forestage area measures 17 x 4 metres (56 x 13 feet) divides into 18 squares.

If we return to the formula this equates to:

General Lighting

Number of lighting zones in area to be illuminated	$= 88$
Number of required colour washes	$= 3$
Number of special or effects lights	$= (88 \times 3) \times 0.2 = 52$
Number of required dimmers in general zones	$\mathbf{= (88 \times 3) + (88 \times 3) \times 0.2 = 316.}$

The cyclorama cloth measures 20 metres wide by 6.5 metres high, and again, due to the height, top cyclorama and bottom groundrow lighting will be required. Therefore with the formula used previously we need to be multiplied by two to take into account the groundrow circuits. So applying the formulae we have:

Number of top cyclorama zones	$= 10$ (number of zones within cyc)
Number of top cyclorama colour washes	$= 4$
Number of groundrow cyclorama zones	$= 10$ (number of zones within cyc)
Number of groundrow cyclorama colour washes	$= 4$
Total number of circuits at top	$= 80$

These 80 circuits could be reduced to 10 x 5kW circuits on the top and a similar number for groundrow fixtures.

For stage level circuits 20% of the over-stage circuits will be applied here as there may be a large number of floor lighting required. This equates to 63 sockets rounded to 60 by the author.

Taking into account the front of house side lighting and the front of house lighting bridges this adds a further 36 zones but in only 2 colours as this is really for conference use so white plus one other colour should be adequate.

Fig 8 shows a summary of my suggested circuit allocation once the TV circuits and non-dims have been added.

OUTLET LOCATION	2.5/3kW DIMMED	2.5/3kW NON DIM	5kW DIMMED
FOH BRIDGE 1	36	4	4
FOH BRIDGE 2	36	4	4
FOH SIDE LEFT REAR	12	2	1
FOR SIDE RIGHT REAR	12	2	1
FOH SIDE LEFT FRONT	12	2	1
FOH SIDE RIGHT FRONT	12	2	1
FORESTAGE GRID	24	4	4
ON STAGE BAR 1	48	4	4
ON STAGE BAR 2	48	4	4
ON STAGE BAR 3	48	4	4
ON STAGE BAR 4	48	4	4
CYCLORAMA			10
STAGE FLOOR RIGHT	30	4	2
STAGE FLOOR LEFT	30	4	2
GROUNDROW			10
UNDER FORE STAGE	4	2	
TOTALS	400	46	56

Fig 8: Summary of High Grade Conference Centre Dimmed and non-dimmed circuit allocation.

The dimmers for the Conference Centre can be accommodated with six high density cabinets and happen to total 512 channels so they fit within one DMX universe.

Like electrical power there are standard sizes of block or cabinets of dimmers. These combinations are often set by the fact that dimmer channel combinations need to be divisible by 3 to match a three phase electrical supply. Thus combinations of 6, 12, 24, 36, 48, 72, 90 and 96 are very common depending upon the type of dimmer packaging. It may be that you are very close to one of the number combinations. If that is true it is economically sensible to try and work around these channel combinations otherwise you might have a 96 channel cabinet containing only a few dimmers!

The cost of a dimmer installation typically equates to between 10 and 15% of the total lighting costs of a performance venue. The greater the number of

TYPE OF VENUE AND SIZE OF STAGE IN m² (width x length)	No OF 2.4/2.5/ 3kW DIMMERS	No OF 5/6kW DIMMERS	TOTAL LOAD 2.4 OR 2.5kW	TOTAL LOAD 5 OR 6kW	ELECTRICAL SUPPLY FOR 2.5kW	ELECTRICAL SUPPLY FOR 5kW
SIMPLE SCHOOL STAGE 42m² – 6m x 7m	36		90kW		375A SP	
SCHOOL HALL & STAGE 120m² – 8m x 15m	60		150kW		208A TPN	
HOTEL BALLROOM 400m² – 16m x 25m	96	12	240kW	60kW	150A TPN	85A TPN
CONFERENCE CENTRE 600m² – 22m x 25m	192	60	480kW	300kW	670A TPN	417A TPN
CITY/CIVIC THEATRE 500m² – 20m x 25m	220	24	550kW	120kW	770A TPN	167A TPN
REPERTORY THEATRE 700m² – 24m x 29m	240	48	600kW	240kW	840A TPN	334A TPN
LARGE OPERA HOUSE 1000m² – 25m x 40m	600	120	1500kW	600kW	2100A TPN	834A TPN
LARGE CONFERENCE CENTRE 1000m² – 25m x 40m	400	56	1000kW	280kW	1390A TPN	389A TPN

Fig 9: Typical Electrical Power and Dimmer Channel Requirements for different venues based on European formats.

individual dimmers the easier it will be to balance and control the lighting. *Fig 9* shows, for the types of venues listed, potential dimmer quantities and the theoretical size (prior to diversity) of the European electrical supplies. These supplies would double in size for a 110 volt installation:

The total electrical supply requirements shown in *Fig 9* have been calculated with every dimmer running at full capacity. In practice these capacities are never reached and a level of electrical diversity can be applied. Typical diversity levels of 40 to 80% can be applied. In larger venues, such as an opera house, *Fig 9* shows a requirement for a total electrical supply of 2934A. In practice it is unlikely that all lighting areas will be lit with all colours and specials simultaneously. Typically we could decide that only two colour washes will ever be used simultaneously resulting in 60% diversity and thus a 1760 Amp 3 phase supply would be installed. For a smaller venue slightly less diversity should be applied, primarily due to the often already restricted supplies, number of dimmers and restricted numbers of luminaires.

4.7   Example 5: News and Current Affairs TV Studio

Firstly it is important to consider the available size of the studio and work out the total square metres of the working area of the studio. Current practice dictates that a light level of around 300 Watts per square metre achieves adequate

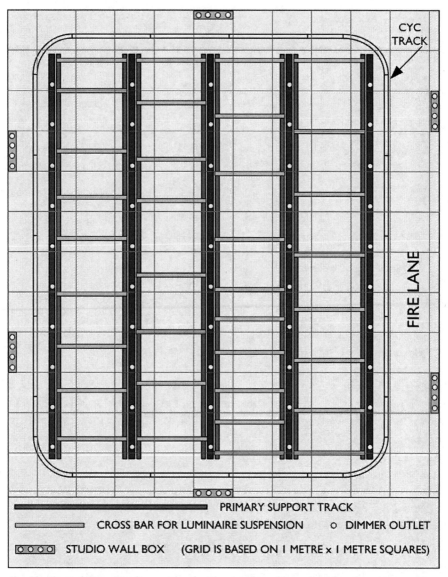

CYC
TRACK

FIRE LANE

PRIMARY SUPPORT TRACK

CROSS BAR FOR LUMINAIRE SUSPENSION   o   DIMMER OUTLET

STUDIO WALL BOX   (GRID IS BASED ON 1 METRE x 1 METRE SQUARES)

Fig 10: Typical News Studio equipped with a track and barrel grid and wrap around cyclorama together with the overhead and wall mounted dimmed outlets.

illumination for most general purpose studios of up to 300 square metres. For larger studios it is recommended that light levels should be generally increased to around 500 Watts per square metre. These figures are guides only; modern camera development is reducing these light level requirements all the time. However, the camera will operate more satisfactorily with *more* light rather than less, with a better depth of field and a less noisy picture. These average light levels may need to be increased to take into account of special lighting requirements such as cycloramas or special effects lighting. It appears to be usual practice now to use automated or moving lights as a form of set dressing and while these may not be directly connected to dimmers they still require an electrical power source and need to be included within electrical power calculations. Some equipment such as teleprompters or partially silvered mirrors in the scenery reduce the amount of reflected light passing through the camera and may again require higher levels of light per square metre to be considered. Similarly, if extreme close-ups from a great distance are needed, All the lighting may need to be rebalanced to provide two stops more light for the camera whose zoom lens sometimes ramps 2 stops.

A simple guide is to first calculate the working size of the studio – the area within the studio on to which light may be required. This area excludes fire lanes, access corridors, areas behind cyclorama cloths, etc. In the example shown we have a small news studio with a wrap around cyclorama. This typically accommodates two news sets and a small weather set. The studio measures 11 x 12 metres (36 x 40 feet) equalling 132m² (1440 square feet). If we are trying to achieve 300 watts per square metre then a total of approximately 132 x 300 = 39,600 Watts or 40kW is required. The problem

TYPE AND SIZE OF STUDIO IN m²	NUMBER OF 3kW DIMMERS	NUMBER OF 5kW DIMMERS	TOTAL LOAD 3kW	TOTAL LOAD 5kW	ELECTRICAL SUPPLY FOR 3kW	ELECTRICAL SUPPLY FOR 5kW
UNIVERSITY/ COLLEGE 100 m²	48		144kW		150A TP	
SMALL BROADCAST 80 m²	36	12	108kW	60kW	150A TP	100A TP
GENERAL PURPOSE STUDIO 120 m²	48	18	144kW	90kW	150A TP	150A TP
MIXED PURPOSE STUDIO 250 m²	60	96	180kW	480kW	300A TP	700A TP
BROADCAST STUDIO 750 m²		700		3500kW		1000A TP
70 m² VIRTUAL REALITY STUDIO	48		73kW		100A TP	

Fig 11: Examples of TV Studio electrical power and dimmer channel requirements.

with rules like this is they do not take into account what space is used and therefore needs to be lit and the empty space. However, allocating dimmer outlets throughout the space maintains lighting flexibility and in this studio barrels with luminaires can be moved for higher or lower lighting density.

Another method of working out the number of dimmers is to take the number of square metres, divide this by two and that equals the number of dimmers for a standard non saturated studio. In this studio this equates to 66 dimmers. The drawing shows 74 including studio floor level wall box outlets - so very close! This rule holds true for most studios with the exception of a saturated lighting studio where a dimmer per square metre is a better guide. Saturated lighting means that the entire grid space of the studio is divided into a matrix and suspension systems like self-climbing hoists or telescopes are installed. On each of these lifting systems a standard rig of luminaires is provided. For studios equipped with cycloramas one also has to consider the number of different colour washes required and add blocks of dimmers to control these cyclorama lights, sufficient to be able to balance the light intensity and also colour mix between combinations of colours.

For those involved in planning studio layouts I enclose a simple guide diagram, *in Fig 11*, showing the suggested power levels per square metre that should be considered.

4.8 Conclusions

The purpose of this chapter was to provide some guidelines as to how to calculate the number of dimmers required in a performance venue. Simple lighting rules were established such as by dividing the area to be lit into a matrix of dimensional squares it is possible to calculate the number of instruments and thus dimmers needed. With some additional factors for cyclorama, side lights and non-dims an approximate design total can be produced. Similar approximate design rules were also established for TV studios.

Having established the rules, examples of different styles of venues at different sizes were given together with actual calculations to show how the final dimmer quantities were arrived at.

These are intended to be guide examples that you can scale up or down from or use as a starting point to work out your system.

4.9 Further Reading

The following books may be found beneficial if a large amount of specific lighting and dimming system design work is to be undertaken.

Control Systems for Live Entertainment by John Huntington published by Focal Press 2nd Edition 2000.

Lighting Control – Technology and Applications by Robert S. Simpson published by Focal Press, 2003.

Lighting Modern Buildings by Derek Phillips published by Architectural Press, 2000.

Lighting by D.C. Pritchard published by Addison Wesley Longman, 5th Edition 1995.

Lighting Technology by Brian Fitt and Joe Thornley published by Focal Press, 2nd Edition 2001.

Lighting Systems for TV Studios by Nick Mobsby published by Entertainment Technology Press, 2nd Edition 2005.

Lighting Techniques for Theatre-In-The-Round by Jackie Staines published by Entertainment Technology Press, 2001.

Practical DMX by Nick Mobsby published by Entertainment Technology Press, 2005.

The Art of Stage Lighting by Frederick Bentham published by Sir Issac Pittman & Sons Ltd., 1968.

Sixty Years of Light Work by Frederick Bentham published by Entertainment Technology Press, 2002.

Stage Lighting Controls by Ulf Sandström published by Focal Press, 1997.

Stage Lighting Design by Richard Pilbrow published by Nick Hern Books Ltd. 1997.

Yesterday's Lights – A Revolution Reported by Francis Reid published by Entertainment Technology Press, 2003.

PORTABLE DIMMER BOXES

Kliegl Portable Dimmer Boxes are designed for traveling theatrical companies, outdoor stages, and other occasions where a temporary switchboard is required. They are built in a trunk-like box, with removable front, in which are assembled all the switches, dimmers, plugging receptacles, et cetera, necessary for the operation of stage lamps, border lights, footlights, and other lighting equipment. Traveling companies find Kliegl Portable Dimmer Boxes of inestimable value for special lighting and color lighting effects, and also useful as an auxiliary to inadequate installations likely to be found in small theatres. They enable road companies to be independent of permanent theatre lighting equipment.

Kliegl Portable Dimmer Boxes are built of wood, lined with sheet metal; mounted on casters to facilitate transportation; switches, cutouts and all live parts completely covered; only control handles exposed. They are built in one or more sections, depending on the amount of equipment to be controlled. Each circuit is controlled by a switch with cutout fused to required capacity, and with plugging-pocket or pin-connector outlets — depending upon the current carrying capacity of the circuits; connections can be made and broken quickly and easily; main fuse switch of proper capacity with flexible stage cable for service supply-line is furnished in any desired length, either 2- or 3-conductor.

Dimmers are banked and installed in bottom of box, in any and as many combinations as required, either interlocking or non-interlocking. In case of interlocking, a master lever permitting dimmer control individually and collectively is provided. One or several circuits may be connected to a single dimmer plate, depending on requirements.

Kliegl Portable Dimmer Boxes operate on either direct or alternating current. Price quotations are furnished on receipt of full information as to the number of circuits and current capacity of circuits to be controlled by dimmers, number of outlets for each circuit, whether dimmers are to be interlocking or non-interlocking, and whether Dimmer Box is to be wired for 2-wire or 3-wire circuits.

Fig. 8. Portable Dimmer Box with fuse-and-switch covers removed

Fig 12: From 1926 Kliegl catalogue – portable dimmers 1926 style, information: McGraw Collection, USA.

5 ARCHITECTURAL DIMMING

The Emirates Towers in Dubai is illuminated by an exterior lighting scheme that is remotely controlled via a central architectural control and dimming system (insert) photos: Delmatic Ltd.

Contents:
- **Wall Box Dimmers**
- **UK Wall Dimmers**
- **USA Wall Dimmers**
- **Commercial Lighting Dimmers**
- **Commercial Lighting Controllers**
- **Dimming Fluorescent Lamps**
- **Conclusions**

5.1 Introduction

This short chapter takes a brief look at the world of architectural dimming which seems to be spanning an ever wider range of diverse solutions. In some parts of the world the residential applications of these systems is immense, with extremely large companies producing many solutions. Historically, architectural dimming was the name given to the dimmers and control systems used to control the houselights in cinemas, theatres and the like. In fact for many years a single 20A dimmer was enough for the average cinema – later progressing to an automatic dimmer where the lights faded up and down in a preset time! This progressed to lighting control in public areas of hotels, museums and in fact almost any application that was not theatrical.

During the past 30 years or so this has grown exponentially from the simple dimmer in the lounge to thousands of channels of dimming used throughout a cruise ship. Many of the bigger systems now use the same dimmers as we would be familiar with in our dimmer room. The systems have now become highly integrated, with residential systems now also controlling curtains, and being linked to home theatre and other integrated control systems. Prior to looking in detail at the entertainment dimmers in the next chapter, let's take a brief look at the other side of the coin and the very large market it has become!

In public spaces lighting control and lighting design are now part of nearly every refurbishment and new-build; the schemes create mood and atmosphere and change with the time of day, mainly automatically. They can sense presence of people, daylight, light levels and constantly change the feel and look of a space.

Many of the architectural dimming systems are directly linked with unique architectural control solutions. These are not part of this book and are discussed in the companion book, *Practical Control*. This chapter looks at the different dimming systems used and concentrates on the smaller systems as hard wired and high density dimmers are already explained next in Chapter 6 with new transistorised solutions detailed in Chapter 7.

5.2 Wall Box Dimmers

As the name implies these are dimmers that fit into a box mounted in the wall. Here again we have different sizes and formats due to the different sizes of electrical back boxes prevalent around the world.

In most cases one country leads the world in producing wall box dimmers, namely the USA. Companies include as Genltye with Entertainment Technology and Lightolier Controls, Leviton with Colortran and NSI, Lutron, with others such as ETC. Around the rest of the world we have Delmatic, Dynalite, iLight, Polaron, Mode Electronics, Anytronics, MK Electric, Crabtree, Leax and lighting manufacturers such as Philips, Osram, Erco and many others – all producing systems to enhance sales of their other products.

If first we look at the standard UK incandescent lamp wall box dimmer we can then consider the more sophisticated versions. For many years in the UK the £10 to £15 wall box dimmer has been available from our equivalent of Home Depot with Homebase, B & Q, Focus and Do It All. Homebase were offering at least four versions when I recently checked out in a store in Bedfordshire.

5.3   UK Wall Dimmers

The latest European dimmers employ the latest micro-controller based circuitry to provide electronic soft-start and overload protection. They are suitable for use with tungsten GLS lamps, mains halogen lamps and for dimming low voltage lighting when used with electronic or wire-wound LV transformers. These types of dimmer are NOT suitable for fluorescent loads. In fact, later in this chapter a brief look into fluorescent dimming is provided. The controls on most of them are very simple – push for on/off and rotate clockwise to increase intensity - and may be connected into a two way switching circuit. The come in many different colours and styles and power ratings. The typical ratings within Europe are 250, 500 and 600 watts. The standard UK single gang electrical plate size is 86 x 86 mm. *Fig 1* shows three standard formats of electrical plates, the offered simple dimmers from one manufacturer and details of the sizing standards.

After these built-into-the-wall dimmers the next group are the unit dimmers designed to handle higher wattage loads as might be found in a staff café or a small meeting room. These tend to be built into industrial enclosures, may look very basic and house a triac or thyristor dimmer usually with a choke producing around 100 to 200μS rise times. These units tend to feature a sensible choke and therefore are moving towards the same professional dimmers as we would use in entertainment. *Fig 2* shows such a typical UK range from one UK manufacturer. *Fig 3* shows the standard unit produced by Strand Lighting in the 1970s that really comprised a JTM or later an STM dimmer module used in another format as a theatrical dimmer. This was the basis of many

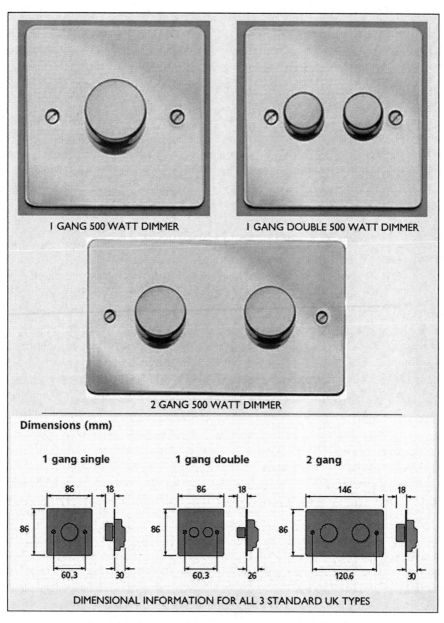

Fig 1: Typical UK Wall Box formats of single and twin gang plates all fitted with 500 watt 230/240 volt 50 Hz dimmers, photos and drawing: MK Electric Ltd.

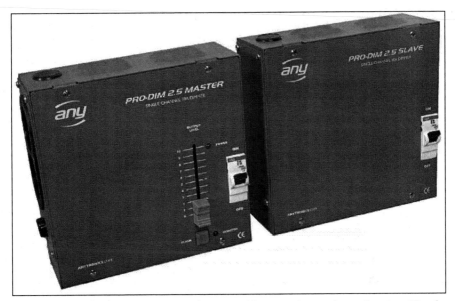

Fig 2: Typical UK High Power Unit dimmers able to receive analogue 0 to +ve 10 volt dc or DMX data input, photos: Anytronics Ltd.

early architectural dimming systems, often being controlled from a simple analogue fader panel.

5.4   USA Wall Dimmers

If we stop here for a moment and look at a similar situation in the USA or in the 120 volt market a completely different range of products is produced. Simple rotary or slider controls exist just like Europe, however there is soon a major departure as wall dimmers with presets, remote controllable units and many more simple solutions are available as shown in *Fig 4*. These products, with preset capabilities, offer a number of user benefits. Some have a location LED that remains on in the dark so that you can easily find the place to turn the lights on. Some have a slider with intensity LEDs by the side to confirm the selected intensity, others have the ability to store the level so that each time the circuit is turned on the lamps come on at the preset level. Others even include a built-in fade up and fade down time just like a theatre console. Others have a built in 'soft-start' of typically 1 second. This ensures that lamps fade up or fade down more slowly. This has an additional benefit in terms of extended lamp life. Because the filament is being 'stretched' more slowly it is

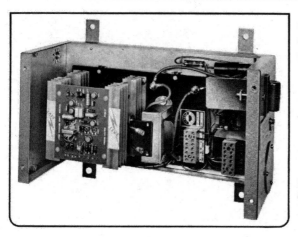

RANK STRAND

Rank Strand Electric,
P.O. Box 70,
Great West Road, Brentford,
Middlesex, TW8 9HR.
Telephone: 01-568 9222 Telex: 27 976

A Division of Rank Audio Visual Limited

**220/240v
50Hz**

Type TU, MTU and PTU Thyristor Unit Dimmers

*Fig 3: Early 'architectural' dimmer from Rank Strand in 1976
photo: The STLD Archive.*

less likely to fail. Each turning on and off cycle results in much less stressing of the filament and therefore prolonged lamp life, when compared to a direct fed lamp. Similar improvements in lamp life can be obtained by under running the lamp by just a few percent.

Maybe it's the number sold but costs in the USA seem to be proportionally lower than European units. A selection of these is shown in *Fig 5*. For example, if we look at the 600 watt units the simplest rotary dimmer from Lightolier or Lutron seems to be available between $7 and $10 (£4 to £6), the versions with presets are available at around

Fig 4: Typical residential lighting control application, photo: Lutron Electronics, Inc.

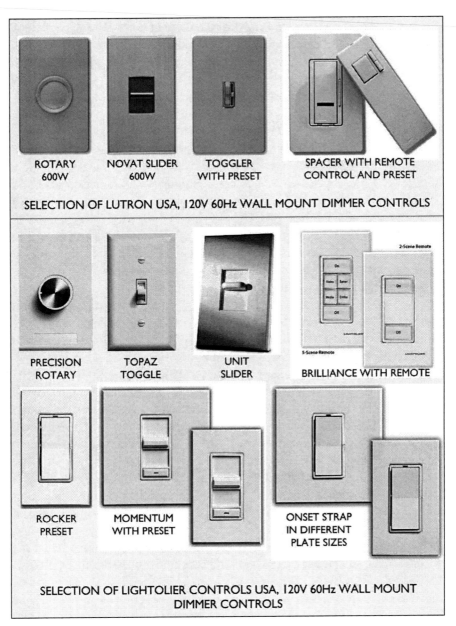

ROTARY
600W

NOVAT SLIDER
600W

TOGGLER
WITH PRESET

SPACER WITH REMOTE
CONTROL AND PRESET

SELECTION OF LUTRON USA, 120V 60Hz WALL MOUNT DIMMER CONTROLS

PRECISION
ROTARY

TOPAZ
TOGGLE

UNIT
SLIDER

BRILLIANCE WITH REMOTE

ROCKER
PRESET

MOMENTUM
WITH PRESET

ONSET STRAP
IN DIFFERENT
PLATE SIZES

SELECTION OF LIGHTOLIER CONTROLS USA, 120V 60Hz WALL MOUNT
DIMMER CONTROLS

Fig 5: Typical USA Wall Box formats of single and twin plates
photos: from listed manufacturers.

$25 to $30 (£14 to £17) and the fully infra red remotely controllable versions around $60 (£35). As in Europe they all come in a wide range of colours and finishes and match plate sizes for other services like power outlets, data and telephone jacks. The ranges extend to higher wattage 1000 watt units using the same face plates and controls, and here the prices climb to around $100.

5.5 Commercial Lighting Dimmers

This part of the market continues to offer controls and dimmers integrated into a wall mounting enclosure. Here again complete systems with dimmers and controls can be provided such as the Lightolier Scenist and Lutron Grafik Eye 2000 and 3000 Series. These are widely used in a single room application or larger residential applications where trying to find space to accommodate remote dimmers can be difficult. These units often allow dimmer channels to be turned into switches allowing control of blinds and curtains (drapes) and in the current home theatre trend into screen control as well.

As soon as you move towards more than one channel of control then we are into so called 'commercial solutions'. Historically the commercial architectural control systems were often based around use of professional analogue input unit dimmers that could be used separately or could be linked together on some sort of back plane to produce a multi-channel solution. An example of this was the Rank Strand Environ range. These were individual dimmers that could be linked together to form a larger channel system. There were also automatic versions of the dimmers that had built-in time fades that were set through 'trim pots'. These could be remotely accessed through push buttons although care was needed if a number of panels were in use, sometimes requiring a Take Control switch. *Fig 6* is a copy of the 1989 Strand Catalogue showing the later version of these dimmers called Environ 2. Strand has produced a wide range of these systems with Microdim, Outlook and Premier – the latter two being large scale processing systems that would link to their range of installed dimmers.

Once multi channel becomes the norm then the next change is whether the system is centrally processed or whether distributed processors are employed. The leading USA based companies here are Lightolier with their Lytemode and Compli controls. Lutron offer the widely used Grafik Eye system and Leviton their Dimensions 4200 and 8000 Series. Crestron, makers of a very large range of integrated controls, also have their own central controller with external unit and cabinet dimmers. Samples of these systems are shown in

PRESET DIMMERS	DIMENSIONS				RATING	TYPE
	H	W	D	Wt		
Modular plug-in automatic dimmers which can be configured into a dimming system comprising a mixture of tungsten or fluorescent loads.	270	135	210	3.5	6A (1.5kW)	Tungsten (P)
	270	135	210	4.0	16A (4kW)	Tungsten (P)
	270	135	210	5.5	32A (7.5kW)	Tungsten (P)
	270	135	210	3.5	6A	Fluorescent (P)
	270	135	210	4.0	16A	Fluorescent (P)
	270	135	210	5.5	32A	Fluorescent (P)

CONTROL STATIONS FOR USE WITH ENVIRON 2 PRESET DIMMERS

- 1-Gang Preset Outstation (4 Pushbutton)
- 2-Gang Preset Outstation (8 Pushbutton)
- 3-Gang Preset Outstation (12 Pushbutton)
- 6-Gang Preset Outstation (24 Pushbutton)
- 1-Gang UP/STOP/DOWN Outstation (3 Pushbutton)
- 2-Gang UP/STOP/DOWN Outstation (6 Pushbutton)
- 2-Gang UP/STOP/DOWN Outstation (9 Pushbutton)

MANUAL DIMMERS	DIMENSIONS				RATING	TYPE
	H	W	D	Wt		
Modular plug-in manual dimmers which can be configured into a dimming system comprising a mixture of tungsten or fluorescent loads.	270	135	210	3.5	6A (1.5kW)	Tungsten (N-P)
	270	135	210	4.0	16A (4kW)	Tungsten (N-P)
	270	135	210	5.5	32A (7.5kW)	Tungsten (N-P)
	270	135	210	3.5	6A	Fluorescent (N-P)
	270	135	210	4.0	16A	Fluorescent (N-P)
	270	135	210	5.5	32A	Fluorescent (N-P)

CONTROL STATIONS FOR USE WITH ENVIRON 2 MANUAL DIMMERS

		Cat No.		
1-Gang Slider Fader		09 110 18		1-Gang Rotary
2-Gang Slider Fader		09 120 15		2-Gang Rotary
3-Gang Slider Fader		09 130 12		3-Gang Rotary
6-Gang Slider Fader		09 160 14		Take Control (Fader plus Take Push)
6-Gang Slider Fader with Master		09 160 06		Photo Cell (including mounting bracket)
				Amplifier and Setting Panel (for Photocell)

ENVIRON 2 ACCESSORIES

Strand Rail (Mounting Plate 1 metre) : Wall fixing for Dimmer Modules

Mains Connection Box : Mains input for Multi-Dimmer installation

Busbar Connecting Set : Links between Modules and to Mains Box

Multi-Phase linking kit : Links Earth and Neutral in 3 Phase installations

Fig 6: 1989 Strand Catalogue and Environ 2 range, photo: Strand Lighting Ltd.

Fig 7. This is really where the break point comes in terms of what is control and what is dimmer related. All the controls shown in *Fig 7* require external dimming resulting in a wide range of wall mount dimmer combinations being offered.

In Europe and the rest of the 230 volt world there is a proliferation of systems from many manufacturers that handle the small, medium and large scale requirements. The market leaders in this area produce an immense range of products that seem to be constantly evolving as this market burgeons into being potentially larger than the entertainment dimmer one. Helvar are a major player and produce a very large range extending from a single channel through to very large building-wide systems, adding their own dimmable ballasts to control fluorescent installations. Polaron with iLight, Zero 88 and Light Processor, all now part of the Polaron Group, mix across both architectural and entertainment markets. Hamilton, Ex-Or, Leax, Dynalite and many others exist with many of the entertainment dimmer manufacturers also producing architectural control systems as a way of increasing the sales of their entertainment dimmers. Anytronics, Strand, ETC, Zero 88, and Mode Electronics are all in this category.

When launched, many of these systems sent analogue data to the dimmers, then unique protocols were developed to make the installation simpler. As protocols, such as DMX, became the norm this resulted in many analogue dimming systems disappearing in favour of only DMX input units. Whilst some manufacturers still continue with their own protocols, others have switched to DMX. An example of this is the Strand Lighting Accent DMX system launched in 2004. This offers the simplicity of a simple wall controller with 8 or 4 presets that can control up to 48 DMX channels per room. This links to any suitable DMX dimmer and you have a low cost control system with say 24 low-cost dimmers for less than £2500 ($4,400).

From here the system become ever more complex but in essence just like a theatre system the dimming blocks are made up from those hard wired and medium/high density units shown in the next chapter. Sometimes the dimming and the control system are linked together so that processing located inside the dimmer rack is remotely accessed from the remote control stations. This is the case with the Strand Outlook and the ETC Unison system, although ETC also offer the Unison processing system as a stand alone system. *Fig 8* shows some examples of the specially manufactured architectural dimmers that were available in early 2006.

Interestingly, the architectural world has its own range of control protocols; some of these are known also to the entertainment world such as the short distance EIA232 and the longer distance EIA485 (this is very similar to DMX) and then we depart into DALI – Digital Addressable Lighting Interface. This is really the opposite of DMX in that it was specifically designed to standardise control of fluorescent ballasts but now has become used for other light sources. DALI never set out to control a building – more to address individually fittings within a single or group of rooms. The cost per fitting of adding a DALI node is low helping to produce a high uptake with the ballast manufacturers. Converters between DALI and EIA232/485 are available enabling linking to other control devices and personal computers. Systems running on LON and Lonworks are common, others running on manufacturers' own Ethernet based networks are becoming prevalent particularly when those manufacturers offer solutions in both theatrical and architectural markets. Some systems in Europe operate on the European standardised EIB – European Installation Bus - although this seems to have had less success than others available. Indeed there seems to be a wide range of these protocols, all happily co-exist and often interfaces between them are available. Needless to say at some point all of these networks need to interface to the external dimmers.

5.6 Commercial Lighting Controllers

The blossoming world of architectural control has become highly intelligent and completely integrated. The home market is well serviced by systems developed in the USA and now also produced by a wide range of manufacturers servicing the 230 volt markets. *Fig 10* shows a typical small network that can run a large residential property through to a small group of conference rooms. But this is just the beginning. The capabilities of these networks are immense and their ability to be linked to Building Management Systems (BMS) to fire and security to heating, ventilation and air conditioning all go to make a completely controlled and managed space that can change as the usage, occupancy or time of day changes. Today the designers' creations are all possible but at an economic cost.

The networks allow local control within a room, global control and managed instructions to all co-exist. This often requires the dimming to be distributed around the building rather than being centralised in a dimmer room. This concept is explained in greater detail relative to entertainment venues in Chapter 7. In commercial spaces it is similar to how an electrical

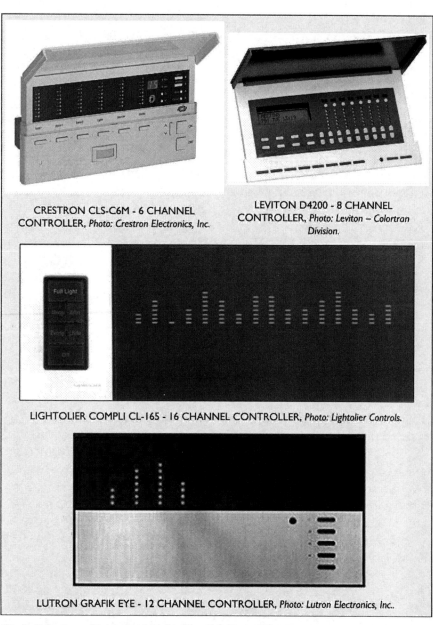

CRESTRON CLS-C6M - 6 CHANNEL CONTROLLER, Photo: Crestron Electronics, Inc.

LEVITON D4200 - 8 CHANNEL CONTROLLER, Photo: Leviton – Colortran Division.

LIGHTOLIER COMPLI CL-165 - 16 CHANNEL CONTROLLER, Photo: Lightolier Controls.

LUTRON GRAFIK EYE - 12 CHANNEL CONTROLLER, Photo: Lutron Electronics, Inc..

Fig 7: Selection of Integrated Multi-Channel Controller connecting to external dimmers, photos: from named manufacturers.

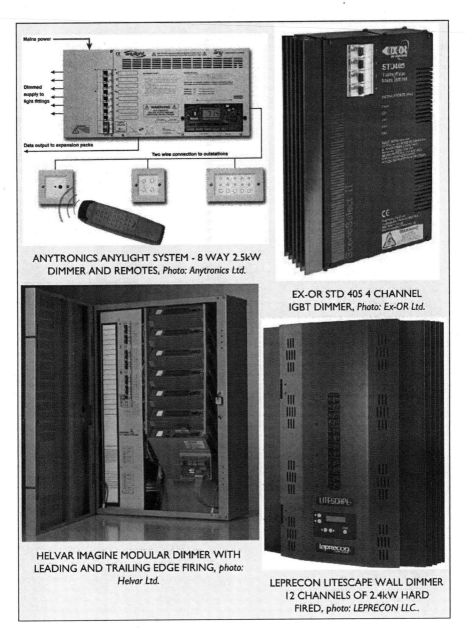

ANYTRONICS ANYLIGHT SYSTEM - 8 WAY 2.5kW
DIMMER AND REMOTES, Photo: Anytronics Ltd.

EX-OR STD 405 4 CHANNEL
IGBT DIMMER, Photo: Ex-OR Ltd.

HELVAR IMAGINE MODULAR DIMMER WITH
LEADING AND TRAILING EDGE FIRING, photo:
Helvar Ltd.

LEPRECON LITESCAPE WALL DIMMER
12 CHANNELS OF 2.4kW HARD
FIRED, photo: LEPRECON LLC..

*Fig 8: Selection of European and USA Commercial Grade Architectural Dimmers,
photos: from named manufacturers.*

HELVAR DIGIDIM 4 – 4 x 10 AMP DIMMER.

HELVAR 425 – 1 x 25 AMP DIMMER.

HELVAR DIGIDIM 5 – 5 x 25 AMP DIMMER.

POLARON MSD/U4/10 4 x 10 AMP DIMMER.

POLARON MSD/C8/10/DSI/PD 8 x 10 AMP UNIVERSAL DIMMER.

LEVITON A 200 18 x 20 AMP DIMMER.

POLARON MSD/U12/10 36 x 10 AMP UNIVERSAL DIMMER.

CRESTRON CNLDM-6 6 x 20 AMP DIMMER.

Fig 9: Further selection of unit and small channel capacity dimming solutions from around the world, photos: from named manufacturers.

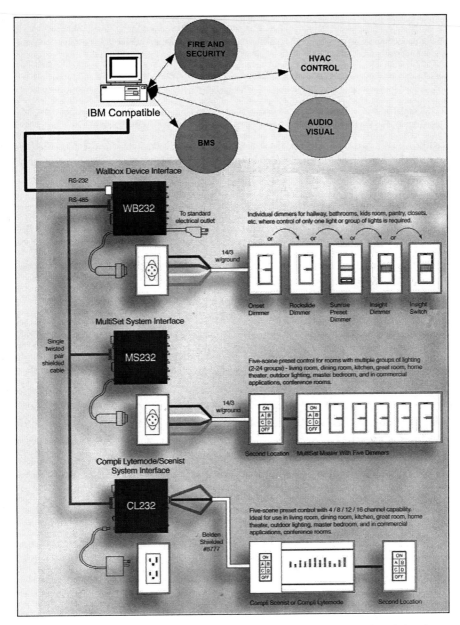

Fig 10: Typical small commercial network from Lightolier Controls in the USA with links to other systems, drawings: Lightolier Controls, Inc and the author.

installation is designed. Here we tend to have a large electrical supply fed into the building or derived from a transformer located in the building. From here a large capacity supply is fed to the 'intake' and from there the supply is broken down into smaller capacity 'feeders' and sent around the building to specific geographic locations or floor by floor. At these locations local distribution takes over with loads connected directly to the local distribution boards or via dimmers and relays. Consequently these are the locations for the dimmers and remotely controlled switches, hence distributing the dimmers around the building. Nothing new in the architectural world, and actually a very economic way of designing a solution! Equally the number of dimmers per floor or per room is low hence the preponderance of small to medium capacity dimming systems.

Figs 8 and 9 show the many different formats that dimmers are available in and interestingly it really does not matter where you are in the world, the channel sizes and capacities are the same - even if the outer box looks different and the electrical supply codes and standards vary.

5.7 Dimming Fluorescent Lamps

Historically this process of dimming fluorescent 'tubes' was achieved by heating the tubes via the heater windings in each end of the tube, this heater supply being derived from a permanent power out from the dimmer – the third wire! The AC voltage was then varied across the fluorescent tube and dimming was achieved before the tube went out at anywhere between 10 and 30% light output. Early systems could often be seen with bands of light and dark blocks moving up and down the tube. These 'Faraday dark spaces' were the result of the arc across the tube not being fully struck – something I know a lot about following my work on the West End production of the show *Jesus Christ Superstar* mentioned in Chapter 2!

Times have changed and dimming of fluorescent fittings is now all about ECG's. So what are ECG's? This abbreviation stands for Electronic Control Gear and is basically an electronic version of the old magnetic ballasts found in all fluorescent fittings until around 10 years ago. Whilst still around, most fitting manufacturers offer solutions with electronic control gear based around high frequency electronics. The control of these devices initially was via analogue 0 to 10 volts. This required power supplies but allowed all sorts of low voltage control systems to be used, just as they were for remote dimmers whose input was often 0 to 10 volts. The problem was to provide enough ways of 2 core cable if one wanted to control individual fittings in terms of intensity and power on and off. With a large office complex this type of control provided good intensity control with 0 to 100% control. However no feedback was provided and unless a considerable number of 2 core cables were installed to a complex switching system individual control was not easily possible.

So the industry solved this problem by developing a solution that enables control of these fittings to be simplified whilst still allowing each fitting or group of fittings to be individually addressed and also to return information. This has been achieved by the DALI protocol mentioned earlier in this chapter. DALI can be run in power cables and simply links between devices. Each device can be given an address or each group of fittings can be given the same address. DALI brought a number of user benefits other than the addressing capability. With Osram gear this includes simple wiring; group linking is not necessary due to the addressability of the system. The ECG's store the scene intensity values and any group assignments, can report status messages back to a central controller and all ECG's reach the same intensity at the same time.

Needless to say there are different manufacturers of these ECG's including Helvar, Lightolier, Philips and Tridonic, to name a few. They all produce different versions to suit the many different lamp types and lengths and some can handle more than one lamp.

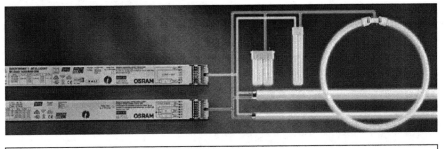

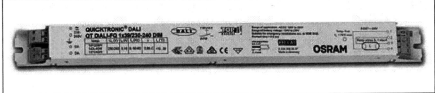

Fig 11: Osram advertising picture from 2000 of their universal electronic control gear and an actual ECG from their current range, photos: Osram GmbH.

5.8 Conclusions

Just before this chapter closes I found a system as I was writing that really seems very clever and so simple if you want to control a residential or small number of rooms. This comes from a UK company called Rako Controls based in Chatham, UK. They have produced a first class range of radio controls and dimmers which simply replace the existing installation in the room(s) with one of their devices, albeit it a wall control plate, infra red receiver and an installed or in line dimmer. The dimmers receive data from a radio receiver and are just like an electronic transformer so they can be inserted easily into a ceiling just like a downlighter. The range is very comprehensive and makes, in my view, a highly flexible solution that anyone can install.

Fig 12: Some of Rako Controls range, photos: Rako Controls Ltd.

This chapter covered very briefly the different types of dimmers found in the architectural world. Out of necessity some of the different types of control systems, protocols and networking solutions were briefly reviewed. Modern methods of dimming fluorescent lamps were also explained and the DALI protocol. The next chapter looks at the many different forms of entertainment dimming.

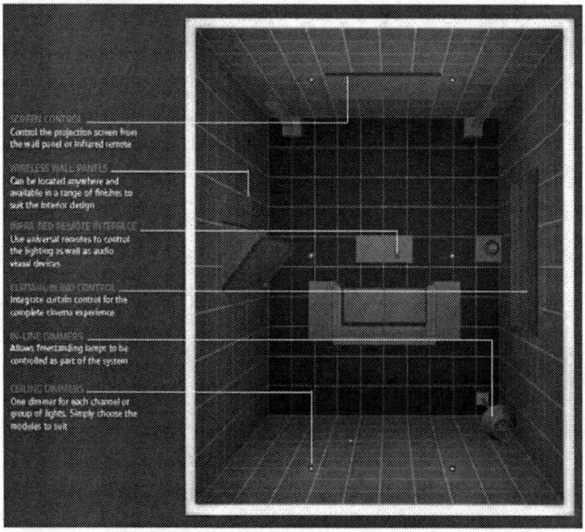

Fig 13: Typical radio control system application, drawing: Rako Controls Ltd.

6 TYPES OF DIMMERS

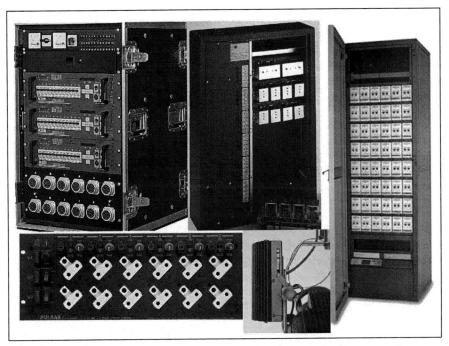

Selection of different types of dimmers 1970s, 1980s, 1990s and 21st Century, photos: ADB Technologies SA., Entertainment Technology, Inc, Pulsar Ltd., Strand Lighting Ltd. and the author.

Contents:

- **Unit Dimmers**
- **Low Cost Portable and Rack Mounting Packs**
- **19 Inch Rack Mountable Dimmers**
- **Professional Rack Mount and Pack Dimmers**
- **Flight Cased Dimmers**
- **Hard Wired Dimmers**
- **High Density Modular Dimmers**
- **Conclusion**
- **Contact Address List**

6.1 Introduction

Current dimmer technology tends to package entertainment dimmers into five distinct categories:

Individual dimmers fitted to luminaires or lighting bars.

Portable packs that may also be rack mounted.

Professional rack mounted packs.

Medium density wall mountable hard wired dimmers.

Modular plug in dimmers contained in floor standing cabinets.

Distributed Dimmers and Dimmer Bars.

This chapter considers each type with a list of potential manufacturers. All are considered suitable for all types of performance and entertainment venue applications.

6.2 Individual Dimmers

Whilst unit dimmers have been used for many years for items such as followspots they have tended to be physically large and have been difficult to integrate into a system as they often could only be controlled locally. In recent years new technology has allowed the economic production of unit dimmers that are small enough to be located on a luminaire or rigged onto a school grid, on a stage bar, in fact virtually anywhere a luminaire can be rigged. The unit dimmer can provide an ideal solution for small and medium size venues as they can be rigged where required just like a luminaire, helping to reduce initial capital costs and reducing the redundancy factor common in most large dimmer installations. Historically, the Magic Lantern from Tim Burnham, when he ran TBA in the UK in the 1980s, is a very good example of a unit dimmer as also is the much later unit from Don Hindle and David Manners for the Freedom range of luminaires, when they owned CCT Theatre Lighting.

This approach can benefit the venue budget as only the required number of dimmers need to be purchased rather than a blanket coverage approach used with most other dimmer types discussed later in this chapter. Typically a museum, studio theatre, TV studio grid, theatre boom or ladder, or school installation, could significantly benefit from this unit dimmer approach.

The latest product in this area is from Entertainment Technology from the USA and is called Bakpak. This product uses IGBT transistor technology making Bakpak small enough to clip onto the luminaire trunnion arm. Bakpak is available in 750W or 1200W for 110 volt countries and 1.2 and 2.4kW versions for 220/240 volt countries. As the unit is microprocessor controlled functions such as voltage compensation, remote DMX data control, local memory storage and, for very small venues or exhibitions, the ability to be programmed to remain set at a level without a control desk. Perhaps more importantly the microprocessor software monitors the current flow, shutting the dimmer down in the event of an overload or short circuit without requiring a

Fig 1: Entertainment Technology Bakpak Unit dimmer
photo: Entertainment Technology Inc.

circuit breaker or fuse. They are also small enough to be used with portable lighting kits. CCT Lighting from the UK also make similar unit dimmer solutions.

I have undertaken some recent research and found that unit dimmers can offer an ideal solution for many applications where having to run a considerable amount of load cabling is difficult and untidy. Hotels, museums, small TV studios, studio theatres, free standing displays or exhibition stands and shopping malls have all benefited from this solution. Using the unit dimmer simplifies the electrical system as only direct power outlets with some lighting data are required, once again helping to control the cost.

A typical unit dimmer lists at around £250 to £300 ($450 to $550) depending on the rating. The easiest electrical system for such dimmers is to wire radial (direct) circuits from an MCB type electrical distribution to a suitably rated power socket outlet. With small power dimmers such as 750W or 1.2kW units even a simple 30A ring system, common in the UK, can be used, or the European 10A radial circuit.

6.3 Portable Packs – Standard

These tend to be available in modules of 3, 6 and 12 channels and are produced by a number of manufacturers across the world. One of the most important criteria is how much interference they generate and how much acoustic noise will be heard from the luminaire filament. In Europe there is a dearth of 6 channel packs produced for use in night clubs, school halls, amateur theatres and rental applications. Portable packs are ideal for these applications but are not suited to television or classical music venues due to their relatively poor interference suppression and the higher levels of acoustic noise heard in the lamp filaments. Typical products in this area are the Zero 88 Betapack (UK), Anytronics 610 packs (UK), Electron Apollo Plus (Greece), Pulsar Rackpak (UK), ADB Micropack (Belgium), Strand Act 6 (UK) and many others produced around the world. Packs of this type tend to be built to a price level and often utilise low grade fuses for output protection. One of the concerns with packs at this price level is that some of them are not designed to operate on a continuous duty cycle. By this I mean the specification sheet might say 6 x 10A or 6 x 2.5kW. If you load up the pack to 60 Amps or 15kW some of them literally start to melt, fuse holders burn out, and the terminals inside the packs burn out. Care is therefore needed when reading the literature because sometimes the manufacturer will say something like maximum load 45 Amps or do not exceed 80% of total specified load.

Many of these portable packs use noise reduction chokes with rise times of around 80 microseconds. Some can be purchased with wall mounting or 19 inch racking kits enabling a number of packs to be housed together to make a dimming system. In terms of economics this makes some sense up to say 24 channels, thereafter alternative larger packing formats offer better value for money and an easier installation. One significant advantage of a 6 pack is that as funds become available another pack can be added. Visiting many smaller educational stages you can immediately see the different generations of packs that have been added over the years. The break point is really at the 24 channel size as this level the cost of the dimmers versus the cost of the installation starts to diverge. At this point the wall mounted cabinet dimmers, discussed later in this chapter, take over as they are easier to install and offer a considerable cost reduction when compared to multiple 6 channel packs.

Probably the epitome of the European portable pack is the Zero 88 Betapack as shown in *Fig 2*. This pack was launched at the end of the 1980s and has gone through various stages of development. Today it is still the best known pack available. Typical costs tend to be around £100 per channel at current (2006) UK list prices with DMX control and MCB protection.

Fig 2: Zero 88 Betapack 2 - 6 Channel portable dimmer pack, circa 2002 photo: Zero 88 Lighting Ltd.

In the USA portable packs exist in a similar format to Europe from manufacturers such as Electronics Diversified, Lightronics, ETC and Leprecon. One of the popular portable pack formats is shown in *Fig 3*. This is truly portable and with DMX control allows packs to be located with booms or lighting bars as required. Typical pack sizes are in 3 or 6 channel formats with 1.2kW or 2.4kW capacities. With a 6 channel pack rated at 1.2kW

Fig 3: Lightronics AS – 62D - 6 Channel
Portable Dimmer Pack
photo: Lightronics, Inc.

from Lightronics they confirm that a maximum load of 4.8kW should not be exceeded. Interestingly, unlike Europe, the rise time per dimmer is quoted as being 350 microseconds.

In both cases the European and USA portable dimmers are based around triacs as the power control device, both in their standard forms utilise replaceable fuses, to maintain their low cost, and both types operate with a DMX input. In the USA similar packs to the European 6 pack are also available. Most of these tend also to be suitable for mounting into 19 inch type equipment racks or flight cases.

6.3   Portable Packs – Rack Mount

These are another derivation of the portable packs previously discussed. They are available throughout the world and are produced from China to Greece with output connectors to match the local electrical specifications and standards. Indeed some manufacturers produce a wide range of the same pack with different connectors to try and maximise their sales across the world. In Europe alone we still have different connectors in many countries. The television and film world seem to have solved this problem by using the Ceeform type connector range shown in *Fig 4*.

In the USA the ratings of the packs are usually 1.2kW, 2.4kW and 6kW with

Fig 4: Example of Ceeform type BS4343
connector range photo: MK Electric Ltd.

versions available in 3, 6 and 12 channel formats with again a number of different connector formats. Examples of the many different types of packs found in the USA are shown in *Fig 5*.

The data sheet for the ETC SmartPack in the USA shows these to be available with Edison, Twist Lock, Stage Pin, Socapex single and double multiway, 6 and 12 ways of Powerlock, and 6 and 12 ways of screw terminals for hard or rack wired formats. These are detailed in *Fig 6*. To match the European market ETC have also produced this pack with UK 15A, Shuko, CEE 17, French Shuko and Harting multiway, altogether necessitating them producing some 14 different rear panels. Maybe one day we can find an international connector for the entertainment market that has 110 and 230 volt versions. Is this where the CEE 17 connector comes in?

Fig 7 details a selection of packs that are available in Europe and the rest of the world. Again this shows the very wide variety of output connectors that are

LIGHTRONIC RA – 121D - 12 x 1.2kW
DIMMERS

ELECTRONICS DIVERSIFIED DIMMEX
DXM24-1 PACK - 24 x 1kW DIMMERS

ETC SMARTPACK - 12 x 1.2kW PACK

ELATION CYBER PAK - 4 x 5 AMP PACK

LEVITON - NSI DDS 8600 - 6 CHANNELS
OF 1.2kW PACK WITH MCB
PROTECTION

LEPRECON MX 1200 - 12 x 1.2kW PACK

Fig 5: Selection of 2006 Portable Packs manufactured in USA
photos: ETC, Electronics Diversified, Inc., Lightronics, Inc. and Leviton – NSI, Inc.

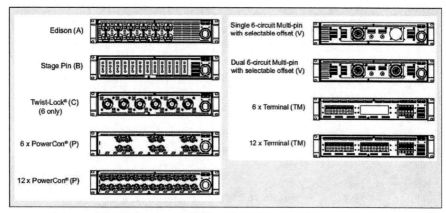

Fig 6: Rear panels available for ETC SmartPack in the USA
photo: Electronic Theatre Controls, Inc.

required. *Fig 28* in Chapter 2 shows what one UK manufacturer, Pulsar Light, provides as connector options for their Rackpak; here 6 types are provided just for the single lamp connections.

Guide list prices for different portable packs, hard wired and standard rack mount packs, current in the spring of 2006, are shown in local currency. This is by no means a complete list, more a sample to show the different formats and prices. Please check these are still current by contacting the manufacturers' web sites detailed at the end of this chapter. Rise time figures for each type are shown in brackets as provided by the manufacturers in their published data. If no figures are quoted this is because they were not available at the time of going to press.

ADB – Belgium

Micropack MIP15/62M/UK – 6 x 2.3kW with single 15 Amp UK sockets – DMX only. (80µS)	£1,008.69
Micropack MIP15/62M/CEE – 6 x 2.3kW with single CEE 17 16 Amp UK sockets – DMX only. (80µS)	£1,008.69
Micropack MIP15/62M/D – 6 x 2.3kW with twin Shuko 16 Amp UK sockets – DMX only. (80µS)	£ 996.49
Microrack 25 MIR/122M/PG/SOC, 12 x 2.3kW dimmers with 2 x Socapex outlets – DMX only. (80µS)	£1,798.91
Microrack 25 MIR25/122M/HAR, 12 x 2.3kW dimmers with 2 x Harting outlets – DMX only. (80µS)	£1,737.79
Microrack 25 MIR25/122M/AMP, 12 x 2.3kW dimmers with 2 sets of Amp connectors – DMX only. (80µS)	£1,562.63

American DJ – USA
DP DMX20L, 4 x 600 watt dimmers with maximum load of
2400 watts, twin Edison – DMX only $ 190.00
DP DMX20L, 4 x 600 watt dimmers with maximum load of
2400 watts, single Edison – DMX only $ 160.00

Anytronics – UK
K066 D610 6 x 10 Amp dimmer pack with 6 twin 15 Amp UK
sockets – DMX and analogue. (150µS)   £ 596.00
K066 D610 6 x 10 Amp dimmer pack with 6 twin Shuko 16
Amp sockets – DMX and analogue. (150µS)   £ 596.00
K066 D610 6 x 10 Amp dimmer pack with 6 twin CEE 16
Amp sockets – DMX and analogue. (150µS)   £ 586.00

Elation Lighting – USA
Cyberpak, 4 x 600 Watt relay or dimmer pack with twin Edison,
maximum load 2400 watts – DMX control. $ 260.00
DP-640, 6 channels of 10 Amp with twin Edison sockets
– DMX control. $ 430.00
DP-DMX20L 4 channel x 10 Amp dimmer pack, maximum
load 20A, twin Edison sockets – DMX control $ 240.00
DP-415, 4 channel x 5 Amp compact dimmer with single
Edison, maximum load 15 Amp – DMX control. $ 160.00

Entertainment Technology – USA
Bakpak single channel unit dimmer 750 watt with wire ends
– DMX only. (worst 400µS, best 800µS) $ 400.00
Bakpak single channel unit dimmer 1200 watt with wire ends
– DMX only. (worst 400µS, best 800µS) $ 500.00

ETC – USA
Smartpack 6 x 20 Amp dimmer with Edison twist lock
connectors – DMX only. (200µS) $1,506.00
Smartpack 6 x 20 Amp dimmer with 2 x Socapex connectors
– DMX only. (200µS) $1,895.00
Smartpack 6 x 20 Amp dimmer Wall mount version with
terminals – DMX only. (200µS) $1,895.00
Smartpack 12 x 10 Amp dimmer with 2 x Socapex connectors
– DMX only. (200µS) $2,235.00
Smartpack 12 x 10 Amp dimmer Wall mount version with
terminals – DMX only. (200µS) $2,235.00

ETC – UK

Smartpack 6 x 15 Amp dimmer with single 15 Amp UK
connectors – DMX only. (200µS)   £   696.00
Smartpack 6 x 15 Amp dimmer with 6 x twin Shuko
connectors – DMX only. (200µS)   £   696.00
Smartpack 6 x 15 Amp dimmer with 6 x single CEE 17
16 Amp connectors – DMX only. (200µS)   £   696.00
Smartpack 6 x 15 Amp dimmer with 2 x Socapex connectors
– DMX only. (200µS)   £   730.00
Smartpack 6 x 20 Amp dimmer Wall mount version with
terminals – DMX only. (200µS)   £   696.00
Smartpack 12 x 10 Amp dimmer with 12 pairs of Powercon
connectors – DMX only. (200µS)   £1,130.00
Smartpack 12 x 10 Amp dimmer with 2 pairs of Socapex
multipin connectors – DMX only. (200µS)   £1,098.00
Smartpack 12 x 10 Amp dimmer Wall mount version with
terminals – DMX only. (200µS)   £1,190.00

Leprecon – USA

LD340 DMX Portable pack with 4 x 1200 watt dimmers with
maximum load of 2400 watts – DMX control. $ 488.00
LD340 DMP-HP Portable pack with 4 x 1200 watt dimmers
with maximum load of 3600 watts – DMX control $ 595.00
LD360 DMX Portable pack with 4 x 1800 watt dimmers with
maximum load of 3600 watts – DMX control $ 522.00
LD360 DMP-HP Portable pack with 4 x 1800 watt dimmers
with maximum load of 4800 watts – DMX control $ 632.00

Light Processor – UK

Paradim Wall mount 6 x 10 Amp dimmer with hard wired
terminals – DMX only.   £   529.00
Paradim Wall mount 6 x 16 Amp dimmer with hard wired
terminals – DMX only.   £   629.00
Paradim Wall mount 6 x 10 Amp dimmer with 6 pairs of
15 Amp UK sockets – DMX only.   £   579.00
Paradim Wall mount 6 x 20 Amp dimmer with hard wired
terminals – DMX only.   £   729.00
Paradim 19 inch rack mount 6 x 10 Amp hard wired terminals
– DMX only   £   499.00
Paradim 19 inch rack mount 6 x 16 Amp hard wired terminals
– DMX only   £   629.00

Paradim 19 inch rack mount 3 x 25 Amp hard wired terminals
– DMX only £ 699.00
Paradim 19 inch rack mount 6 x 20 Amp hard wired terminals
– DMX only £ 699.00
Paradim 19 inch rack mount 6 x 10 Amp with single 15 Amp
UK sockets – DMX only £ 529.00
Paradim 19 inch rack mount 6 x 10 Amp with twin 15 Amp
UK sockets – DMX only £ 599.00
Paradim 19 inch rack mount 6 x 10 Amp with single CEE 17
16 Amp sockets – DMX only £ 599.00
Paradim 19 inch rack mount 6 x 16 Amp with single CEE 17
16 Amp sockets – DMX only £ 649.00

Lightronics – USA
AS 40D 4 x 600 watt portable pack with DMX and LMX
control input. $ 405.00
AS 42D 4 x 1200 watt portable pack with DMX and LMX
control input. $ 608.00

LSC – Australia
EPAK/X, 12 x 10 Amps with twin Socapex sockets – DMX
control. A$3,300.00
EPAK/SE, 12 x 10 Amps with twin Shuko sockets – DMX
control. A$3,300.00
EPAK/T, 12 x 10 Amps with hard wired terminals – DMX
control A$3,179.00

Multiform – UK
Masterpac 6 x 10 Amp rack mount pack with 6 x 15 Amp
UK sockets – analogue only. £ 540.00
Masterpac 6 x 10 Amp rack mount pack with 6 x twin
Shuko 16 Amp sockets – analogue only. £ 525.00
Masterpac 6 x 10 Amp rack mount pack with hard wired
terminals – analogue only. £ 500.00
Rackpac 4610 6 x 10 Amp rack mount pack with twin 15
Amp UK sockets – DMX and analogue. £ 480.00
Rackpac 4610 6 x 10 Amp rack mount pack with twin Shuko
16 Amp sockets – DMX and analogue. £ 470.00
Rackpac 4610 6 x 10 Amp rack mount pack with twin French
Shuko 16 Amp sockets – DMX and analogue. £ 470.00

Rackpac 4610 6 x 10 Amp rack mount pack with hard wired
terminals – DMX and analogue.   £ 470.00

NSI (Leviton) – USA
DS 12–12, 12 x 1200 watt with choice of connectors – DMX
only. $2,279.00
DS 12–12, 12 x 1200 watt with hard wired terminals – DMX
only. $2,279.00
DS 12–24, 12 x 2400 watt with choice of connectors – DMX
only. $3,420.00
DS 12–24, 12 x 2400 watt with hard wired terminals – DMX
only. $3,420.00
NRD8000, 8 x 1200 watt with maximum load of 9600 watts
with choice of connectors – DMX only. $ 600.00

Pulsar – UK
Minipak 27730, 3 x 10 Amp portable unit with single 15 Amp
UK connectors – analogue 0 to 10 volt only.   £ 209.00
Minipak 27780, 3 x 10 Amp portable unit with twin Shuko 16
Amp connectors – analogue 0 to 10 volt only.   £ 209.00
Unipak Skt – 1 x 10 Amp portable unit with twin 15 Amp
sockets – DMX control.   £ 215.00
Rackpak 29502AADX 2U, with 6 x 5 Amp dimmers hard
wired to terminals – DMX and analogue control.   £ 379.00
Rackpak 29502STDX 2U, with 6 x 5 Amp dimmers hard
wired to terminals – DMX and analogue control.   £ 431.00
Rackpak 21118STDX, 4U, 6 x 10 Amp rack or portable pack
with 6 twin 15 Amp UK sockets and status controls – DMX
and analogue.   £ 589.00
Rackpak 21118BRDX, 4U, 6 x 10 Amp rack or portable pack
with 6 twin 15 Amp UK sockets with MCB protection
– DMX and analogue.   £ 695.00
Rackpak 21118DX, 4U, 6 x 10 Amp rack or portable pack with
6 twin 15 Amp UK sockets - DMX and analogue.   £ 520.00
Rackpak 21112STDX, 4U, 6 x 10 Amp rack or portable pack
with 6 twin Shuko 16 Amp sockets and status controls
– DMX and analogue control.   £ 589.00
Rackpak 21119STDX, 4U, 6 x 10 Amp rack or portable pack
with 6 twin CEE 17 16 Amp sockets and status controls
– DMX and analogue.   £ 589.00

Strand Lighting - UK

> Act 6, 6 x 10 Amp wall mount pack with 6 twin 15 Amp UK
> sockets – DMX and analogue. £ 490.00
>
> Act 6, 6 x 10 Amp wall mount pack with 6 twin Shuko 16 Amp
> sockets – DMX and analogue. £ 485.00
>
> Act 6, 6 x 10 Amp wall mount pack with 6 twin CEE 17 16
> Amp sockets – DMX and analogue. £ 495.00
>
> SD6, 6 x 10 Amp rack mount or portable pack with 6 x 15
> Amp UK sockets – DMX only. £ 464.00
>
> SD6, 6 x 10 Amp rack mount or portable pack with 6 x twin
> Shuko 16 Amp sockets – DMX only. £ 469.00
>
> SD6, 6 x 10 Amp rack mount or portable pack with 6 x CEE 17
> 16 Amp sockets – DMX only. £ 485.00

Zero 88 Lighting - UK

> Betapack 2, 6 x 10 Amp portable or rack mount with 6 twin 15
> Amp UK sockets – DMX and analogue £ 570.00
>
> Betapack 2, 6 x 10 Amp portable or rack mount with 6 twin
> Shuko 16 Amp sockets – DMX and analogue. £ 570.00
>
> Betapack 2, 6 x 10 Amp portable or rack mount with 6 twin
> CEE 17 16 Amp sockets – DMX and analogue. £ 625.00
>
> Rack 6, 6 x 10 Amp rack mount with 6 x single 15 Amp UK
> sockets – DMX only. £ 425.00
>
> Rack 6, 6 x 10 Amp rack mount with 6 x twin Shuko 16 Amp
> sockets – DMX only. £ 450.00
>
> Rack 6, 6 x 10 Amp rack mount with 6 x single CEE 17
> 16 Amp sockets – DMX only. £ 475.00
>
> Alpha Pack 2 – 3 x 10 Amp dimmers with single 15 Amp UK
> socket – DMX and analogue. £ 299.00
>
> Alpha Pack 2 – 3 x 10 Amp dimmer with 3 twin Shuko sockets
> – DMX and analogue. £ 299.00
>
> Alpha Pack 2 – 3 x 10 Amp dimmer with 3 triple Swiss sockets
> – DMX and analogue. £ 299.00
>
> Install 6, 6 x 10 Amp dimmers in wall mount package with hard
> wired terminals – DMX control only. £ 460.00
>
> Install 6, 6 x 10 Amp dimmers in wall mount package with 6
> pairs of 15 Amp UK sockets – DMX control only. £ 515.00
>
> Install 6, 6 x 10 Amp dimmers in wall mount package with 6
> pairs of Shuko sockets – DMX control only. £ 515.00

The $ dollar prices are from the USA, the A$ dollar prices are from Australia.

One subject very dear to my heart is compliance with standards, and in 2004 the revised DMX standard was released by ESTA and PLASA – DMX512-A. In this standard the task group spent considerable time trying to remove the problem with connectors and now make compliance of using the correct connector mandatory if the manufacturer wants to confirm the product is compliant with the standard.

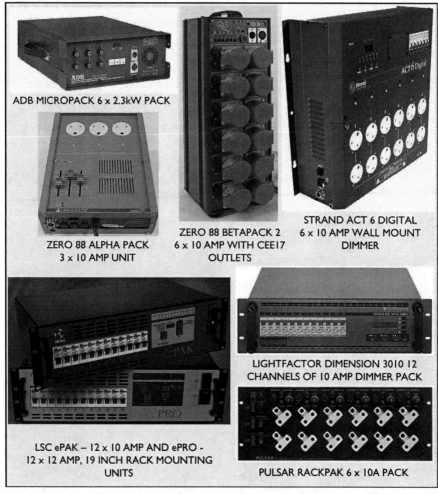

Fig 7: Selection of European Portable and Rack Mount dimmers, photos: ADB Technologies SA. (Belgium), Lightfactor Sales Ltd.(UK), LSC Lighting Systems (Aust) Pty Ltd. (Australia), Pulsar Ltd. (UK) and Strand Lighting Ltd. (UK).

However, looking at many of the lower cost dimmers listed in the price guide I see many are still using 3 pin XLR connectors. The difference in cost is an issue of course, but we are talking pence and cents not pounds and dollars here! If all would switch to the 5 pin XLR life would become so much easier. Imagine the confusion in non-professional users when a control desk arrives with a 5 pin XLR connector and yet the dimmers have a 3 pin. I am convinced that many of the problems blamed on DMX are due to these stupid issues of connectors where someone makes up an adaptor cable and creates the problem. So, manufacturers, please think carefully when your next round of product upgrading takes place!

Fig 8: Pulsar 2U Rackpak with fuse blown and load connected indicators and local intensity control, photo: Pulsar Ltd.

It is interesting to review the different price levels that exist in the USA with Europe and to see the way that the different portable formats have developed. Many more dimmers suitable for stand or truss mounting seem to exist in the USA than Europe where the electrical regulations and safety codes try more and more to hide the dimmers away in a locked electrical or dimmer room. Equally, the facilities offered and the maximum load capacity differ between them. Some dimmers like the Pulsar pack, shown in *Fig 7*, provide additional user benefits including indication of connected load and fuse failure and local channel by channel intensity controls for local level setting and testing.

When looking at these types of low cost packs there are a number of questions that should be asked before choosing a solution, the answers are shown in italics.

Is the pack to be mounted on a stand or close to the luminaires or is it to be housed in a controlled area such as a dimmer or electrical room?

If the pack is to be stand mounted then you will have to use the truly portable units like the Zero 88 Alpha Pak, Pulsar Mini Pak or in the USA then the NSI, Lightronics, Elation Lighting and American DJ portable 4 channels pack.

If the pack is to be mounted in a controlled area do you want them to be equipped with sockets so that a number of different outlets can be patched in when required or are you going to install a dimmer per outlet socket for the system?

If the dimmer is going to be wired directly to an outlet socket then you can use the lower cost hard wired terminal type dimmers where no output sockets are fitted to the dimmer. This does make the system easy to understand and is ideal for educational or non professional user systems. However, where budgets are restricted it is often beneficial to have (say) 50 to 75% more outlets wired around the venue back to patch cords that can then be plugged into the dimmer socket outlets as required. This helps keep the number of dimmers, and therefore the budget, controlled without limiting the lighting flexibility. Most manufacturers offer portable or rack mountable packs with or without sockets.

If you have elected to use the 6 or 12 channel packs are you intending to leave these as portable units or are you intending to 'rack them up' or mount them on the wall?

Common sense is an issue here, as is safety and long term security. In most venues it is also safer and more secure to have a fixed location. This makes the idea of wall mounting or housing 19 inch type packs within a proper 19 inch rack very sensible. However, if the packs have patchable outlets on the front then any proposed rack design needs to consider how the cords are plugged into the dimmers whilst maintaining security. Using security screws can help to dissuade the opportunist thief but a lockable door can completely hide the temptation. Whatever format is adopted, remember that the dimmers emit heat and therefore you cannot completely seal up the rack when in use. The wall mounted packs clearly cover this point in their original design.

If you are going to leave them as portable packs how are the packs going to be connected to a source of electrical power?

These are very important questions that span across issues of electrical safety, Health and Safety (major issue in Europe), electrical distribution and protection requirements, location of the electrical supplies, how is the pack going to be connected to the control desk and how are the luminaires (fixtures) to be connected to the dimmer? If the packs are to be used in multiple locations then a series of safe electrical connections are needed. These issues are discussed in Chapter 8. If the packs are to be mounted on to lighting stands then it is often possible to power the packs from a standard electrical outlet, helping to explain why some of the packs are limited to a maximum safe electrical load. The author's view is that any portable dimmer that is being connected to equipment that may be remote from the dimmer or has the dimmer mounted on to it, such as a stand, benefits from being connected via a residual current

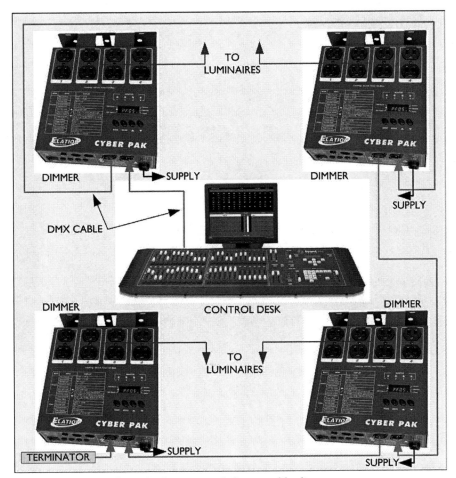

*Fig 9: Typical simple DMX data network for portable dimmers
photos: Elation Lighting Inc. (USA) and Strand Lighting Ltd. (UK).*

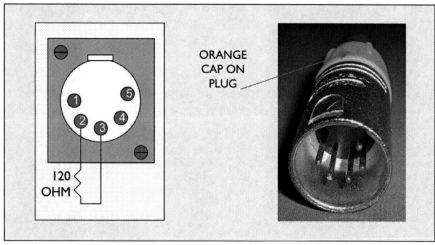

Fig 10: 5-pin XLR Male Termination Wiring and example of a Terminator plug.

breaking device. These are automatic, are very safe and reliable to use, and protect everyone no matter how experienced, when the system is in use. Again these issues are discussed in Chapter 8.

All portable packs will need to be connected to a control desk, and if there are multiple packs located around a venue this can create a mess of loose cabling that is difficult to understand, forms a tripping hazard and is itself prone to reliability issues. One way round this problem is to have a simple data network installed that links from a control position to dimmer plug-in points, daisy chain style, located around the performance space. Fig 9 shows the actual control network required for a simple 4 lighting stand installation where a 4 channel pack is locally connected to a standard electrical supply outlet and the DMX data cabling required, to complete the network. With any DMX network the critical element is making sure that a terminator is fitted in the last DMX receiver in the network. In Fig 9 the last dimmer pack is the one fitted with the terminator. These are simple devices that can be purchased for a few pounds or dollars from most distributors. For those wanting to make one up Fig 10 shows they comprise of a 120 Ohm resistor connected across Pins 2 and 3 of a 5 pin XLR – or pins 2 and 3 if a 3 pin XLR connector is in use!

In summary, the low cost portable rack and wall mount dimmers offer an ideal solution for many entertainment related venues as well as multiple channel solutions for hotels, restaurants, places of worship, museums, schools and colleges. Their cost ensures they can be widely used by almost everyone with typical cost per channel figures of between £60 to £120 per channel in UK and $70 to $150 in the USA depending on the channel rating, format of the dimmer and connector types. Almost all packs offer DMX and in 2006 this really is the way forward, whilst some analogue control desks do continue to be manufactured these will undoubtedly be phased out in the next couple of years. Buying DMX solutions now will avoid this unnecessary cost.

6.4   Professional Portable and Rack Mount Packs

A number of manufacturers produce high specification packs or rack mountable units with higher rise time chokes and better noise reduction compared to the lower cost units discussed in the previous section. Often these units are housed in more professional and rugged packages, are designed for continuous operation, use over-rated power control devices for improved reliability and are generally built to much higher specification levels.

Included within this section are products such as the ADB Memopack and Memorack units, the higher current versions of the ETC SmartPack, LSC ePro packs, Strand CD80 packs and others from Leprecon, Celco, Lightronics, Avolites and Electronics Diversified. Usually these packs have a conservative power rating matching the professional markets of theatre, film and television where the packs will be fully loaded and left turned on for long periods of time. This tends to require better packaging and cooling, often adds some sophisticated user benefits in terms of operational software and generally produces a pack at a higher price but with improved levels of reliability and operational facilities.

These types of unit tend to offer considerably higher rise times in the range of 200 to 400µS and therefore lower interference with much reduced acoustic filament noise. The packs are available in 6 or 12 channel blocks of 3kW and 3 or 6 channel blocks of 5kW for Europe and 12 channel blocks of 2.4kW and 6 channel blocks of 6kW for the US markets. Relatively small, they can be mounted into 19 inch equipment bays, be used free standing, or can be used as part of rolling racks – dimmers in flight cases.

These packs are designed for continuous operation at full rated load provided they are fed with a full capacity electrical supply. Many of them include fan

Fig 11: Selection of Professional Portable and Rack Mount dimmers, photos: ADB Technologies SA. (Belgium), Anytronics Ltd. (UK), Electronics Diversified Inc. (USA), Leprecon (USA), Lightronics Inc. (USA), NSI- Leviton Inc. (USA), Strand Lighting Ltd. (UK) and Zero 88 Lighting Ltd. (UK).

cooling to keep the pack size small. The benefit of this level of technology often comes with he significant user controls built into the processing inside the pack. Almost of them are now digitally controlled accepting a direct DMX control signal. Once a processor has been included then a wide variety of additional features can be added. These include channel by channel patching where each channel within a pack may be given a different DMX channel address. Each channel may be allocated a different dimmer curve with the choices of linear, preheat, S law, non-dim, TV and others are available. The dimmers may be able to store a number of memories and then be instructed to fade automatically to one of these in the event of loss of DMX data or via a push button remote control panel.

The other added advantage is that many of these packs use thyristors as the power control devices. These offer more accurate firing and higher current ratings allowing reliable use of re-settable circuit breakers for output protection instead of the fuses often employed on the lower cost packs.

Guide list prices for different portable, rack mount and hard wired professional packs, current in the spring of 2006, are shown in local currency. This is by no means a complete list, more a sample to show the many different products available and the price range. Please check these are still current by contacting the manufacturers' web sites detailed at the end of this chapter. I should confirm that the items listed are not the complete range from any of the manufacturers – rather they are samples from their range for readers to compare prices and facilities in their local market. Rise times are quoted in brackets where they are available from the manufacturers' literature or websites

ADB – Belgium
> Memopack 15XT MP15/XT/63M/CEE – 6 x 3kW with single
> CEE 17 16 Amp sockets – DMX only. (200μS)   £1,552.00
> Memopack 15XT MP15/XT/63M/D – 6 x 3kW with twin
> Shuko 16 Amp sockets – DMX only. (200μS)   £1,552.00
> Memopack 15XT MP15/XT/35M/D – 3 x 5kW with single
> CEE 17 32 Amp sockets – DMX only. (200μS)   £1,504.00
> Memopack 30XT MP30/XT/123M/CEE – 12 x 3kW with twin
> CEE 17 16 Amp sockets – DMX only. (200μS)   £2,552.00
> Memopack 30XT MP30/XT/123M/D – 12 x 3kW with twin
> Shuko 16 Amp sockets – DMX only. (200μS)   £2,552.00
> Memopack 30XT MP30/XT/65M/CEE – 6 x 5kW with twin
> CEE 17 32 Amp sockets – DMX only. (200μS)   £2,442.00

Memorack 15 MR15/63M/CEE – 6 x 3kW with single CEE 17
16 Amp UK sockets – DMX only. (200µS)   £1,509.00
Memorack 15 MR15/63M/D – 6 x 3kW with twin Shuko 16
Amp sockets – DMX only. (200µS)   £1,509.00
Memorack 15 MR15/35M/CEE – 3 x 5kW with single CEE 17
32 Amp UK sockets – DMX only. (200µS)   £1,490.00
Memorack 30 MR30/123M/AMP – 12 x 3kW with twin AMP
multiway connectors – DMX only. (200µS)   £2,075.00
Memorack 30 MR30/FLY/123/SOC – 12 x 3kW with twin
Socapex multiway connectors – DMX only. (200µS)   £2,530.00
Memopack 30 MP30/FLY/63M/AMP – 6 x 5kW with twin
AMP multiway connectors – DMX only. (200µS)   £2,249.00
Memopack 30 MP30/312/HAR – 3 x 12kW with Harting
multiway connector – DMX only. (200µS)   £2,278.00

Anytronics – UK

K111 Smartdim D1225, 12 x 12 Amp rack mount 3U dimmer
with hard wired terminals – DMX and analogue. (170µS)   £1,138.00
K112 Smartdim D1225, 12 x 10 Amp rack mount 3U dimmer
with rear plate punched for 4 x Socapex connectors – DMX
and analogue. (170µS)   £1,138.00

ETC – USA

Smartpack 6 x 20 Amp dimmer with Edison twist lock
connectors – DMX only. (200µS) $1,506.00
Smartpack 6 x 20 Amp dimmer with 2 x Socapex connectors
– DMX only. (200µS) $1,895.00
Smartpack 6 x 20 Amp dimmer Wall mount version with
terminals – DMX only. (200µS) $1,895.00

ETC – UK

Smartpack 6 x 15 Amp dimmer with single 15 Amp UK
connectors – DMX only. (200µS)   £ 696.00
Smartpack 6 x 15 Amp dimmer with 6 x twin Shuko connectors
– DMX only. (200µS)   £ 696.00

Smartpack 6 x 15 Amp dimmer with 6 x single CEE 17 16 Amp
connectors – DMX only. (200μS) £ 696.00

Smartpack 6 x 15 Amp dimmer with 2 x Socapex connectors
– DMX only. (200μS) £ 730.00

Smartpack 6 x 20 Amp dimmer Wall mount version with
terminals – DMX only. (200μS) £ 696.00

Smartpack 12 x 10 Amp dimmer with 12 pairs of Powercon
connectors – DMX only. (200μS) £1,130.00

Smartpack 12 x 10 Amp dimmer with 2 pairs of Socapex
multipin connectors – DMX only. (200μS) £1,098.00

Smartpack 12 x 10 Amp dimmer Wall mount version with
terminals – DMX only. (200μS) £1,190.00

Jands – Australia

HP12TR 12 x 2.5kW 3U, rack mount dimmer with twin
Socapex multiway outlets – DMX only. (240μS) £1,946.00

HP12WMTR 12 x 2.5kW 3U, rack mount dimmer with 24
Wieland outlets – DMX only. (240μS) £1,946.00

HP12WMMC 12 x 2.5kW 3U, rack mount dimmer with twin
Socapex multiway outlets – DMX only. (500μS) £2,140.00

HP6C-H 6 x 6kW 3U, rack mount dimmer with hard wired
terminals – DMX only. (500μS) £1,946.00

HUB24EC 15 x 10 Amp dimmed and 9 x 16 Amp direct in
flight case with CEE 17 16 Amp connectors – DMX only.
(150μS) £3,450.00

HUB24Es 15 x 10 Amp dimmed and 9 x 16 Amp direct in flight
case with Shuko 16 Amp connectors – DMX only. (150μS) £3,450.00

NSI (Leviton) – USA

DS 12–12, 12 x 1200 watt with choice of connectors – DMX
only. (400μS) $2,279.00

DS 12–12, 12 x 1200 watt with hard wired terminals – DMX
only. (400μS) $2,279.00

DS 12–24, 12 x 2400 watt with choice of connectors – DMX
only. (400μS) $3,420.00

DS 12–24, 12 x 2400 watt with hard wired terminals – DMX
only. (400μS) $3,420.00

Strand Lighting – USA
  CD80 portable or rack mounting pack with 12 x 2400 watt
  dimmers with twin connectors per channel – DMX control.
  (350µS) $3,490.00
  CD80 portable or rack mounting pack with 24 x 2400 watt
  dimmers with single connectors per channel – DMX control.
  (350µS) $5,748.00
  CD80 portable or rack mounting pack with 6 x 6000 watt
  dimmers with twin connectors per channel – DMX control.
  (350µS) $3,120.00
Zero 88 Lighting – UK
  Spice 1210 Harting, 12 x 10 Amp, 3U rack mount with twin
  Harting Multiway connectors – DMX control. (80µS)   £1,425.00
  Spice 1210 Socapex, 12 x 10 Amp, 3U rack mount with twin
  Socapex Multiway connectors – DMX control. (80µS)   £1,425.00

6.5 Flight Cased Dimmers

When planning a dimming system for a multi-purpose venue another avenue that can be explored is to consider the use of flight-cased dimmers or rolling racks as they are called in the USA. These are generally used by rental companies to provide dimmers for all forms of temporary shows or within venues that have multiple performance spaces and no fixed dimming installation. In recent years, with performance venues seeking to earn revenue from almost any opportunity, multi-purposes spaces have been turned into full blown theatres or dry hire spaces. For example, we have seen full blown opera staged in exhibition halls. To keep capital costs to a minimum 'dimmers on wheels' have become an attractive alternative to outright purchase of installed dimming. In a complex with more than one stage they have the advantage that they can be moved from stage to stage as usage demands. Equally, in dry hire TV studios having a pool of flight-cased dimming which allows them to be moved from studio to studio to match production requirements is beneficial.

The flight cases are manufactured by a number of companies such as ADB, Avolites, Celco, Colortran, Compulite, ETC and LSC. Many lighting rental companies around the world offer these products, allowing an empty venue or studio to be built with equipment hired in as required. In many cases these rental companies utilise the simplest forms of portable packs discussed earlier in this chapter for low cost solutions or the more sophisticated professional

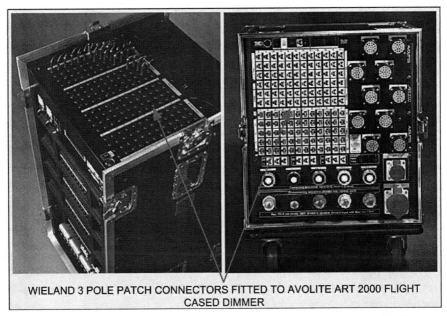

WIELAND 3 POLE PATCH CONNECTORS FITTED TO AVOLITE ART 2000 FLIGHT CASED DIMMER

Fig 12: Examples of typical patching facilities using Wieland connector as fitted to Avolite flight cased dimmers, photos: Avolites Ltd.

versions where better interference suppression or acoustic noise reduction is required.

If flight-cased dimmers are being considered it is advisable, during the planning stage, to define locations where these cases are to be located. The flight cases tend to be fitted with cooling fans and conventional choked dimmers and therefore emit both heat and the ubiquitous dimmer 'buzz'. Locating them in the corner of one venue may work in some applications, in others a dedicated room or cordoned off area may be required. Remember that wherever they are located there is a substantial electrical and fire risk. In these locations power provisions should be made to connect the dimmers to a source of electricity. Within Europe the standard power connectors and ratings are based on the CEE 17 type 63 and 125 Amp three phase connector range. In the film and rock and roll world other connectors, such as Powerlock and Camlocks, are used. Alternatively an electrical isolator or busbar chamber into which loose cables can be terminated could be used. If a busbar chamber is selected ensure that a local isolation device is provided upstream to enable the supply to be switched off prior to the cables being terminated. Some users specify that any floor-mounted flight-cased dimmers should be powered via RCD devices to ensure that the venue's electrical safety is maintained. With a large amount of loose electrical cabling and items being rented from many sources adding RCD protection makes sense and often ensures that insurance companies will cover the installation and the contingent risk.

Flight cases used in the rental markets are often equipped with a means of connecting multicore cabling from say six lamp bars to the flight case. In these applications it is often desirable to be able to patch the lamps on the six lamp bar to the dimmer channel. For this reason many of the rolling racks are equipped with a patch bay, and more often than not a Wieland type connector is used because these are small and can therefore be packed at a high channel density into a relatively small space. Fig 12 shows two views of such a patching system within Avolites flight-cased dimmer racks. The advantage of this type of patching is that there can be one, two, three or even four connectors per channel allowing parallel connections to be easily achieved.

Most manufacturers offer a very wide range of items that can be selected from when designing your flight case; it's a bit like buying a car where the options list runs to many pages! Here the choices relate to power rating of dimmer, rise time of dimmer – low, medium or high, load connectors, patching or direct connection, if patch how many outlets per channel, voltmeter – yes/no, current meters yes/no 3 separate or 1 with a switch, residual current protection per case or per pack, electrical protection per pack or per case, loop out for power yes/no and many more.

The major questions and comments have been listed below:

No of dimmers required in the flight case?

Remember the larger number of dimmers the greater the weight and the number of personnel required to lift the rack safely.

Ratings of dimmers – Europe 2.5/3/5/6/12kW, USA 1.2/2.4/6/12kW?

The ratings often reflect on the applications that the flight case can be utilised on. Theatre/Rock and Roll/Touring/Events tend to use lower wattages than TV or Film. It is often better to keep the higher power dimmers in one flight case rather than add higher rated dimmers to each case. This often results in 24, 36 or 48 way 2.5/3kW racks with 18, 24 or 36 way 5/6kW cases.

Type and number of output connectors per dimmer channel?

This is a critical issue and often affects the overall size of the rack.

Some users want to use a connector per channel as this matches typical usage – this is common in TV and film. Others prefer to bring back multiple channels of load on multiway connectors – widely used in theatre and touring markets. If multiway connectors are selected, how many per rack? The usual solution is to provide at least twice as many ways as there are dimmer channels, as this allows pairs of luminaires to be created. The next question is whether to pair the outlets at the dimmer or to send these via a patch panel, allowing the user to pair as required. The type of connectors is really market and country dependent. For racks that will travel internationally it makes no difference as the only connection of concern is the main power. Here loose tails, CEE 17, Powerlock and Camlock have become international.

The rack facilities are areas where cost can become the major consideration and yet these facilities can often save the show when problems develop or can avoid the problems occurring. What is really required and what benefits do these options provide?

Here items such as residual current electrical protection can make a system safe but may nuisance trip! This is really a fallacy; modern RCD's only trip if faults occur and really do protect 'your' equipment from others who take less care than 'you' do. Equally, adding protection per pack prevents damage to dimmers and ensures only one pack looses power if an overload occurs. Adding a voltmeter and protection for mis-wiring of the power supply helps protect the rack before anything is turned on and saves large re-wiring bills! Adding current meters helps to balance the electrical phases and prevent overloads occurring as the rack engineer can adjust the phases to avoid an overload during rehearsals.

The dimmer rack can often be called upon to act as the electrical distribution system requiring direct or switched direct supplies to be provided and fed to similar locations to the dimmable luminaires.

Many manufacturers now produce relay or non-dim switching versions of their dimmer packs. Indeed some manufacturers provide non-dim laws and are happy to allow dimmers to be used as inductive load switches provided the channel is de-rated by up to 50%. So, depending on the type of dimmer, it may be wise to add some direct power outlets that are switched on and off with a circuit breaker. Alternatively, true DMX controlled non-dim relays or dimmer channels switched to non-dims

COMPULITE – ISRAEL EXAMPLE OF FLIGHT
CASED COMPUDIM SYSTEM

AVOLITES – UK EXAMPLE OF STANDARD
ART 2000 24 WAY FLIGHT CASED DIMMER

JANDS – AUSTRALIA EXAMPLE OF HUB 24
FLIGHT CASED DIMMER AND
DISTRIBUTION SOLUTION

ADB – BELGIUM EXAMPLE OF MEMORACK
30, 36 WAY FLIGHT CASED 3kW DIMMER

ETC EUROPE – EXAMPLE
OF SMARTPACK FLIGHT
CASED DIMMER

LSC – AUSTRALIA EXAMPLE OF
e24 FLIGHT CASED SOLUTION

*Fig 13: Examples of typical flightcased dimmer solutions from around the world,
photos: ADB Technologies SA. Avolites Ltd., Compulite R&D Ltd., ETC Europe Ltd.,
Jands Pty Ltd. and LSC Lighting Systems (Aust) Pty Ltd.*

could be provided. In all cases these will need to be fitted with standard power connectors allowing items like smoke machines to be powered. Racks fitted with patching benefit from allowing the direct circuits to be patched to the multiway feeds allowing items like moving lights to be direct powered.

All modern dimmer flight cases operate on DMX lighting data, some are fitted with diagnostic measuring devices that can feed data back to the local rack processor or remotely to the lighting console or to the 'rackman' PC. Should the dimmer racks can become the centre of distribution of the data as well as dimmed and direct power?

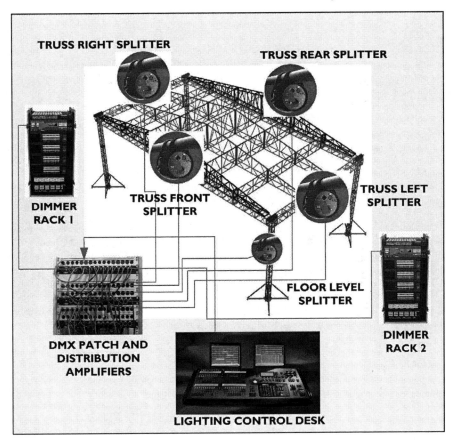

Fig 14: Typical distributed DMX network on a touring truss system
photos: Avolites Ltd., ETC Europe Ltd. and LSI Projects Ltd.

My view is to keep the lighting data separate within another flight case containing all of the active and passive lighting data components. In my companion book, 'Practical DMX', considerable detail is provided on exactly this issue. Fig 14 shows this scenario with a flight cased DMX data rack working with separately cased dimmers.

The diagnostic data can be produced from a number of sources – the dimmers, colour scrollers, possibly moving lights. Each of these systems have all evolved within a manufacturer's domain. New developments with the Remote Device Management (RDM) standard should rationalise some of this and will require significant changes in the active components used within a DMX network. These will now need to be bi-directional so that from a lighting desk you will be able to configure the address of a dimmer rack or a moving light. With all of these new benefits this makes an ever stronger case for centralising the lighting network into one case rather than providing some facilities across multiple racks. Longer term I believe that the artistic elements will remain within the lighting console whereas engineering issues will be moved to an 'electricians control' that will control dimmer laws, address settings, receive feedback on operational status and problems and generally enable the 'electrician' to run the lighting engineering.

Guide list prices, from the Spring 2006, are provided for different flight-cased dimmers. By the very nature of these types of product offering so many options these must be considered as 'guide prices' only for the basic or standard flight case. Almost all manufacturers offer a custom engineering service and you would be well advised to contact them at the earliest opportunity. Companies such as ETC have a detailed options pack that you pick from and email or fax back, and they are then able to confirm an accurate cost. So please check these are still current by checking the manufacturers' websites detailed at the end of this chapter or alternatively any of their local distributors.

ADB – Belgium

48 way x 3kW Memorack 30 type flightcase with 96 ways of
Socapex outlets wired to patch complete with 4 pole MCB
power protection per pack with power inlet via Ceeform 125
Amp. (200μS rise time) £18,475.00
18 way x 5kW Memorack 30 type flightcase with 18 ways of
CEE 17 32 Amp outlets wired to dimmers complete with

4 pole MCB power protection per pack with power inlet via
Ceeform 125 Amp. (200µS rise time) £14,597.00

Avolites – UK

Art 2000 T4 basic flight cased system, 48 way x 16 Amp
dimming with 20 Socapex connectors (120 ways) wired
back to Wieland patch bay complete with MCB power
protection for each 12 way pack and input via Camlock or
Power lock connectors. (240µS rise time) £10,013.00

Art 2000 T4 full spec flight cased system, 48 way x 16 Amp
dimming with 20 Socapex connectors (120 ways) wired back
to Wieland patch bay complete with MCB power protection
for each 12 way pack and input via Camlock or Power lock
connectors. (240µS rise time) £10,863.00

Art 2000 T2 basic flight cased system, 24 way x 16 Amp
dimming with 10 Socapex connectors (60 ways) wired back
to Wieland patch bay complete with MCB power protection
for each 12 way pack and input via Camlock or Power lock
connectors. (240µS rise time) £ 6,778.00

Art 2000 T2 full spec flight cased system, 24 way x 16 Amp
dimming with 10 Socapex connectors (60 ways) wired back
to Wieland patch bay complete with MCB power protection
for each 12 way pack and input via Camlock or Power lock
connectors. (240µS rise time) £ 7,456.00

Art 2000 T4 basic spec flight cased system, 24 way x 32 Amp
dimming with 24 CEE 17 32 Amp output connectors hard
wired to dimmer channels complete with MCB power
protection for each 12 way pack and input via Camlock or
Power lock connectors. (240µS rise time) £ 9,194.00

Art 2000 T4 full spec flight cased system, 24 way x 32 Amp
dimming with 24 CEE 17 32 Amp output connectors hard
wired to dimmer channels complete with MCB power
protection for each 12 way pack and input via Camlock or
Power lock connectors. (240µS rise time) £ 9,744.00

Art 2000 T4 basic spec flight cased system, 12 way x 32 Amp
dimming with 12 CEE 17 32 Amp output connectors hard
wired to dimmer channels complete with MCB power
protection for each 6 way pack and input via Camlock or

Power lock connectors. (240µS rise time) £ 6,365.00

Art 2000 T2 full spec flight cased system, 12 way x 32 Amp dimming with 12 CEE 17 32 Amp output connectors hard wired to dimmer channels complete with MCB power protection for each 6 way pack and input via Camlock or Power lock connectors. (240µS rise time) £ 6,844.00

Art 2000 T2 basic spec flight cased system, 12 way x 32 Amp dimming with 12 CEE 17 32 Amp output connectors hard wired to dimmer channels complete with MCB power protection for each 6 way pack and input via Camlock or Power lock connectors. (240µS rise time) £ 6,365.00

Art 2000 T4 full spec flight cased system, 12 way x 32 Amp dimming with 12 CEE 17 32 Amp output connectors hard wired to dimmer channels complete with MCB power protection for each 6 way pack and input via Camlock or Power lock connectors. (240µS rise time) £ 6,844.00

Art 2000 T4 basic spec flight cased system, 6 way x 63 Amp dimming with 6 CEE 17 63 Amp output connectors hard wired to dimmer channels complete with MCB power protection for each 3 way pack and input via Camlock or Power lock connectors. (240µS rise time) £ 9,623.00

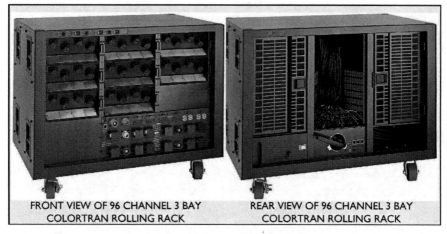

FRONT VIEW OF 96 CHANNEL 3 BAY COLORTRAN ROLLING RACK

REAR VIEW OF 96 CHANNEL 3 BAY COLORTRAN ROLLING RACK

Fig 15: Colortran 96 channel rolling rack with patch, photo: Colortran Inc.

Art 2000 T4 full spec flight cased system, 6 way x 63 Amp
dimming with 12 CEE 17 63 Amp output connectors hard
wired to dimmer channels complete with MCB power
protection for each 3 way pack and input via Camlock or
Power lock connectors. (240µS rise time)   £10,273.00

ETC – USA

Smartpak Touring dimmer rack with 12 x 20 Amp dimmers
with DMX input, 120 volt multiway output connectors, 225
Amp main incoming breakers and Camlock loop through
connection. (200µS rise time) $ 8,136.00

Smartpak Touring dimmer rack with 24 x 20 Amp dimmers
with DMX input, 120 volt multiway output connectors, 225
Amp main incoming breakers and Camlock loop through
connection. (200µS rise time) $13,722.00

Jands – Australia

Hub 24, 24 output x 10 Amp digitally controlled flight cased
dimmer and direct power rack with UK 15 Amp sockets.
(80µS rise time)   £ 3,450.00

Hub 24, 24 output x 10 Amp digitally controlled flight cased
dimmer and direct power rack with Shuko 16 Amp sockets.
(80µS rise time)   £ 3,450.00

6.6   Medium Density Hard Wired Cabinet Dimmers

These tend to be the 'backbone' dimmer for theatre applications due to their
cost, ease of installation, dimming quality and physical size. A cabinet dimmer
basically comprises of a wall or floor mounting enclosure into which are
mounted a number of dimmers all controlled from one central processor. The
dimmer modules are often the physical dimmer elements used within the same
manufacturer's portable dimmers. The electrical wiring is then connected from
the cabinet to the socket outlets around the venue.

The economy provided in cost is due to the fact that one processor can
control 12, 24 or even 36 dimmers in one cabinet compared with the packs
where only 6 or 12 channels are involved. The cabinet construction allows
noisy chokes to be mounted via acoustic damping mounts to reduce noise
from the dimmer cabinets themselves. High quality 250 microsecond rise

Fig 16: Popular European LD90 cabinet dimmer from Strand Lighting photo: Strand Lighting Ltd.

time chokes can be used and pairs of thyristors for better control of the dimmer firing. Popular products in this area using thyristors for power control include the ADB Eurorack and ETC Unison. Other products using triacs such as Strand's LD90 are also available. Cabinets tend to be produced with 2.5, 3 and 5kW dimmer ratings. All of them are also available with non-dim relays or contactors. The cabinets have the advantage that it is possible to build cabinets of all 3kW, or all 5kW or combinations of 3 and 5kW. In some cases non-dims can also be inserted. The Unison has a further advantage in that plug-in modules are provided, enabling any combination of ratings and relays to be employed. This makes installation of mixed dimming capacity systems very easy.

One unique problem to the UK is based on consultants' requirements of splitting electrical phases to geographic locations within a theatre. This is a historic requirement dating from the period where electrical safety was more important than balanced phases. During this period one electrical phase was always allocated to the over-stage lighting, another to the front of house and the third to the stage and under-stage levels. This resulted in many cabinet dimmer installations carried out in the 1960s, 70s and 80s being single phased. This resulted in expensive electrical installations and considerable out of balance loads. Modern cabinet dimmers are almost always designed to operate with a three phase electrical supply with eight dimmers allocated to each of the three electrical supply phases. When these dimmers need to be installed as replacements for the older single phase solutions problems can develop. This can show up as load wiring being too short to be spread across the new cabinets or requirements to run non sequential DMX addressed channels in the same rack. Some of the cabinet dimmers do not offer channel by channel DMX address selection – they only offer a global address setting. This makes their use very difficult in refurbishments and in applications where the electrical design is still based on geographical phase layouts. Good quality professional cabinets follow the facilities or their larger brothers, the high density cabinets. Here the processor allows each channel or the entire rack to be individually addressed, to be allocated a different dimmer law, to have the output voltage controlled/limited, to have the response speed adjusted and to be stored into back-up and remotely controllable memories.

Remember if this type of dimming solution is to be used, never mount the cabinet dimmers onto a wall that can transmit noise into the auditorium or into a stage area. If they must be mounted on a venue structural wall mount them via Neoprene or equivalent damping materials. Always try to ensure that each cabinet is fitted with a means of electrical isolation close to the cabinet. This allows isolation of each cabinet for maintenance and also a degree of electrical sub protection between a large capacity supply and each dimmer cabinet.

Cabinets of this type tend to generate considerable levels of hot air and are often fitted with cooling fans, and these again generate noise. Remember that with a number of these cabinets in the room housing the dimmers, additional cooling may be required. Details of how to calculate the resulting heat output are provided in Chapter 3.

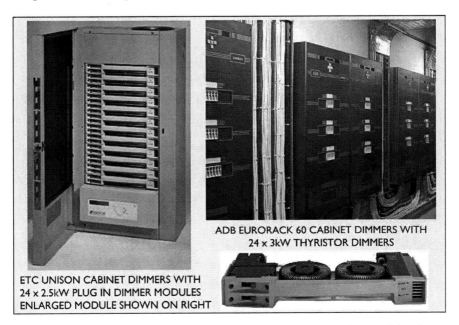

ADB EURORACK 60 CABINET DIMMERS WITH
24 x 3kW THYRISTOR DIMMERS

ETC UNISON CABINET DIMMERS WITH
24 x 2.5kW PLUG IN DIMMER MODULES
ENLARGED MODULE SHOWN ON RIGHT

Fig 17: Two types of cabinet dimmers, the hard wired ADB Eurorack 60 and the plug in module ETC Unison, photos: ADB Technologies SA. and ETC Europe Ltd.

In recent years manufacturers have been forced to offer low cost versions of the installed cabinet solutions to cope with electrical safety regulations and also the demand for ever lower cost dimming solutions. Accordingly Anytronics with their Contractor range, ADB with Eurorack 50, Electron with their new Premium, Light Processor with Paradim and Strand with the LD24 and latterly Wallrack have produced solutions that are very low in cost. These range from £70 to £100 per channel around 30 to 50% less than the more professional range, bringing them closer to the budgets of schools and colleges. I have found these to offer ideal solutions in many applications ranging from hotels, restaurants, clubs, small theatres and virtually any venue where the budget is restricted. This type of cabinet solution has superseded the separate architectural dimmers that historically were manufactured to suit the needs of architectural lighting consultants' dimming requirements for hotels, museums and other applications.

In fact these professional and lower cost cabinet dimmers are now widely used across almost all lighting applications due to their size, compatibility with different types of lighting loads, and ability to store memories that can be remotely accessed and their reliability.

When planning an installation of this type of dimming there are a number of issues that should be considered. Firstly they need to be accommodated into a controlled space such as a dimmer room. This needs to be force-cooled if the temperature rises above a safe working temperature. Typically most cabinet dimmers will operate reliably up to 35 degrees Celsius. In some cooler climates this makes only an extraction fan necessary. In the warmer climates, depending upon the number of channels used, it may be necessary to include air conditioning within the dimmer room. This type of cabinet generates heat at the rate of 2% of the total load that the electrical supply allows to be connected. I mention it like this as often electrical diversity is applied resulting in say 120 x 2.5kW dimmers but only enough power to run 96 at 2.5kWs.

Fig 18: Premium Installation dimmer from Greece photo: Electron SA.

Therefore the maximum heat that can be produced is restricted to 96 x 3kW x 2%, in other words 4.8kW's of heat per hour.

Unlike portable dimmers where we are dealing with a relatively small number of channels and thus load cables, this type of cabinet allows a large number of channels to be controlled. Consequently, a large number of cables need to be managed when being routed into the cabinets. Some of the cabinets allow cables to enter from all four sides, some from the top only, some allow cable access from the bottom only. Therefore careful design is required to ensure that the number of cables can be routed around the room to reach the relevant dimmer. Remember that the cables might be entering the room from different directions, and this often happens with front of house and stage level cabling.

Therefore considerable space within the room may need to be given over to turning these cables and their containment system as they enter the room and then joining them together into a centralised feeder system into the dimmer cabinets. The types of cabling and containment vary across the world and it is not the job of this book to detail these solutions. However there are general aspects which need to be passed onto electrical contractors to ensure long term reliability.

Whatever type of cable containment is to be used the route that this follows to reach the dimmer should never obstruct any of the cooling vents or extraction grilles – nor should it limit the radiation of heat if the cabinet forms part of the general heat sink. If the cable entry is from the bottom then the safest solution is to lift the cabinets up on the wall, allowing the containment to be sited underneath. Any good contractor will size the containment in accordance with the local electrical regulations or codes but will also allow additional capacity for say 25% to 40% more cables to be added later. If the solution entails running each cable in an individual containment this would require 24 separate 25mm or larger conduits to enter the dimmer cabinet. With the physical size of some cabinets this might be difficult. To solve this problem a header box could be created that allows the conduits to be bushed into the box and then the dimmer cabinet sited on top.

If cable trays are being used it is often possible to run major trays horizontally and then smaller dropper trays down between cabinets, a system like this is shown in the photograph of the ADB Eurorack system in *Fig 17*. The same is also true if electrical trunking is being used. This is like an enclosed cable tray and often allows different types of cable to be used to what would be used on an open cable tray. However, because it is enclosed, different factors apply

Fig 19: Example of DIN rail mounted screw down terminals, photo: the author.

when calculating the required size of the trunking; these relate to bunching of cables, temperature and distance and again are subject to local regulations.

It should also be remembered that as well as load cabling we also have to accommodate the power feeder cables which will typically be around 100 Amp 3 phase for a European 24 channel system or 200 Amp 3 phase for a USA system, so cables from 35mm^2 to 120mm^2 may need to be included. In addition, data cables will need to enter the first rack and then be looped from cabinet to cabinet. As these are usually rated as low voltage cables they cannot be included within containment carrying mains voltage cables. Therefore separate conduits, tray or trunking is often required to contain these cables. There is no problem running power and data cables side by side but there should be a segregated barrier between them to ensure that no high voltages can penetrate the data inputs.

Many of these dimmers use screw-down terminals that are often mounted on DIN rail, and examples of these are shown in *Fig 19*. When using these terminals it is a good idea to instruct the electrical contractor to crimp ferrules onto the ends of the cables before terminating them into the terminals. These produce a more reliable connection than just using the bare cables as these can work loose with age and have been known to cause arcing and burning out problems unless they are regularly inspected and tightened. Good practice

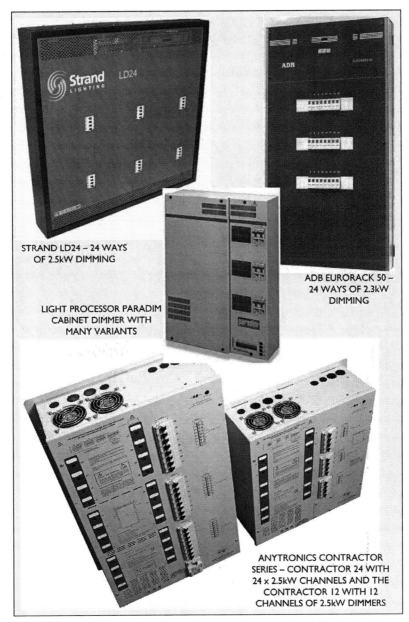

STRAND LD24 – 24 WAYS
OF 2.5kW DIMMING

ADB EURORACK 50 –
24 WAYS OF 2.3kW
DIMMING

LIGHT PROCESSOR PARADIM
CABINET DIMMER WITH
MANY VARIANTS

ANYTRONICS CONTRACTOR
SERIES – CONTRACTOR 24 WITH
24 x 2.5kW CHANNELS AND THE
CONTRACTOR 12 WITH 12
CHANNELS OF 2.5kW DIMMERS

*Fig 20: Selection of lower cost cabinet dimmers, photos: ADB Technologies SA.,
Anytronics Ltd., Lightfactor Ltd., and Strand Lighting Ltd.*

looks at the tightness of this type of terminal during any annual electrical inspection. This is easily done by taking a sample of a few connections in each cabinet, if all of them are tight there should not be a problem. If some are found to be loose then it is wise to tighten them all. Recent terminal developments might have taken a turn for the worse! Some manufacturers have started to fit 'push fit' terminals. These provide a spring loaded terminal which opens when the cable is inserted and then locks the cable in place. Past experience of this type of terminal has not encouraged me! They are highly sensitive to cable size and manufacturers never seem to understand the different electrical regulations on cable sizes we meet across the world. So, I have to be convinced that they prove to be as easy to use as the literature states and that they prove to be more reliable than the earlier versions I have encountered.

Guide list prices are shown for some of the 12 and 24 way standard and low cost cabinets currently available, again current as of Spring 2006. They are quoted in local currency where applicable. Once again, quoted prices should be verified with a local stockist or the manufacturer as many options are offered for each of the quoted products. All products listed are complete with single pole MCB protection per channel. Rise times are again shown in brackets where the manufacturer's publish this data.

STANDARD CABINETS
ADB – Belgium

Eurorack 60 243 with 24 x 3kW dimmers and DMX input. (200µs rise time)	£3,896.00
Eurorack 60 243 with 24 x 3kW dimmers and 3 x RCDs each protecting 8 dimmers with DMX input. (200µs rise time)	£4,898.00
Eurorack 60 123 with 12 x 3kW dimmers and DMX input. (200µs rise time)	£2,974.00
Eurorack 60 123 with 12 x 3kW dimmers and 3 x RCDs each protecting 4 dimmers with DMX input. (200µs rise time)	£3,976.00
Eurorack 60 125 with 12 x 5kW dimmers and DMX input. (200µs rise time)	£3,816.00
Eurorack 60 125 with 12 x 5kW dimmers and 3 x RCDs each protecting 8 dimmers with DMX input.(200µs rise time)	£4,816.00
Eurorack 60 65 with 6 x 5kW dimmers and DMX input. (200µs rise time)	£2,890.00
Eurorack 60 65 with 6 x 5kW dimmers and 3 x RCDs each protecting 2 dimmers with DMX input. (200µs rise time)	£3,892.00

Eurorack 60 123+65 with 12 x 3kW and 6 x 5kW dimmers
with DMX input. (200µs rise time) £4,112.00

Eurorack 60 123+65 with 12 x 3kW and 6 x 5kW dimmers and
3 x RCDs each protecting 6 dimmers (4 x 3kW and 2 x 5kW)
with DMX input. (200µs rise time) £5,114.00

Eurorack 60 123SW with 12 x 3kW contactor switched outputs
with DMX input. £4,126.00

Eurorack 60 123SW with 12 x 3kW contactor switched outputs
and 3 x RCDs each protecting 4 contactors with DMX input. £5,128.00

Avolites Ltd. – UK

Art 2000 Install system with 24 x 16 Amp dimmers. (240µs
rise time) £3,037.00

Art 2000 Install system with 24 x 16 Amp dimmers, DMX input
and one Residual Current Circuit Breaker for the entire rack.
(240µs rise time) £3,333,00

Art 2000 Install system with 24 x 16 Amp dimmers, DMX input,
patching to 48 outlets – different types available and one
Residual Current Circuit Breaker for the entire rack. (240µs
rise time) £3,830.00

Art 2000 Install system with 24 x 16 Amp dimmers, DMX
input, patching to 48 outlets – different types available, one
Residual Current Circuit Breaker for the entire rack and mains
input isolator. (240µs rise time) £4,050.00

Art 2000 Install system with 12 x 16 Amp and 6 x 32 Amp
dimmers, DMX input, one Residual Current Circuit Breaker
for the entire rack and mains input isolator All housed in 1
rack (240µs rise time) £3,122.00

Art 2000 Install system with 48 x 16 Amp dimmers, DMX input,
patching to 96 outlets – different types available and two
Residual Current Circuit Breakers – one for each of the two
racks – must be sited together. (240µs rise time) £7,064.00

Art 2000 Install system with 24 x 16 Amp and 12 x 32 Amp
dimmers, DMX input, two Residual Current Circuit Breakers
– one for each rack and 2 mains input isolators. – 2 racks
which must be sited together (240µs rise time) £6,609.00

Colortran – USA

I Series E dimmer Rack complete with 12 dual 2.4kW
dimmer modules (500µs rise time) $8,541.00

ETC – Europe

Unison Cabinet with 12 plug in dual 225µs rise time 3kW
dimmer modules with DMX input. £3,609.00

Unison Cabinet with 12 plug in dual 225µs rise time 3kW
dimmer modules with RCD protection per channel and
DMX input. £5,300.00

Unison Cabinet with 12 plug in single 225µs rise time 5kW
dimmer modules with DMX input. £4,101.00

Unison Cabinet with 12 plug in single 225µs rise time 5kW
dimmer modules with RCD protection per channel and
DMX input. £5,051.00

Unison Cabinet with 12 plug in dual 3kW Non-dim switching
modules with DMX input. £3,465.00

Unison Cabinet with 12 plug in dual 400µs rise time 3kW
dimmer modules with DMX input. £4,074.00

Unison Cabinet with 12 plug in dual 400µs rise time 3kW
dimmer modules with RCD protection per channel and
DMX input. £5,765.00

Unison Cabinet with 12 plug in single 350µs rise time 5kW
dimmer modules with DMX input. £4,689.00

Unison Cabinet with 12 plug in single 350µs rise time 5kW
dimmer modules with RCD protection per channel and
DMX input £5,640.00

Unison Cabinet with 6 plug in dual 225µs rise time 3kW dimmer
modules with DMX input. £2,276.00

Unison Cabinet with 12 plug in dual 225µs rise time 3kW
dimmer modules with RCD protection per channel and
DMX input. £3,062.00

Unison Cabinet with 6 plug in single 225µs rise time 5kW
dimmer modules with DMX input. £2,525.00

Unison Cabinet with 6 plug in single 225µs rise time 5kW
dimmer modules with RCD protection per channel and
DMX input. £3,311.00

Unison Cabinet with 6 plug in dual 3kW Non-dim switching
modules with DMX input. £2,204.00

Unison Cabinet with 6 plug in dual 400µs rise time 3kW
dimmer modules with DMX input. £2,501.00

Unison Cabinet with 6 plug in dual 400µs rise time 3kW
dimmer modules with RCD protection per channel and
DMX input. £3,100.00

Unison Cabinet with 6 plug in single 350µs rise time 5kW

dimmer modules with DMX input. £2,816.00
Unison Cabinet with 12 plug in single 350µs rise time 5kW
dimmer modules with RCD protection per channel and
DMX input. £3,240.00

Strand Lighting – UK
LD90 cabinet complete with 24 x 2.5kW dimmers with DMX
input. (100µs rise time) £3,425.00
LD90 cabinet complete with 24 x 2.5kW dimmers with DMX
input and 3 x RCD each protecting 8 dimmers. (100µs rise
time) £4,145.00
LD90 cabinet complete with 12 x 5kW dimmers with DMX
input. (100µs rise time) £3,934.00
LD90 cabinet complete with 12 x 5kW dimmers with DMX
input and 3 x RCD each protecting 4 dimmers. (100µs rise
time) £4,654.00
LD90 cabinet complete with 24 x 2.5kW contactors with
DMX input. £4,287.00
LD90 cabinet complete with 24 x 2.5kW contactors with
DMX input and 3 x RCD each protecting 8 contactors. £5,007.00

LOWER COST CABINETS
ADB – Belgium
Eurorack 50 242 with 24 x 2.3kW dimmers and DMX input.
(80µs rise time) £2,951.00
Eurorack 60 242 with 24 x 2.3kW dimmers and 3 x RCDs each
protecting 8 dimmers with DMX input. (80µs rise time) £3,369.00
Eurorack 50 242/CEE with 24 x 2.3kW dimmers and 24 x CEE
17 16 Amp or 24 x twin Shuko 16 Amp sockets and DMX
input. (80µs rise time) £3,448.00
Eurorack 50 242/CEE with 24 x 2.3kW dimmers and 24 x CEE
17 16 Amp or 24 x twin Shuko 16 Amp sockets and 3 x
RCD's each protecting 8 dimmers with DMX input.
(80µs rise time) £3,865.00
Eurorack 50 242/CEE with 24 x 2.3kW dimmers and 24 x UK
15 Amp sockets and DMX input. (80µs rise time) £3,554.00
Eurorack 50 242/CEE with 24 x 2.3kW dimmers and 24 x UK
15 Amp sockets and 3 x RCD's each protecting 8 dimmers
with DMX input. (80µs rise time) £3,971.00

Anytronics Ltd. – UK

    Contractor 12, 12 ways of 12 Amp dimming or switching with DMX input in wall mount enclosure including one RCD on main supply. (170μs rise time)   £1,010.00

    Contractor 12, 12 ways of 12 Amp dimming or switching with DMX input in wall mount enclosure. (170μs rise time)   £ 852.00

    Contractor 24, 24 ways of 12 Amp dimming or switching with DMX input in wall mount enclosure including RCD on main supply. (170μs rise time)   £1,810.00

    Contractor 24, 24 ways of 12 Amp dimming or switching with DMX input in wall mount enclosure. (170μs rise time)   £1,652.00

Strand Lighting – UK

    LD24 cabinet complete with 24 x 2.5kW dimmers with DMX input. (80μs rise time)   £1,850.00

    LD24 cabinet complete with 24 x 2.5kW dimmers with DMX input and 3 x RCD each protecting 8 dimmers. (80μs rise time)   £2,570.00

Zero 88 Ltd. – UK

    Chilli 1210i with 12 channels of 10 Amp dimming and DMX input. (80μs rise time)   £1,050.00

    Chilli 1210i with 12 channels of 10 Amp dimming and DMX input with one RCD for entire rack. (80μs rise time)   £1,225.00

    Chilli 1216i with 12 channels of 16 Amp dimming and DMX input. (80μs rise time)   £1,250.00

    Chilli 1216i with 12 channels of 16 Amp dimming and DMX input with one RCD for entire rack. (80μs rise time)   £1,425.00

    Chilli Pro 1210i with 12 channels of 10 Amp dimming and DMX input. (80μs rise time)   £1,375.00

    Chilli Pro 1210i with 12 channels of 10 Amp dimming and DMX input with one RCD for entire rack. (80μs rise time)   £1,575.00

    Chilli Pro 1610i with 12 channels of 16 Amp dimming and DMX input. (80μs rise time)   £1,575.00

    Chilli Pro 1610i with 12 channels of 16 Amp dimming and DMX input with one RCD for entire rack. (80μs rise time)   £1,775.00

    Chilli 2410i with 24 channels of 10 Amp dimming and DMX input. (80μs rise time)   £1,925.00

    Chilli 2410i with 24 channels of 10 Amp dimming and DMX input with one RCD for entire rack. (80μs rise time)   £2,120.00

Chilli Pro 2410i with 24 channels of 10 Amp dimming and
DMX input. (80μs rise time) £2,125.00
Chilli Pro 2410i with 24 channels of 10 Amp dimming and
DMX input with one RCD for entire rack. (80μs rise time) £2,345.00
Chilli Pro 2416i with 24 channels of 16 Amp dimming and
DMX input. (80μs rise time) £2,475.00
Chilli Pro 625i with 6 channels of 25 Amp dimming and DMX
input. (80μs rise time) £1,250.00
Chilli Pro 625i with 6 channels of 25 Amp dimming and DMX
input with one RCD for entire rack. (80μs rise time) £1,425.00

6.7   High Density Modular Dimmers

These types of dimmers have traditionally been employed in the larger venues, concert halls or broadcast TV studio applications where large numbers of dimmers are required with high levels of performance. As venues are being refurbished, with an ever increasing number of dimmer channels required, this type of dimmer is finding high usage as it allows more dimmers per square metre than any other type and the costs have fallen significantly over the past 15 years. The dimmers must be easily maintainable and ideally offer facilities for dimmed and direct power outputs.

A number of manufacturers offer solutions in this category: these include ADB with their Eurodim 3, Colortran in the USA with their i96 range, ETC with their Sensor range, Entertainment Technology in the USA with Capio Plus, IES/ETC with their Matrix and Strand Lighting with CD80 and SLD96 and recently the EC21.

All of these products tend to be slightly more expensive per channel than the cabinet solution but offer many user benefits. All offer the ability to have one or two control processors enabling instant back-up should one processor fail. Modules can be easily removed for maintenance or alternative modules inserted. Often this allows module slots to accept a dimmer or alternatively contactor controlled non-dims can be inserted. Processors tend to be more sophisticated, offering additional user facilities including online fault reporting where the status of each dimmer is regularly scanned and reported continuously to a remote PC or even the lighting console. These facilities can be very important where hundreds of dimmers may be in use and venue time is costing thousands of pounds per hour.

High density cabinets tend to be designed to accept combinations of

Fig 21: ADB Eurodim 3 Modular Dimmer 2004, photo: ADB -TTV Technologies.

2.5/3, 5/6 and 10/12kW within the same cabinet, making planning an installation very simple. Common sizes of cabinets allow up to 96 or 108 channels of dimmers to be accommodated in one cabinet, thus each cabinet requires large amounts of electrical power and generates large amounts of heat. This requires careful planning of such an installation and inevitably means good cooling of the dimmer room. Consideration should also be given to the location of the dimmer room relative to the venue. Good practice dictates that cabinets of this type should be mounted on acoustic damping materials between the cabinet and the floor to avoid noise transmission through the floor into the building structure.

Cabinets of this type of dimmer tend to be able to accommodate larger sized noise reduction chokes and thus rise times tend to be much greater than the portable or hard wired types previously described. Typical values tend to be of the order of 500 microseconds although the method of measuring rise time appears different between manufacturers. Acoustic consultants tend to prefer these types of dimmers as they offer much reduced acoustic filament noise and are often available with rise times as high as 800 microseconds for use in noise sensitive buildings such as TV and recording studios and concert halls.

In areas where electrical power is subject to fluctuations, some of the modular dimmers offer a facility to automatically stabilise the output voltage.

Normally the dimmer processor is instructed to maintain a given output voltage within 1% for up to a 10% change of input voltage. Clearly such a system can never output more voltage than the given input voltage and will always need a degree of headroom to allow the electronics to operate. Whilst the European and US electrical supplies are relatively stable, in many other countries this facility is widely used in order to maintain the output voltage avoiding annoying 'dips' in light level during a show.

These high density cabinets are very powerful and include significant amounts of single or double processing. The double processor versions enable instant switch-over should one processor fail. This option is often selected for the larger theatrical venue or the TV studio where many 'live' broadcasts are to be transmitted. Most of them feature on-board LCD type user displays where on-board diagnostic fault reports can be displayed together with menu selectable functions that the user can programme. Most of the racks offer similar facilities although they often achieve them in slightly different ways.

Some of the major facilities have been summarised below:

Fig 22: Strand EC21 dimmer with capability to use thyristor and sine wave dimmers and switching modules circa 2006 photo: Strand Lighting Ltd.

- Channel by Channel DMX address setting in addition to setting a global address for the whole rack.
- Selection of dimmer law and non-dim switch on and off functions – these can include Linear r.m.s. voltage, Linear r.m.s voltage with pre-heat, TV – different national laws such as EBU, BBC, ORTF etc, Fluorescent, non-dim with and without hysteresis, Theatre S law and some offer user creatable laws.
- Selection of response speed of processor or interpolation of number of bytes on the DMX signal to provide long fade time smoothing.

- The memory system will allow memories to be created and edited from the keyboard, to be created by 'snap shotting' the DMX or Ethernet input, to be played back in any sequence locally or from a remote control.
- The processor enables a fail safe state to be created in the event of loss of input DMX or Ethernet data – this will hold last intensity settings until new values are received, fade to black (off) in an adjustable time set in seconds or fade to a memory selected from the memory store.
- The output voltage per channel shall be user settable based on compensating for an over-voltage input or to set the channel by channel or entire rack output voltage down by a percentage to improve lamp life. The voltage reduction circuit will be reliable enough to reduce 230/240 to 110/120 volts. This circuit shall clamp the output voltage to the set level even when the cabinet is powering up or down.
- The menu system will be able to select the functions of the local rack but will also be able to address other similar racks forming the dimmer network – even if these are in a remote location.
- Set up rack identity for any local displays or network identification.
- Calibration of local measuring devices such as voltage transformers and temperature sensors.
- All the user-created data will be downloadable to a PC either via a network link or via an RS232 port fitted to the processor.
- Local test facilities should be provided enabling each channel to be turned on at an adjustable intensity level between 1 and 100%.
- Set passwords to allow access to specific parts of the system software.
- Importantly any data stored within the processor should be retained indefinitely without the need for electrical power or batteries.

These professional dimmers often include a number of other benefits such as having dual DMX inputs each with their own patch or facilities to copy the patch from DMX Input 1 to the patch for Input 2. These allow a main and a back-up desk to be separately connected to the dimmer cabinet. Alternatively in a touring venue the second input can become the input into which the touring system is connected to use the house facilities. Many of these dimmers also include On or Off line diagnostic systems that can report significant amounts of useful data back to the lighting console or via the network to a PC.

Typical diagnostic information can include but is not limited to:

- Confirmation of DMX status on both inputs.
- Confirmation of selected dimmer laws and other user programming.
- Confirmation of dimmer location, phase of supply and DMX input patch.
- Output voltage from a dimmer.
- Load current per phase of a cabinet and also current per dimmer.
- Confirmation of temperatures within the cabinet, temperature hot spots, status of air filters, how many fans are operational or installed.
- Operational hours worked and thus when maintenance is due.
- Status of channel circuit breaker – open (tripped) or closed.
- Ability to measure the loads connected to the dimmer and then store these as the Known Loads. Thereafter it should be possible to ask the rack to compare the re-measured loads with the known loads are show were there are any differences and thus where faults have occurred. The system should be able to diagnose problems with the control electronics.

Recent developments from ETC/IES in Holland, ADB in Belgium and Strand Lighting and Entertainment Technology in the USA have all released high density dimmer cabinet solutions offering IGBT based or sine wave controlled dimming.

A transistor differs from a thyristor in that it can be controlled to vary gradually the current, not just to switch it on. IGBT dimmers are the commercially practical implementation of reverse-phase dimming, a technique of power control developed through generations of thyristors and MOSFET transistors for dimmers in the mid 1980s. The MOSFET was not widely adopted due to its sensitivity to heat, and poor early reliability, but eventually these products proved they could be used reliably to turn off the current rather than turning it on and could reduce a significant amount of sine wave distortion and harmonic problems with previous designs, and at the same time, eliminate the need for a choke. More of this in the next chapter.

It is impossible to provide guide prices for the different combinations of high density dimmer cabinets and modules as all manufacturers have so many different formats and options. It would appear that a 96 channel theatrical cabinet equipped with 2.5 or 3kW dimmers in Europe would have an average price of £15,000, and in the USA this would be around $25,000.

6.8 Conclusions

This chapter looked at the different types of standard dimmer packages and their costs in different parts of the world. Care is needed in selecting the right product for the application and further thought should be given if the budget only allows a partial solution initially with the requirement to add further dimmers in the future. As can be seen, there is a wealth of different products available at different price levels. With modern digital technology dimmers can be purchased and almost forgotten save for sensible maintenance in cleaning out fan filters or carrying out the annual inspection. A list of some dimmer manufacturers has been included at the end of this chapter which, together with the list of useful contact addresses at the end of the book, provide contact points for manufacturers and distributors who are all very willing to help with advice and packaged solutions.

A brief introduction was made concerning transistor dimming and

Fig 23: Entertainment Technology Capio Plus dimmer using IGBT transistor technology producing a near silent economic dimming system circa 2005, photo: Entertainment Technology, Inc.

the next chapter looks at the modern trends and packaging options offering yet further choice in design of a dimming system.

6.9 Useful Contact Details

A.C. Lighting Ltd (UK)	www.aclighting.co.uk
A.C. Lighting Inc (USA)	www.aclighting.com
ADB-TTV Technologies SA. (Belgium)	www.adblighting.com
ADB UK.	www.lsiprojects.com
American DJ Supply, Inc. (USA)	www.americandj.com
Anytronics Ltd. (UK)	www.anytronics.com
Artistic Licence (UK) Ltd.	www.artisticlicence.com
Avolites Ltd.	www.avolites.com
Colortran Inc. (USA)	www.colortran.com
Compulite Systems (2000) Ltd.	www.compulite.com
Elation Professional, Inc. (USA)	www.elationlighting.com
Electron SA (Greece)	www.electron.com.gr
Electronic Theatre Controls Ltd. (UK)	www.etcconnect.com
Electronic Theatre Controls Inc. (USA)	www.etcconnect.com
Electronics Diversified, Inc. (USA)	www.edionline.com
Entertainment Technology Inc. (USA)	www.etdimming.com
ESTA (USA Standards)	www.esta.org
Howard Eaton Lighting Ltd. (UK)	www.helluk.com
Jands Pty Limited. (Australia)	www.jands.com.au
Light Processor Ltd. (UK)	www.lightfactor.co.uk
Leprecon LLC. (USA)	www.leprecon.com
Lightronics Inc. (USA)	www.lightronics.com
Lite-Puter Enterprise Co., Ltd.	www.liteputer.com.tw
LSC Lighting Systems (Australia)	www.lsclighting.com.au
Multiform Technology Ltd. (UK)	www.multiform-uk.com
NSI Corp – Leviton Inc (USA)	www.nsicorp.com
PLASA (UK Standards)	www.plasa.org
Robert Juliat (France)	www.robertjuliat.com
Pulsar Light of Cambridge Ltd. (UK)	www.pulsarlight.com
Stagetec Ltd. (Compulite UK)	www.stagetec.co.uk
Strand Lighting Ltd. (UK)	www.strandlighting.com
Strand Lighting, Inc. (USA)	www.strandlighting.com
TMB (UK)	www.tmb.com
TMB (USA)	www.tmb.com
USITT (USA Standards)	www.usitt.org
Zero 88 Lighting Ltd.	www.zero88.com

THEATRE DIMMERS—Continued

Round Type Interlocking Dimmers.

end frame, an angle iron at the lower back of the frame, and an angle iron bar placed midway on the horizontal arm of the frame.

The operating levers are mounted on a shaft which is carried on self-centering bearings on an extension of the horizontal arm of the end frame, and the levers are so mounted in both the interlocking and non-interlocking types.

Cut C

Cut C indicates arrangement of dimmers for rear of board mounting with operating handles mounted on the front of switch board. This construction costs approximately twenty per cent. more than Cut A arrangement.

See page 51 for additional cuts showing dimmers, mountings and dimensions.

We will gladly furnish estimates on special arrangements to suit particular requirements.

INFORMATION REQUIRED

1. State whether system is 2 or 3 wire.
2. Voltage of circuit.
3. Number and type of lamp i. e., carbon or metal filament, per dimmer.
4. State cut showing arrangement of dimmers desired.
5. Give complete information regarding space limitations.
6. State arrangement of colors desired.

Fig 24: Kliegl catalogue from 1914, information: McGraw Collection, USA.

7

NEW TECHNOLOGY DIMMERS

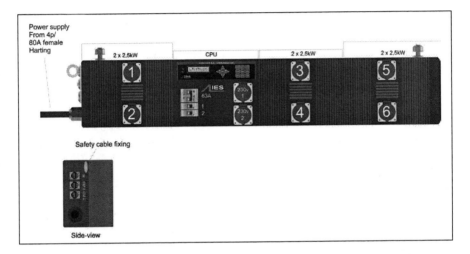

Distributed Dimmer manufactured by IES in Holland in 2003 for MTV TV studio in London containing 6 x 2.5kW IGBT reverse phase dimmers
drawing: IES bV now ETC bV.

Contents:

- **Introduction to Transistors – MOSFET and IGBT**
- **Reverse Phase Transistor Dimming**
- **Sine Wave Dimming – theory and new dimmer types**
- **Distributed Dimming – types and applications**
- **General Issues Using Transistor Dimming**
- **Conclusions**

7.1 Introduction to Transistor Dimming

Some explanation of electronic theory is required here to enable the transistor principles and benefits to be understood. The thyristor and triac dimming systems work on the leading edge of the sine wave. The transistor solution works on the trailing edge due to the transistor working via the proportional control principle. For this reason transistor dimmers are often known as 'reverse phase or trailing edge dimmers'. Some transistor dimmers can be switched between leading or trailing edge dimming, allowing different types of load to be reliably dimmed.

With a thyristor/triac dimmer always using the rising waveform edge this tends to generate sharp switching edges of the controlled waveform. With a transistor we can allow the sine wave to build up and then to control the point it is switched off, not suddenly but in a controlled way. This gentle switch-off removes the fast switch-off process of the thyristor and dramatically removes the harmonic interference that is generated, possibly removing altogether the need for a suppression choke.

Like all good ideas there are problems to be overcome, the first is that the transistor is not as efficient as the thyristor, producing a higher voltage drop when fully switched on and some high losses in the non saturated non fully switched on state. The worry here is that the more perfect the circuit is designed to create the perfect curve then the greater the losses through the transistor and the less efficient the dimmer. Remember that efficiency often shows up as heat generated by the dimmer. Transistors are much less tolerant to voltage and current issues than purpose designed switching devices such as triacs and thyristors. This requires additional protection circuitry and software to protect transistors, something that is not so critical with conventional dimmers.

There are two types of transistor that have been used in dimmers: one is the IGBT standing for Insulated Gate Bi-polar Transistor, the other is the MOSFET standing for Metal Oxide Silicon Field Effect Transistor. The MOSFET has been around for some time, has been widely used even though the devices are voltage controlled, needs little gate current, does not suffer from thermal runaway and devices can be connected in parallel to increase current carrying capacity. This has resulted in them being widely used in audio amplifiers. Their drawbacks are that they are sensitive to electrostatic discharge and that their forward voltage ratings have not been good enough for use in dimmers.

The IGBT on the other hand has been through much wider acceptance and use and is really a mix of a MOSFET and a bi-polar transistor. The latter is a device made up on an n-p-n and a p-n-p transistor. This means that the device has a safe and wide operating range, needs little gate current and has a low saturation voltage. The IGBT benefits from being fast to turn on and slow to turn off. Most of the higher power transistor dimmers on the market currently use IGBT devices.

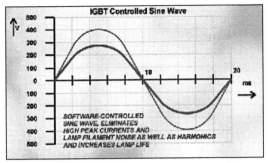

Fig 1: IGBT Sine Wave dimmer output waveform, graph: ETC bV. (IES bV.)

The modern IGBT dimmer switches power off to the lamp at a point during the half cycle. In the same way as the thyristor chops the waveform, so too does the IGBT. But due to the switch-off condition and the fact that the IGBT is a transistor, it is possible to control the fall time and curve shape of the current precisely. Within the control software an optimum switch-off curve is stored to reduce the unwanted effects experienced with a thyristor or triac dimmer. The controlled way that this current is managed is at the very heart of an IBGT transistor dimmer.

A further benefit from the use of IGBTs is that the acoustic performance of the system is improved. This can easily be checked. If a 1kW Par Can is connected to the output of a standard triac or thyristor dimmer and then an IGBT dimmer, with both dimmer types set to the same 60% intensity level, listen to the noise at the lamp in the Par Can. The filament clearly resonates (buzzes) with the triac or thyristor dimmer – even with a good quality 350µS rise time choke – but when connected to the IGBT dimmer the lamp is virtually silent. A detailed look at the developments that transistor technology has started to bring follows in this chapter.

7.2 Reverse Phase Transistor Dimming

As stated previously, the transistor has a major advantage over thyristors and triacs in so far as they are not switching devices but electronic elements that can actually control the flow of current through the device. As explained earlier in this chapter, conventional triac or thyristor dimmers rapidly switch current through these devices giving rise to harmonic currents and interference when the switching actions occur.

Triac and thyristor dimmers reduce the amount of interference they create by use of inductive chokes connected between the device and the load. These have major disadvantages in terms of adding weight to the dimmer and added heat dissipation created by the voltage drop across the choke. The action of the choke and the switching create high peak currents requiring the power devices and other components to withstand considerably higher voltages than normal.

The transistor devices allow the circuit designer much greater flexibility and also allow the flow of current to be controlled considerably more accurately. This permits almost the reverse operation of power control that is used in conventional dimmers. The IGBT device allows the current to flow at the beginning of the half cycle and gradually to be switched off later in the cycle. The total amount of power fed to the load can then be controlled without the step increase in current seen in triac or thyristor dimmers. This reduction has considerable advantages: there are no longer high peak currents, no choke is required and the voltage drop created by the choke is eliminated. This 'reverse-phase' approach ensures that the large current surge seen each half cycle in a conventional thyristor dimmer is eliminated, and any harmonics created go to balance out the harmonic currents experienced by other dimmers in the system. It should be noted that these conventional current surges can give rise to peak currents of 20 times the nominal – this results in 84A for a 1kW lamp and 168 Amps for a 2kW lamp. The resulting technology is extremely versatile, and initially resulted in a number of solutions being produced for applications where the lowest levels of interference and noise are specified. These solutions tended to be configured in a low density formats which accommodated the higher heat dissipation required to meet the noise limits.

The IGBT power device is actually less efficient than a thyristor with a voltage drop across the device of around 3 volts compared to the thyristors 0.7 volts. However, when the choke loss is added to the thyristor loss this can reach up to 10 volts compared to the IGBT's device loss of only 3 volts. All of this ensures that the IGBT dimmers dissipate less heat, weigh less and can be manufactured in physically smaller enclosures.

Perhaps the major benefit comes in the considerably reduced amount of acoustic noise generated in the lamp filaments. As the IGBT device turns on at the zero crossing point the filament current is controlled and no longer subject to the high peak currents on each half cycle the filament is subject to considerably less stretching and vibration. This results in an equivalent rise time of greater than 800 μS. Even the best standard thyristor based modular dimmers used in concert halls can only produce rise times of between 400 and 600 μS using very large chokes.

However, using IGBT technology within a 'reverse phase' dimming system, whilst having some significant benefits, does have some drawbacks. We have already shown that a transistor differs from a conventional dimmer in that it can be controlled to gradually vary the current, not just to switch it on. By gradually turning off the current rather than turning it on, a reverse phase angle dimmer reduces the filament noise in a similar fashion as a forward phase SCR dimmer without the need of a choke.

Using a transistor as a switch (on or off) produces minimal heat, while using a transistor to directly control the voltage to a load creates a lot of heat. The more time spent by the transistor in the 'analogue mode', the more heat it produces. Some designs quote rise times of approximately 800μS with either a rise time or a fall time. In these designs the transistor is required to operate in analogue mode for the entire time duration of 800μS. This may raise the transistor operating temperature past the limits set by the manufacturer. Some current designs protect the IGBT from failure by turning it off early; whilst this produces less heat it also reduces the fall time and consequently increases the acoustic noise in the lamp filament.

My belief, following tests on solutions that I have installed, is that the IGBT does have a place in the market and certainly is a better dimmer than a conventional unit however care must be taken in viewing different manufacturers' literature as some who are trying to push us towards sine wave dimmers are trying hard to convince us that the IGBT reverse phase solution has no benefit over conventional dimmers. It is true that some reverse phase dimmers are intelligent enough to detect that some connected loads cannot be dimmed in reverse phase mode so the dimmer switches automatically to forward phase. In this mode then it is true they will create harmonic neutral currents just like a conventional dimmer.

This type of reverse phase dimming relies on some very careful processor design and some very clever software. The processor controls the point of turn-off in the half cycle corresponding to the selected output level. The software control allows for the speed of response and the current flow through the IGBT. Sensing of the current flow through the IGBT circuit removes the need for a protection device save for a short circuit 'fire' protection fuse. Once the microprocessor is used to manage the current flow through the IGBT other facilities and user benefits such an integral diagnostics, voltage and current measurement, remote programming, and analysis of the DMX signals, can be added at almost no additional cost. IGBT based dimmers are now produced by ETC Europe (previously called IES bV) and Entertainment Technology (part of Genlyte Group). Both companies produce packs, bars and modular high density dimmers.

Discussing these issues with Jan de Jonge, who was the Managing Director of IES bV before this became part of ETC, there are a number of points about IGBT technology that should be considered, these comments relate to the particular products IES produced at this time.

"Since 1995, IES have produced a range of dimmers using IGBT devices in conjunction with our own custom hardware and software technology. The IES technology monitors voltage, current and temperature at a rate of 40kHz (equates to 400 times within each half cycle at 50Hz) *and dynamically adjusts the operation of the IGBT to ensure that the current waveform is optimised for performance and protection of the IGBT and the load circuit. In a normal overload situation, using a conventional triac dimmer such as a filament failure or a wiring fault, a high current builds up within microseconds and after a delay, during which time a thermal or magnetic protection device (MCB) responds to the overload, power is then mechanically disconnected. With an IES dimmer, an over current is measured within 2μS and the dimmer switched off in another 5μS. This is much faster than any thermal or magnetic circuit breaker can react to, and therefore also protects cables and other components in circuit. As the fault could be either temporary due to a filament briefly shorting out as it collapses or permanent due to a developed short circuit the IES dimmer software checks the circuit repeatedly over a period of 10 seconds. If the fault has been cleared, the dimmer software instructs the processor to perform a soft start bringing power back to the circuit. An added benefit of this feature is when multiple paralleled loads are connected to one dimmer, as might be the case with cool 575 or 600W profiles where three or four could be used in parallel, if one filament fails with a momentary short circuit, power is not mechanically disconnected and the other three lamps are not affected. However, if the fault continues, the dimmer is disabled until remedial action is taken."*

I should add a note here and confirm that this is indeed the case as I have suffered from exactly this situation where one lamp out of three did fail in a spectacular way but the dimmer remained operational.

Jan continued: *"For some time, IGBT dimmers were considered unreliable, slow to respond to a snap change, and could not work successfully in a chase situation. It is interesting that the main drive for the use of the IES IGBT technology, and the early adopter of it, has been the rock and roll industry, so there is obviously a solution! The reason for the assumption that IGBT dimmers are slow dates back to the early MOSFET devices. In order to protect the device from the effects of inductive load cables and high impedance mains supplies, the dimmers went through a gradual switch-on process from cold. During this time the dimmer was able to measure the rate of change of current and take action if the IGBT device was at risk of being damaged by a short circuit or over current demand. The technique is still used, but the speed of the measurement is now running at 40kHz, plus the latest IGBT devices are now capable of withstanding high overload currents. This ensures that the speed of a cold lamp start has improved to the point where it is equivalent to a triac dimmer. A continuous chase or flash effect is noticeably faster using IGBT than a digital triac dimmer.*

"The reliability issue is only proved by experience. In the first months of the initial IES installations in Europe, higher levels of device failures than expected were recorded, and much effort was put into selecting devices and re-writing the software to achieve the performance of the dimmers and the added features suggested by users. There had been a much wider variation in device specification tolerance than had been expected. Also, mains supply voltage and impedance varied widely throughout Europe which, added to the different characteristics of installed load cables, gave rise to early concerns about IGBT mortality rates. However, detailed research on a number of sites identified the criteria and this provided the route to a universal solution."

I was part of the team that installed the later generation of IES modules when these were first installed in the UK in 1998 in a distributed dimming applications for a TV studio, coincidentally with low impedance mains supply. I can confirm that these have worked

Fig 2: IES PM4 Power Module with 4 x 2.5kW dimmers installed on a TV studio lighting grid circa 2001, photo: the author.

faultlessly ever since. The initial problems experienced with installed versions of IGBT devices were quickly corrected and by mid-1999 the design of the IES IGBT circuit and power ratings was finalised. Since then I have been involved in nearly 20 such installations using these IES IGBT reverse phase solutions and all have worked with no greater failure rates than would be experienced with conventional dimmers in a similar installation.

7.3 Sine Wave Dimming

The latest in dimming technology is the sine wave dimmer. If an oscilloscope is connected to a sine wave dimmer output a pure sine wave will be seen. The intensity of the light is controlled by the amplitude of the sine wave. Other dimmer technologies control a light's intensity by chopping parts out of the mains waveform, and this can cause annoying acoustic noise and electrical interference problems.

Sine wave dimming eliminates the inherent problems with forward phase control, namely the noise and harmonic distortion. Harmonics are discussed in detail in Chapter 8. Audible noise from lamp filaments and cables is uncontrollable and can be very distracting particularly if the lamps are located close to the audience. Acoustic noise is unpredictable at the design stage as it depends on the structure of the lighting installation, the lighting system power supply and the geometry and layout of individual lamp filaments - and in some cases the layout of the electrical cabling and containment systems.

In a building electrical system, harmonic currents cause interference with other equipment and consume supply authority energy which is added to the venue's electrical bill; this is basically 'lost' energy to the venue and is an 'unseen' consumption. This increases costs at the initial installation phase and thereafter in the running costs. Capital costs exist because the electrical system for a traditional dimming scheme has to accommodate a reactive power component created by harmonic currents.

When designing the electrical system for a lighting installation the regulations in each country take account of the harmonics likely to be travelling through a cable. In the UK the Institute of Electrical Engineers (IEE) regulations typically add between 20 and 40% to cover the heating and loss effects of harmonics. If this is applied through the electrical system then cables can get over-rated, containment systems can get larger, transformers and generators have to be larger capacity, and so on. Additionally supply transformers dissipate heat when subjected to harmonic currents which can shorten their lifespan.

Discussions on cable reductions and transformer sizes must comply with the country electrical regulations as many countries stipulate cable sizes for a given current, over a defined cable length either surface mounted or fixed to tray or within trunking. It will take a good electrical engineer to argue cable and supply reductions with some electrical authorities.

Reading data on ETC/IES web site suggests that *"experience with sine wave dimming controlling auditorium lighting applications has indicated that there are substantial savings in re-lamping. One theatre in The Netherlands has reported that the conversion of their venue's auditorium lighting scheme from phase-control to sine wave dimming has been repaid within 12 months in terms of fewer lamp replacements, less maintenance and lower energy bills."* The suggested reason *"is that sine wave dimmer eliminates the 50Hz inrush of current when the lamps are at a dimmed level, and it is this pulsing inrush current which stresses the filament leading to failure."*

The elimination of interference on the mains system can also ensure that lighting power no longer has to be segregated on a separate mains transformer.

Recent developments have lead to the rapid availability of sine wave dimmers. IES, now a division of ETC, lead the way with the first sine wave installation being carried out in 2002 at the Lyttelton Theatre in London's Royal National Theatre. I was part of an LSI Projects team which installed 100 channels of 5kW IES sine wave packs at a TV studio in the UK in 2003. Subsequently products from ADB in Belgium, Bytecraft in Australia, ETC in the USA and Strand in the UK are now in the process of being launched or

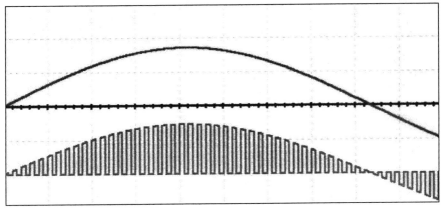

Fig 3: Pulse width modulated sine wave sliced waveform, graph: Strand Lighting Ltd.

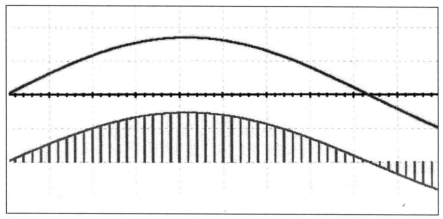

Fig 4: Pulse width modulated to almost full power, graph: Strand Lighting Ltd.

have been launched and installed. Strand's current EC21 literature confirms that a number of venues across the world have selected sine wave versions for their new systems in Canada, China, USA and UK. ETC's Sensor literature confirms system sales in the USA.

The sine wave dimmers currently available utilise high frequency pulse width modulation control to drive the IGBTs. If we look at this in more detail with the aid of some waveform diagrams it might help to explain this technology.

The pulse width modulation circuits tend to operate above 40kHz, and this means that the 50 or 60 Hertz mains waveform is going to be cut into thousands of pieces every second. This is shown graphically in *Fig 3*.

If we now look at the same waveform with a lamp almost fully turned on we see that the width of the pulses has changed; this is shown in *Fig 4*.

The pulse width modulated signal cannot be connected directly to the load; the signals must be fed through a high frequency filtering circuit to convert them into a sine wave. So yes a sine wave dimmer does have a filter choke, but somewhat smaller in size than a conventional dimmer as the sine wave inductor is working at a much higher frequency. The result of the filter choke is shown in *Fig 5*. The first waveform is the supply input waveform. The lower waveform is the filtered dimmer output showing that the amplitude is 50% of the incoming supply. Varying the duty cycle of the pulse width modulation varies the output voltage and thus the lamp intensity.

Importantly this technique of controlling the sine wave produces a number of major user benefits. Because no fast-acting switches with on or off instructions

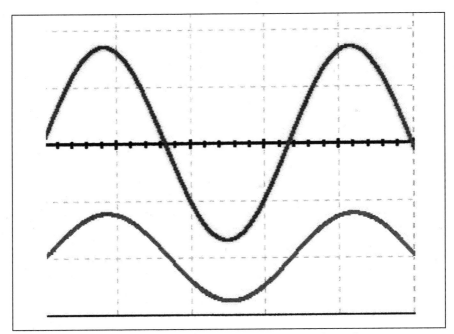

Fig 5: Line input waveform and resultant output voltage waveform after passing through filtering network, graph: Strand Lighting Ltd.

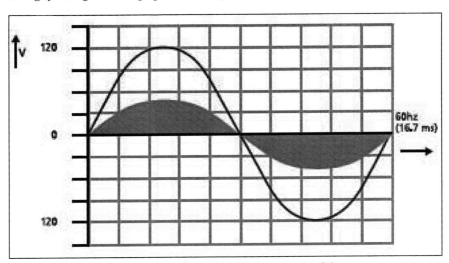

Fig 6: ETC Sine wave output waveform of 120 Volt Sensor Module graph Electronic Theatre Controls, Inc.

STRAND EC 21 DUAL 2.5kW Truesine SINE
WAVE DIMMER MODULE 2005

IES MATRIX II 4 x 5kW iSINE SINE
WAVE DIMMER MODULE 2005

ETC SENSOR DUAL 2.4kW SINE WAVE
DIMMER MODULE 2005

ENTERTAINMENT TECHNOLOGY CAPIO plus DUAL 2.5kW IGBT REVERSE PHASE
DIMMER MODULE 2004

*Fig 7: Selection of transistor reverse phase and sine wave dimming modules
photos: Entertainment Technology, Inc., ETC Europe Ltd., ETC bV. (IES bV.) and
Strand Lighting Ltd.*

are used there is almost no harmonic distortion created and with a standard
lamp current is consumed throughout the power cycle. This has a huge benefit
in terms of the way other types of load can be dimmed. For non-linear loads
as might be experienced with an HMI ballast or low voltage LED fitting
the load characteristic is passed through to the power line. The sine wave

dimmer looks transparent to the load and does not affect the voltage or current characteristics of the load.

Many loads cannot be controlled from a conventional phase controlled dimmer due to the fact the waveform is no longer a true sine wave. An ideal dimmer is therefore one that will deliver voltage and current to the load as if it were connected directly to the supply. The auto-transformers discussed earlier in this book are an ideal way of determining what can be dimmed or not. With sine wave technology fans and small motors, LED fixtures, cold cathode, neon, discharge ballasts, fluorescent ballasts and others can be dimmed successfully.

Currently the resulting sine wave distributed packs are physically larger than reverse phase versions and result in plug-in modules currently occupying nearly double the space of a thyristor equivalent. This means that cabinets of 48 x 3kW instead of 96 x 3kW and 24 x 5kW instead of 48 x 5kW would be required. This philosophy is confirmed as Strand Lighting launched their new sine wave dimmer called EC21 in 2005. This design replaced their previous SLD range and was forced upon them to accommodate the sine wave technology. ADB is continuing to use their Eurodim 3 cabinet as sufficient space allows the sine wave technology to be used albeit at a 50% reduction in channel capacity. Potentially we might be back to historic larger dimmer rooms and more electrical power distribution to feed a larger number of dimmers. Sine wave solutions are currently evolving; at this stage the very high capital cost can appear prohibitive to all but the largest and most prestigious users.

Sine wave solutions are in their infancy, and as the techniques evolve the currently high initial cost will fall, new cooling systems will evolve and we will be in the harmonic free zone! Harmonics cost the power generators large sums of waste energy every year, so it is therefore inevitable that energy suppliers will drive forward the move towards less harmonics. However, conventional dimmers are not doomed. I believe any new standard will need to be introduced slowly and dimmers bought now, of whatever type, will still legally be operational in 10 to 15 years time.

To those involved in specifying or buying large scale dimmer systems it should be remembered that currently sine wave solutions have one major drawback. At this time sine wave dimmers are three to four times the price of thyristor and twice the price of reverse phase dimmers. So in 2006 choosing sine wave takes a clear head, particularly as lighting budgets are continually being reduced. Like all new technology there will be teething problems, and whilst everyone learns, patience is needed. The second edition of this book

Fig 8: ADB Sine wave dimmer module for Eurodim 3 launched in 2005
photo: ADB Technologies SA.

will no doubt report some very positive movement forward with sine wave
becoming more the 'norm' than the 'odd one' out!

7.4 Distributed Dimming

Over the past eight years a number of alternative packages have been developed
which allow the dimmers to be located with the luminaires. I say eight years,
actually some fifteen years ago a company in the USA, called Entertainment
Technology founded by Gordon Pearlman and Steve Carlson, developed the
Intelligent Strip. This has remained in production ever since its inception
through the different owners of the company including with the present owner
Genlyte Group.

The concept was simple, to produce a dimmer strip that looked like a piece
of electrical containment with the standard socket outlets built in, just as you
would find in many a theatre. The difference was that the Intelligent Power

System (IPS) strip also contained IGBT dimmers. Using the technology discussed earlier in this chapter, Entertainment Technology were able to build into a very small space 6 channels of 1.2kW or 3 channels of 2.4kW rated 120 volt dimming. Remember that to us Europeans this represents 6 channels of 2.4kW or 3 channels of 5kW dimming, – so no mean achievement in 1988!

Reading through the current sales literature the characteristics that made the development unique in 1988 are still valid today. *"The strips are completely solid state, enabling them to operate silently without mechanical noise and to operate at 450μS in forward or reverse phase mode. This dramatically minimizes lamp, ballast, or transformer noises in the space. Since IGBT technology does not use filters or chokes, IPS dimmers are more efficient, with a maximum 2.5 voltage drop at full, are lightweight at less than 2 lbs (0.9kg) per dimmer, and produce less heat than conventional dimmers."*

"IPS dimmers offer an extended feature set that is unsurpassed in today's conventional dimming equipment. Every IPS dimmer has an on-board, intelligent microprocessor, which adjusts and maintains proper voltage and current in response to changes detected in the load and electrical service. The microprocessor automatically suppresses surges, protects against dead shorts, and extends lamp life. Other features include a built-in raise and lower focus button for convenient fixture testing, aiming, and setup."

One of the other benefits unique when launched was built-in diagnostics that were called Talkback. This provided dynamic feedback of load size and type, short circuit, temperature and overload. They claimed that IPS dimmers also significantly reduced neutral harmonics by operating them in 'Low Harm Mode' which was actually reverse phase mode.

These early IGBT transistor dimmers provided dimming control of the following load types: incandescent, neon, cold cathode, electronic low-voltage, magnetic low-voltage and quartz halogen. They were also compatible with most brands of fluorescent non-dim ballasts in a non-dim configuration. They automatically adjusted to forward or reverse phase dimming to suit the type of connected load. Significantly there was no minimum load and they could dim from 1 watt to their rated load. The voltage drop across the pack was only 2% of the connected supply voltage so around 2.5 volts only at 120 volts. All of these facilities still exist in the current product.

This product developed the term for remotely locating dimmers around the venue, namely 'distributed dimming'. It was not the first approach to placing dimmers where they could be located or where the cable runs were shortest or

Fig 9: Intelligent Power System Dimmer Strip with 6 x 1.2kW 120 volt dimmers circa 2003, photo: Entertainment Technology, Inc.

where the power supplies were located. Theatres had been built with installed dimmers located in more than one location often to ease the electrical cable costs. However it did launch a new concept in placing dimmers around the venue that could be moved around, removing the necessity of installing a large number of dimmers, only to use 70% of them in any show.

The modern concept of distributed dimming is to find a package that suits the requirements of the venue. This may be that there are installed dimmers for part of the system, dimmer bars or strips for other parts and possibly some dimmer modules or boxes or packs for other parts of the system.

Recent years have seen a number of different packages being developed. Entertainment Technology has continued to take the IGBT dimmer and to package this into different formats to the point today they have wall boxed dimmers, portable dimmer boxes, dimmer strips and dimmer raceways. In Europe the most prolific developer of solutions has to be IES in Holland. Like Entertainment Technology, IES is no longer the small innovative company it was and in 2004 became part of ETC. Entertainment Technology became part of Rosco Laboratories and more recently Genlyte, also owners of Vari-Lite and even more recently (Summer 2006) Strand Lighting. In both cases the financial and technical resources now given to these two companies has seen them both blossom and grow. IES developed dimmer bars, portable modules and the installed dimmer, all based around IGBT technology and all linkable on their network providing a completely distributable dimming solution.

Technically distributed dimming versus hard wired dimming solutions need careful consideration such as:

- Initial capital cost.

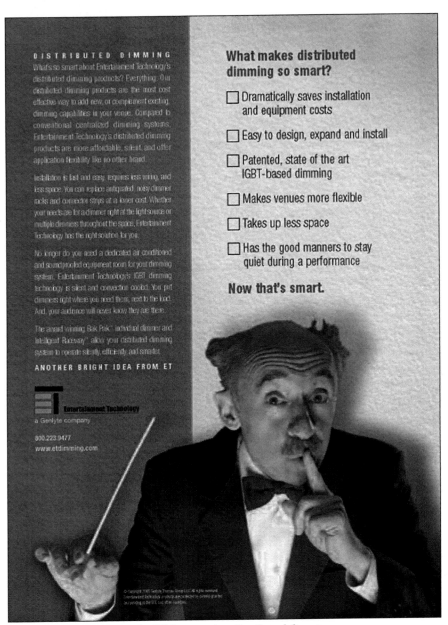

Fig 10: Advertisement in the USA promoting distributed dimming
advert: Entertainment Technology, Inc.

- Required turn around time between shows.
- Applications venue will be used for – type of productions.
- Existing or new electrical and data systems to be used.
- Is this a new installation or an addition to an existing installation?
- Quality of required dimming solution and acceptable acoustic noise levels?

These different aspects are discussed in following sub sections.

7.4.1 Initial Cost?

To calculate the initial cost of an installed versus a distributed solution is not simply comparing one equipment 'wish' list with another. This is a complex calculation if it is to be handled correctly. One of the major costs of any dimmer installation is actually not the dimming equipment, it is the electrical materials and labour cost to connect the dimmers to the supply(s) and to the socket outlets around the venue.

This is difficult for us technicians to cost and requires a complex analysis by a qualified electrical contractor or engineer. In this process the cost of the power distribution should be considered both for the fixed and the distributed. Equally, the actual location of the distributed solutions, how they are to receive their power and how the loads will be connected should not be forgotten. On one recent project distributed sine wave dimmer bars were selected for use over a stage area. As the lighting bars were part of a power flying system then attached distributed dimmer bars had to receive their power via a cable management system. This had to deliver a number of heavy three phase electrical supplies and the necessary lighting data services. For a proper analysis in this situation the cost of the cable management system required for either approach would have to be included.

I have summarised in the simplest form the costs that should be included to produce a cost comparison for an installed versus a distributed solution. Out of space necessity this must really be used to provoke a thought process and will vary per installation.

Item	Installed	Distributed
Equipment:	Cost?	Cost?
Power distribution:	Cost?	Cost?
Cable management:	Cost?	Cost?
Feeder cables	Cost?	Cost?

Load cables	Cost?	Cost?
Feeder cable containment	Cost?	Cost?
Load cable containment	Cost?	Cost?
Data cable and connections	Cost?	Cost?
Data cable containment	Cost?	Cost?
Any additional data processing cost?	Cost?	Cost?
Any required additional structural pickup costs?	N/A	Cost?
Any additional rigging system costs?	N/A	Cost?
Any additional rigging time related costs?	Cost?	Cost?

7.4.2 Required Turn-around Time?

The item that probably needs some further explanation is the last one in the list : "any additional rigging time related cost?" This can be an important issue because it may be that additional rigging time and thus labour costs need to be included if the dimmers have to be moved around and rigged in addition to the lighting instruments. This would add rigging time to any show rig and therefore has a cost that should be included if a complete true analysis is to be carried out.

Turn-around time is the time taken to strike one show and put in the next whether this is in a theatre, TV studio, conference centre or concert hall. In some venues this has no impact because the shows are not continuous. In others where there is a daily, weekly or fortnightly changeover this can be an important consideration. With installed dimmers, whether they be in one dimmer room or in fixed distributed locations there is no impact on turn-around time.

However imagine a multi-purpose theatre-in-the-round space found in a larger college with lighting bars installed over the performance space and a number of bar locations around the auditorium. *Fig 11* shows the conventional installed solution with the dimmer channel numbers shown on the lighting bars. *Fig 12* shows the same venue with only power and data connection points, ready to accept a distributed dimming solution.

In this example time would need to be allowed to rig the dimmer boxes or

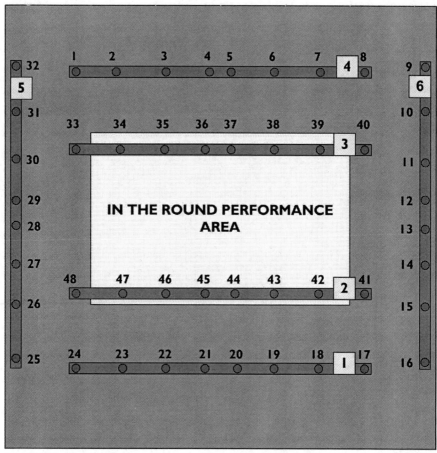

Fig 11: Simple multi-purpose theatre-in-the-round auditorium with conventional installed dimmed and DMX data outlets.

modules or bars shown as *Fig 13*. Additional time would need to be included to connect extension cables from the dimmers to the lighting instruments although this may not be that different from a standard venue where the outlets never seem to be in the right location. Consequently the turn-around time between the conventional *Fig 11* solution and the distributed solution of *Fig 12* would be longer due to the time required to rig the dimmers. That is unless the distributed dimmers become the standard rig! This is where the cost analysis becomes important. If the *Fig 10* system is changed to then be based around installed distributed dimmer bars, there is no difference in turn-

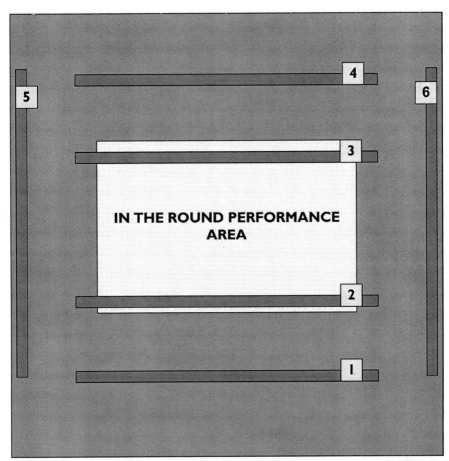

Fig 12: Simple multi-purpose theatre in the round auditorium with installed lighting bars only and fixed DMX data outlets.

around time, the electrical costs are lower as only power feeds need to be sent for each dimmer bar, and the data outlets are similar to the installed solution. So in this example the distributed solution MUST be lower in cost and can use SCR, reverse phase or sine wave dimmers and the cost comparison ratio will remain the same.

7.4.3   Type of Productions Staged In The Venue?

One might ask what difference this makes. Well the type of venue and its productions go together and this does seem to have an effect on whether a distributed solution will be viable or not if only economics are considered.

In TV applications experience has shown me that for the smaller News and Current Affairs studios distributing the dimming around a fixed or tracking lighting grid can work fine. In these applications the dimmer boxes, modules or bars all operate well and there is an initial cost advantage in following the distributed solution. However, acoustic noise can be a consideration, even with relatively close-talk microphones, and the reverse phase or sine wave solution may be required depending on the height of the lighting grid. This seems to work very well in studios from 40 to 150 square metres. Once the

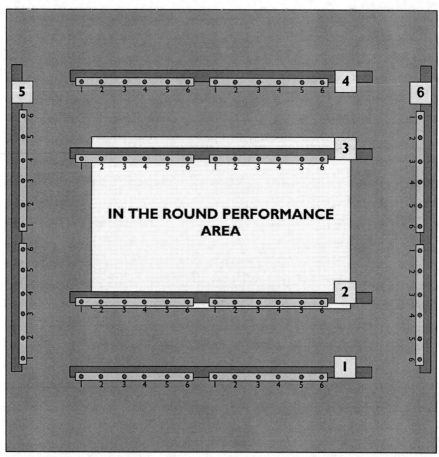

Fig 13: Simple multi-purpose theatre-in-the-round auditorium with installed distributed 6 way dimmer bars fed from fixed DMX data outlets.

studio starts to be equipped with alternative suspension solutions such as pantographs, self-climbing hoists or telescopes, the situation may change. With the single lighting instrument hung on a pantograph or a telescope then a single channel distributed dimmer can be considered, but this is the same cost as installing a fixed outlet. However if the studio is of the saturated type there is an initial cost benefit in only providing enough dimmers to equip say 60% of the space and then moving them around to suit the production needs. With self-climbing hoists with two or three channels of dimming adding a 2 or 3 channel dimmer box or module provides a sensible solution and again the redundancy issue can be considered.

In a museum or space that is constantly changing such as a hotel ballroom then rigging dimmers as required makes a great deal of sense because the system retains the complete flexibility that the architect and consultant specified initially.

In an educational space with the cost of the portable or rack mounted packs it is almost inevitable that both work well and the size of the venue and the scale of the productions will govern what works best. My experience suggests that in the primary schools with a simple stage then the smart bar or portable dimmer mounted on a stand is a true distributed dimming solution. When the stage becomes larger in the high schools or colleges the installed solution with 24 way lower cost cabinets is probably the lowest cost solution. In these applications acoustic noise and dimmer performance is not so critical as one might find in a TV studio or professional theatre.

In professional theatre the venue format seems to govern the choice of solution more so than the style of production. In most theatres installing dimmers for fixed front of house bridges and slots makes sense as there is little benefit in complicating the installation and lighting instruments will always be needed in these locations. Over the stage area it is a very different matter as considerable costs can be saved by placing dimmers on the flown over-stage lighting bars. The power feed cables, whilst large, occupy a lot less overall diameter than multiple channel load cabling. Therefore, mixing the types of dimmer packages can allow cost and end user flexibility; in some theatre applications allocating 50 – 60% to be installed with 40 – 50% being distributed seems to work well with the overall cost being spent more on dimmers and less on contracting. It is very definitely worth considering use of distributed packs or modules on moving structures where managed cable costs can be high and reducing the number of cables can reduce costs and improve system reliability – although do not forget that adding the dimmers to these bars may restrict the load carrying capacity for rigged equipment or increasing the lifting capacity requirements.

7.4.4 Re-use of Existing Cabling or Fit New Cabling?

This is a very important aspect as re-use of existing cabling almost always governs that the new installation must be similar in format to the existing one otherwise major costs will be incurred. Where the number of dimmers is being increased it is possible to re-use the existing cabling if it tests out okay, then adding more installed dimmers or distributed units as best suits the installation. What clearly does not work is mixing installed and distributed dimming onto existing cabling.

Where new cabling is required the costs need to be calculated completely, so again the earlier list should be used, not forgetting to include all the conduits, other containment cables and of course the labour to install it. Usually a local electrical contractor can provide you with average rates to install per metre of cable for a given size. Whilst not completely accurate it will provide comparable costs between the two potential solutions.

7.4.5 Is this a new installation or an addition to an existing installation?

This point has really been answered in previous sections save that maybe you want to change the venue to improve lighting flexibility or you are planning for a temporary change to suit a certain production. One obvious advantage of adding distributed dimmers is that all they need is a protected power source and access to the data network. Therefore it is very easy to add on additional dimmers with the minimum of installation cost. Remember this could simply be adding a 12 channel dimmer pack on the fly floor, or a flight cased rack on stage with multicore up to ladders or temporary bars.

I would suggest that following a distributed solution works very well if a completely new set of lighting locations are required. Where the solution is not so effective is if you have 240 dimmers installed throughout a theatre and you want to globally increase this to, say, 360 ways. Here the best solution is to add more of the installed dimmers and the additional cable ways. That is unless the scheme has a shortage of dimmers in a specific area. Here this may involve adding a single high current feed and adding a 'block of dimmers' in another dimmer room or flight case or via installed dimmers within socket boxes. Always remember that electrical and safety regulations may preclude some ideas due to potential hazards such as fire, cable routing or electrical connection issues.

Recent experience with a medium size venue has taught me that you do have to consider carefully what you want to achieve in the design and then double check the costs. It is easy to convince oneself that the numbers are correct - so get someone else to check them for you, otherwise embarrassing moments can occur in design meetings!

7.4.6 Quality of Required Dimming Solution and Acceptable Acoustic Noise levels?

When looking at any dimming system today engineers and specifiers need to consider in detail the quality of the delivered solution and the potential acoustic noise that it may generate.

The electrical supply authorities are keen to reduce the amount of electrical pollution present on their networks, and audiences are all too often sitting within auditoria that are polluted with electrically generated noise. When the grand Matcham theatres were designed the audiences saw and heard a show without any of these aspects even being worried about. Technology has brought us some wonderful solutions for the designer's tool box but like all good ideas there are some drawbacks. Certainly the noise present in the auditorium in some shows has passed the level of acceptability. Listening recently to Richard Pilbrow, being interviewed at Showlight in Munich in 2005 by David Taylor, Richard made a plea concerning moving lights, colour scrollers and noise in the auditorium: *"Please make the damn things quiet. It is the duty of a lighting designer to make the show less noisy for the audience"*. More and more designers and specifiers are being forced to consider the generated noise as it has definitely reached the point of interfering with enjoyment of some shows.

This book only looks at the dimming aspect rather than the greatest source of noise which are the motorised instruments and the colour changers. However, having recently sat in a theatre equipped in the early 90's and been forced to hear constantly changing acoustic noise levels from the instruments as well as listening to them creaking and cracking as they heated up and cooled down, there *is* something we can do!

Acoustic noise from luminaires is generated from two sources. The first and largest source is from dimmer-generated acoustic noise usually heard as a buzzing sound that tends to change frequency as the intensity changes. The secondary noise is directly related to specific luminaires. Some of them creak and crack as they warm up and cool down, others remain quiet throughout their heating and cooling cycle. Experience soon shows which are the quiet ones and which are the noisy instruments.

ENTERTAINMENT TECHNOLOGY DIMMER BOX – 6 x 1.2kW OR 3 x 2.4kW – 120V

ELECTRONICS DIVERSIFIED Big STIK DIMMER BAR – 6 x 1.2kW OR 3 x 2.4kW -120V

ETC (IES) SMART BAR - 6 x 2.4kW (120V OR 240V) – other versions available.

ETC (IES) SMART MODULE -
AVAILABLE IN MANY VARIANTS
120 OR 240V

Fig 14: Examples of different packages of distributed dimmers, photos: ETC Europe Ltd., Electronics Diversified, Inc, and Entertainment Technology, Inc.

Choosing conventional dimmers with high rise time chokes or using reverse phase dimmers both help to reduce this noise. Making them acoustically near silent requires sine wave dimmers. Reducing electrical pollution is helped with reverse phase dimmers but using sine wave dimming solutions can make substantial reductions. So, back to the question in hand. If you are specifying or installing now, then my view is that you have a duty to consider using a sine wave solution; it may be rejected on cost but should at least be responsibly considered.

7.4.7 Other Considerations

The remaining issues that should be considered are not necessarily so obvious and more difficult to relate to or cost for. If distributed dimming is used there is no longer a need for a dimmer room and any associated costs for cooling this room to acceptable temperature levels. This might seem like an irrelevance but in today's space allocation and room costing structure this can become a serious consideration. Clearly there will always need to be an electrical room in which the electrical switchgear can be located. However this can occupy a relatively small space; dimmer rooms, even with high density dimmer racks, need a much larger space and often fall within building regulations due to their high potential fire risk. Therefore distributing installed dimmers around the building by (say) having a dimmer room adjacent to the stage grid, one sub stage and one within the front of house areas will substantially reduce electrical cabling costs but the actual room and infra-structure costs such as air conditioning can be high. Moving the dimmers to (say) the over-stage bars by using powered bars, putting dimmer boxes on to the stage walls or floor with perhaps some installed dimmers for front of house may produce a more flexible solution at a lower cost. So do not forget these aspects during the design process.

7.5   Other Distributed Solutions

In the USA Entertainment Technology manufacture a product called Raceway. This is just like a length of electrical containment and built into this are dimmer modules. As each Raceway is built to order, the designer can define the number of dimmers and their ratings within a given length of Raceway. The Raceway is suspended from a lighting bar or mounted along a lighting bridge just like a socket distribution system. As with their other reverse phase dimming solutions these Raceway units include built-in diagnostics and software to manage short

Fig 15: Installed Over-Stage Intelligent Raceway Dimmer Bar
photo: Entertainment Technology, Inc.

circuits and overloads making the device completely safe to be remote from the electrical supply and protective devices. Data from the dimmers can be fed back to a central location and read on a PC or lighting console. This solution allows one supply cable to be fed to the Raceway, often managed by a cable winding or management system. Remember that the unit will also require DMX or Ethernet data as the control signal. Whilst the bars are available with 230/240 volt dimmers, no European distributors currently exist for this product. Clearly work would need to be done to comply with European standards such as using different connectors and cable colours and well as metric metalwork, but to me this seems like such a good idea somebody should pick it up.

To try and help show ways in which different products can be applied I have included some suggested applications I have used and found to work very well.

Four channel reverse phase and sine wave packs can be used in TV studios or theatre stages for dimming cyclorama lights as they tend to directly match the four colour cyclorama luminaires used for top cyc and groundrow lighting. Packs can be placed by the cyc lights or adjacent to the groundrow with a considerable reduction in acoustic noise emission.

Fig 16: 4 channel reverse phase dimmer pack used as a distributed solution on TV studio floor feeding groundrow instruments, photo: Jan de Jonge.

With an open format performance space where a lighting grid is fixed above the performance area a very simple solution is to fix packs or lighting bars directly to the grid as shown in *Fig 17*. The uniform nature of the grid? being made up of a 1 metre x 1 metre matrix, makes it ideal to distribute the dimmers uniformly over the grid. In this case the dimmers are shown receiving power from a CEE 17 32 Amp connector, and these have been distributed uniformly over the grid allowing modules to be plugged in as required across the grid. Similarly, DMX data outlets have been provided, wired back to a central patch bay where powered distribution equipment is provided. Again, these are uniformly distributed across the grid. Both these power and data formats allow dimmers and other DMX devices to be located where required, ensuring complete flexibility.

On a recent visit to a large UK opera house I was surprised to see the format where dimmed circuits were being delivered to the side stage ladders. The existing layout is shown in *Fig 18*. This involved a whole series of dimmed circuits being delivered by a festoon system down to the ladders where the

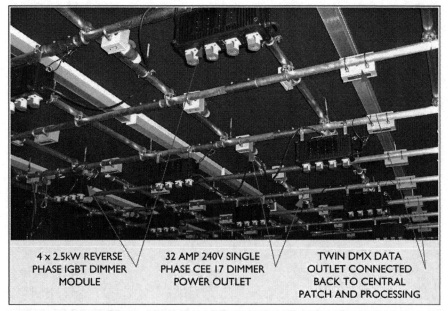

| 4 x 2.5kW REVERSE PHASE IGBT DIMMER MODULE | 32 AMP 240V SINGLE PHASE CEE 17 DIMMER POWER OUTLET | TWIN DMX DATA OUTLET CONNECTED BACK TO CENTRAL PATCH AND PROCESSING |

Fig 17: 4 channel x 2.5kW packs mounted directly to uniform lighting grid and methods used to connect power and data, photo: the author.

feeds were terminated into 16 Amp CEE 17 sockets. I was visiting because a consultant had thought that maybe converting this system to a distributed one might simplify the whole solution, improve reliability and put more dimmed channels onto each ladder. The proposal involved adding a 6 channel dimmer module to each of the ladders requiring a power and data connection only. The power would be delivered via an extruded power truck running adjacent to the walkway. This solution could use standard SCR, reverse phase or sine wave boxes or modules. The proposal is still under review due to budget constraints.

One other recent project that I had the opportunity to visit was another opera house in Europe. In this project the venue staff had decided, during a major dimmer upgrade, to utilise distributed and installed sine wave solutions. The sine wave solution was selected as a means of reducing acoustic noise and to reduce electrical pollution after a careful study had shown that the reduction in energy costs would qualify for a government energy grant to cover some of the equipment cost.

The final selected solution comprised a combination of installed and distributed sine wave dimmers. A total of 424 x 2.5kW, 144 x 5kW and 26 x 10kW dimmers were provided by way of 864 equivalent dimmers. This manufacturer's product offered an advantage in that 5kW dimmers can be converted into two 2.5kW dimmers.

For the over-stage lighting bars a total of 50 power bars were supplied providing a total of 300 dimmers. Each Power Bar is fitted with three 2.5kW and three 5kW sine wave dimmers which are capable of dimming 4kW HMI sources and switching up to 6kW HMIs – together with three 24V 150W power supplies for auxiliary equipment such as mechanical dimming shutters, colour scrollers and automated lights. Each channel

Fig 18: View of Side Stage Ladders showing festoon cable feeds, photo: the author.

is protected both electronically and by means of an RCBO, with each dimmer channel reporting faults, status, programming and other data back to a control position via their own diagnostic network. The Power Bars are fed via power cables wound on cable reelers in time with the rise and fall of the motorised flown bars. This is a very good example of how mixing conventional installed and distributed dimmers provides user benefits and flexibility.

One question that is often asked is does the weight of the power bar or module not restrict the flying capacity of the flown bar or the lighting grid? No is the simple answer! As the weight of the IGBT and sine wave dimmer is low, typically 10kg for a 4 x 2.5kW and 9kg for a 2 x 5kW pack they can be suspended from the lighting grid or flown bar without significantly restricting the bar's lifting capacity. The unit dimmer versions can be fixed to the luminaire or located in almost any suitable position. Remember for stage floor circuits the packs can be located directly on the floor just like an electrical breakout box.

With these solutions considerable cable costs are saved between the dimmer room and the top termination boxes feeding the flown bars or lighting grid.

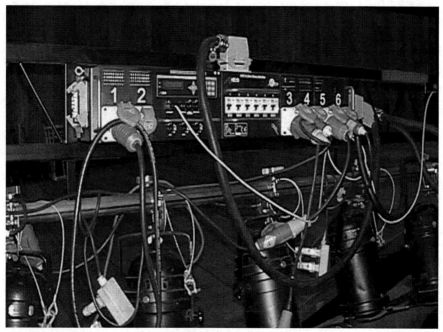

Fig 19: Special Power bar as developed for European Opera House photo: Rick Dines.

Where flown bars are of the raise and lower type there is always the issue of how to manage the feeder cables. With a centralised dimming solution one might have to cable-manage a considerable number of circuits, and therefore cables. With a distributed solution only mains power and data are required. This can result in considerable savings as the size and capacity of the cable windlass, or reeler or winder is almost directly proportional to the number of cores or circuits being managed. Potential electrical and radio frequency interference is reduced as is the acoustic noise transmission. I have been involved in some 26 distributed dimming projects in the past nine years where distributing the dimmers across the lighting grid or bars close to the luminaires has proved to offer ideal solutions for small to medium sized venues. Combination solutions have been shown to work well in the medium to large scale venues. In fact I am currently involved, as this book goes to press, in the first multi TV studio complex that will be completely equipped with distributed sine wave based dimmer modules and bars. This completes in 2007, so the second edition should detail the results of this project!

My first such crude installation was based on mounting six channel dimmer packs in cradles on the lighting grid. This was not ideal because the packs were large and heavy and emitted large amounts of dimmer 'buzz'. This was probably the first 'true' distributed dimmer installation in the UK and was chosen because the user did not have space for fixed dimmers and wanted an economic solution with high levels of flexibility.

Planning a distributed dimmer installation requires similar consideration to that of a hard wired solution save that the number of dimmer channels required may be less as no redundancy need be allowed, other than one or two spare dimmer modules or bars for maintenance purposes. The areas to be lit should be considered and an instrument plan worked out otherwise it is not possible to work out where the dimmers will be required, unless this is a matrix type grid shown earlier in this chapter. This dictates the number of dimmers required and their ideal locations. It details what quantity of dimmer will be required, the best combination of channels and their capacities and where they should be located. This allows consideration of whether unit dimmers, dimmer bars or distributed packs/boxes would form the best solution. Equally consideration should be given as to whether these should be conventional, reverse phase or whether sine wave types would be most appropriate.

The packs and bars should be fitted with hanging clamps and safety bonds. They are then installed, by the venue electricians, onto the lighting grid as they rig the fixtures. As the sets change so the instrument locations and dimmer positions can change to suit. One word here is that the packs are best located where they can be reached easily if DMX address or any programming needs to be carried out. Mounting them on the end of a lighting bar close to a catwalk or above the luminaires on a front of a lighting bridge, works well. If 2, 4 or 6 channel packs are to be used these can be powered from a single phase supply of 16, 32 or 63 Amp. Alternatively, three phase supplies can be safely used with each pack or bar accepting three phases if they are in channel modules of 3. In some countries use of 3 phase power to equipment regulations requires careful labelling and specific types of electrical protection. Equally, where higher current power sources are in use that portable equipment plugs into, added protection such as RCDs or RCBOs should be considered essential. These electrical aspects are reviewed in the next chapter.

7.6 Conclusions

So now there is an alternative to the conventional thyristor or triac dimming solution. Both have their place, each has their advantages, either in price or technical advantage - as well as their disadvantages. The reverse phase solution has an acoustic noise benefit together with the size and weight advantage. The sine wave solution has one further benefit in terms of reduced electrical harmonic emission. As this book goes to press there is a serious concern among electrical engineers and standards institutions that the amount of harmonic distortion, some call it pollution, has reached dangerously high levels. This is said to be causing considerable problems with electronic equipment, not to mention cabling and lost energy. Standards institutions are now trying to drive through legislation that may require all manufacturers to reduce considerably the amount of distortion produced by their equipment. Dimmers will not escape this legislation, and electronic design engineers are currently seeking ways in which dimmer technology can be re-designed to reduce these problems.

The reverse phase solution is considerably better than thyristor or triac dimmers, but the author believes it is the sine wave solution that will ultimately be adopted universally. With Strand Lighting about to install a large system in Toronto, ETC, via IES, having already installed well over 3,000 channels by 2005, ADB having launched their sine wave modules in 2005 and Bytecraft, in Australia, already manufacturing and shipping, the world is moving to 'controlling the sine wave'. The greater the volume sold the lower the price may become. However, there are physical restrictions created by the higher heat dissipation which will see dimmer cabinet quantities or sizes grow to accommodate the additional heat.

It is interesting to see the way that sine wave technology is being specified by consultants and end users. One recent major London concert venue saw 90% of the dimmers being specified as conventional with 10% specified as sine wave. The sine wave dimmers were selected to control the lighting over the acoustic shell, where noise was a major issue. In another major project, completing some three years hence, used for many forms of live stage based entertainment and also used for TV events, conventional dimmers were specified again. Yet in a new opera house in Denmark virtually all of the over-stage dimmers were sine wave with the rest of the installation conventional thyristor. Some of the cost of the over-stage distributed solution was recovered on the reduced cost of the automatic raise and lower cabling system costs. These decisions confirm that the venue type, the show application and local requirements all affect the choice and of course the overall cost of what is always a large part of any lighting system.

My view, in early 2006, is that sine wave solutions should now be considered at the design stage. Regulations will come into force at some point as the cost of power generation escalates and more energy suppliers fight with the public about the building of additional power generation plants. In the USA we have already seen some energy generators offer to pay for conversion of conventional 1 and 2 kW profiles into lower energy luminaires such as the ETC Source 4 and Altman Shakespeare. Another similar example occurred in Holland in the refurbishment of the Amsterdam Opera where the Dutch Government gave an energy efficiency grant to allow the purchase of sine wave dimmers. Maybe this

Fig 20: The simplest distributed dimming system, photo: ETC Europe Ltd.

will lead to an alternative Arts funding body! So give the new technology a try, experiment with distributed dimming and do not just follow what has gone before. These new technological distributed installations are being further strengthened by the major changes to the lighting data networks with RDM and Ethernet and do bring many user benefits.

7.7 Useful Contact Details

ADB-TTV Technologies SA. (Belgium)   www.adblighting.com
ADB UK.   www.lsiprojects.com
American DJ Supply, Inc. (USA)   www.americandj.com
Anytronics Ltd. (UK)   www.anytronics.com
Compulite Systems (2000) Ltd.   www.compulite.com
Elation Professional, Inc. (USA)   www.elationlighting.com
Electronic Theatre Controls Ltd. (UK)   www.etcconnect.com
Electronic Theatre Controls Inc. (USA)   www.etcconnect.com

Electronics Diversified, Inc. (USA)	www.edionline.com
Entertainment Technology Inc. (USA)	www.etdimming.com
ESTA (USA Standards)	www.esta.org
Leprecon LLC. (USA)	www.leprecon.com
Lightronics Inc. (USA)	www.lightronics.com
NSI Corp – Leviton Inc (USA)	www.nsicorp.com
PLASA (UK Standards)	www.plasa.org
Stagetec Ltd. (Compulite UK)	www.stagetec.co.uk
Strand Lighting Ltd. (UK)	www.strandlighting.com
Strand Lighting, Inc. (USA)	www.strandlighting.com
USITT (USA Standards)	www.usitt.org

*Fig 21: Pulsar Datapak 18 x 10 Amp dimmer
rack circa 2005,
photo: Pulsar Light Ltd.*

8 ELECTRICAL SYSTEMS

Modern TV studio equipped with conventional tungsten lighting and installed dimmers, photo: Jim Curruthers.

Contents:

- Electrical Supplies and Protection
- Use of Technical Earth
- Harmonic Distortion and Power Factor
- Electrical Protection and Distribution Equipment
- Residual Current Devices
- Phasing of Venue Installations
- Socket Outlets and Production Lighting Boxes (PLB's)
- Cable Sizes
- Earthing Requirements
- Geographic Layouts
- Diversity
- Non-dim, Working Light and House Lights
- Conclusions

8.1 Introduction

Probably the most important part of any lighting scheme is the electrical system; very little will operate without electricity! If the system design is poor, considerable problems can develop; if the system is incorrectly specified, costs can escalate or there is not enough power to accommodate the lighting designer's requirements. Additionally, other venue requirements are compromised and the venue appeals less to potential users, performers and the public alike.

This section looks at the electrical systems required in typical entertainment venues, the size of the power supplies, their location, facility and outlet box specifications, installation of lighting data networks, circuit distribution, types of connectors and generally all items related to the installation of a lighting system.

Electrical safety aspects are discussed in greater detail than in previous chapters together with prevention and protection measures. Confirmation of standards and advisory practises are shown for items such as Residual Current Circuit Breakers, something that has become a highly debated subject in performance venues often due to poorly selected or specified protective devices.

Parts of this chapter take a look at new technology and how this affects the design of electrical systems, in particular the effects of distributed dimming and DMX controlled luminaires are considered. Consideration must be given as to how dimmed and non-dimmed outlets should be allocated, an issue that has become much more important with the advent of motorised luminaires and other effects. The control of other lighting systems such as working, rehearsal and house systems are also considered, as these often have to be integrated into one master lighting control system. Linking these to building-wide management systems can be critical for some types of venues for emergency evacuation or conversion from one audience/show format into another.

8.2 Electrical Supplies

When planning a scheme it is essential to look at the size of the electrical supply required to run the complex. Only part of this relates to the lighting. Large supplies will also be required for heating and air conditioning, the rigging system if power flying or motorised lifts and elevators are involved, temporary on stage power supplies for touring shows, any catering requirements, offices and workshop areas.

With a large complex the size of the supply may necessitate the installation of a local supply transformer with all of the requirements of space to house and protect this. However, it is a false economy to install a large supply 'just in case I might need it'. Standing electrical supply charges are very high so it is always better to be realistic rather than extravagant. It is always possible to add in a generator for that very large show that may only occur once a year!

The size of supply requirements is ever changing as new technology emerges into everyday lighting designs. Lamp technology has advanced considerably from the early days of stage lighting. Some of these sources are discharge units that are being used in motorised movement or colour changing luminaires; they often have integral dimmers and therefore need direct power rather than dimmed supplies. The 1990s saw the advent of the low wattage dichroic profiles such as the 575 watt ETC Source 4, Altman Shakespeare and the 600W CCT Freedom and the Strand Lighting SL. These produce nearly as much light as a conventional 1/1.2kW profile whilst requiring less electrical power. GE lighting has recently launched an 80 volt lamp with a considerably longer lamp life than conventional 240 volt units producing more lux per watt thus saving energy.

For those of you being asked to size the electrical supply in a new or refurbished performance venue, let's hope you have a good crystal ball. This chapter attempts to detail the levels of power demand used in modern lighting schemes, so the reader will be able to apply these experiences to other buildings. A number of examples of actual schemes have been included to assist in this process.

As with all systems, someone always knows something! Electricity is no different and many systems that I have seen over the past 20 years bear a direct testimony to a lack of understanding. Like rigging and suspension systems, you need an expert to help plan an electrical system. Electrical systems are complex, need the same degree of care over safety as a mechanical system, and dramatically affect the lighting flexibility and operational quality of any venue.

This book is really only concerned with the dimming part of a lighting systems but with electrical supplies and installations we need to have an understanding of the over-all electrical system in a performance venue so that when planning a system mistakes can be avoided.

One of the first issues to be considered is that of the total power requirement and thus the capacity of the incoming 'feeder' into the building. The total power feed will include items such as those described below; the figures shown are based on a real multi-purpose UK venue with a 600-seat theatre and a 100-seat studio theatre with small performance possibilities in the foyer and cafe areas. The incoming building supply fitted to the building was 600 Amp Three Phase.

Outgoing Supplies:	Load	Supply Provided Building Wide:
Air Conditioning and Heating System	188kW	315 Amp Three Phase
Catering Supplies	80kW	125 Amp Three Phase
Lighting for All Office	5kW	10 Amp Three Phase
Office Power inc UPS	10kW	25 Amp Three Phase
Exterior Lighting	26kW	45 Amp Three Phase
Control Rooms	12kW	63 Amp Single Phase
Working & Conventional Lighting around building	40kW	63 Amp Three Phase.
Non Technical Ring Mains	12kW	32 Amp Three Phase.
Studio Theatre Systems:		
Production Lighting System	60kW	100 Amp Three Phase.
Sound Technical Power	*12kW*	*63 Amp Single Phase*
Theatre Systems		
Production Lighting System	200kW	315 Amp Three Phase
Sound Technical Power	*40kW*	*63 Amp Three Phase*
Temporary On Stage Power – Lighting	80kW	125 Amp Three Phase
Temporary On Stage Power – Sound	*12kW*	*63 Amp Single Phase*
TOTALS	**777kW**	**1407 Amps 3 Phase**

The items marked in italics correspond to electrical services which were subject to a technical earth and do not use the primary building earth. This is a very important issue in all types of building where large amounts of technical equipment are installed, and this is discussed in more detail later in this chapter.

Ultimately when the electrical systems are being designed one should always try and split up the electrical services into specific functions such as Heating, Air Conditioning, Lighting, General Power, Production Lighting and Technical Power. Each one of these services would then have a centrally located protective device and a means of electrical isolation. Normally these are located in a ground floor main Switch or Intake room.

From here power is distributed floor by floor or area by area to sub-distribution boards carrying the same dedicated services as the intake distribution boards. Each of these services has a common neutral, phase and earth connection; any electrical disturbances, harmonic distortion, transients or other unwanted interference will travel around the entire electrical system.

Any such interference can be very noticeable on audio and video signals by means of a 'buzzing' sound on loudspeakers or the ring intercom or horizontal 'hum bars' travelling up and down the video monitor. On sound systems a definitive hum or loud clicks and bangs are often audible due to earthing problems or 'earth loops'. One way of reducing this interference is by ensuring that the sound and video equipment is always fed from one main isolator with power fed in a star format off the incoming supply. Single phase is another route often used when specifying power supplies for sound and communications systems. Care must always be taken to try and keep the building electrical supply well balanced, as this will keep the peak electrical demand at an acceptable level. A good quality installation with trunking properly bonded with segregation between power trunking and low current services can guarantee interference is minimised from the first stage of construction. This also helps balance the supply, something which is mandatory in some parts of the world, before the supply authority will connect the electrical service! Good quality equipment with sensible rack and linking cabling can further help to minimise any further problems.

Secondly, ensure that the technical systems have their own earth, which is completely independent of the building earth or the electrical supply company's earth.

This can often be difficult for electrical contractors to comprehend and no end of problems can occur as they run containment systems around the building forgetting that the Technical Earth is separate from the general earth, often resulting in more earthing loops and problems. Good practice suggests that wherever possible always run the largest size of earth conductor, matching the electrical standards, around technical installations clearly labelling this Tech Earth. Insulate the power and technical sockets from the containment system by fitting paxolin or other insulation material between the socket face plates and the metal trunking or back box.

Some manufacturers, such as MK Electric in the UK, produce special 13

Amp sockets fitted with an insulation block for this very application. On a recent project I was commissioning, substantial problems were occurring on the sound system with 'buzzes' and 'bangs' heard throughout the testing period. This was compounded by constant 'dimmer buzz' as the lighting system was faded up and down. After some considerable investigation it was discovered that at just one socket box out of over 100 boxes, the contractor had grounded the technical earth to mains earth by failing to fit an insulation bush. On another project the sound engineer complained to me that every time I faded up the colour wash on stage the sound system went crazy! I subsequently discovered that one borrowed Par Can being used had a neutral earth short on the cable entry at the back of the Can!

For this reason we should design installations of Technical Outlet boxes, containing sound and video tie lines, talkback and other services so that they are always kept separate from lighting outlet boxes. Lighting is connected to the general earth apart from where lighting equipment is located in a control room or other joint technical areas. Here care must be taken, make sure the

Fig 1: Typical 1970's Electrical Intake Switch room, photo: the author.

lighting equipment being located in these technical areas is fitted with 'galvanic isolation'. This ensures that there is no physical connection between the control desk and the dimmers; a device called an opto-coupler is commonly used. This basically accepts an electronic signal and electronically converts this to light pulses. An optical sensor (photo transistor) then receives these signals and via electronics converts them back into usable signals. As there is no physical connection, complete isolation is achieved.

This may sound cumbersome but the opto-isolator receiver and transmitter is the size of the end of a match stick, is highly reliable, and ensures complete isolation between control and power devices. This isolation, typically rated at 1500 volts, breaks the control earth connection, allowing the lighting equipment in the technical area to be connected to Tech Earth and remote equipment, like dimmers, to be connected to general earth. Be careful, some of the lower cost dimmers and control desks offered for small venue usage, such as schools and colleges, are not fitted with galvanic isolation and problems can and do occur. Manufacturers are very poor in confirming which products are isolated and which are not, although the new DMX512- A standard does make it mandatory to label products that are isolated.

One practice, common in the UK, is to run the Tech Earth throughout the technical installation and then to join this via an earth jumper bar to the building earth in one place, usually the intake room. Within an entertainment complex this requires the theatre technical wall boxes, control rooms, amplifier room and any connected remote areas such as the sound studio to be connected to Tech Earth. In fact this is not quite true, as some modern sound and video distribution amplifiers tend to be fitted with optical isolation. This completely isolates one video or audio feed from another, preventing some of the global noise problems occurring. Planning for the worst case scenario is still favoured by the author.

8.3 Harmonic Distortion and Power Factor

During the past 30 years electrical supply authorities have seen ever more energy efficient ways of producing and controlling light. Unfortunately this has created other problems. With fluorescent fittings, discharge lamps, dimmers and switch mode power supplies a very large amount of harmonic distortion can occur. Harmonic distortion is the unwanted generation of frequencies which are a multiple of the fundamental or base frequency - 50 Hertz in the case of Europe. For example, the 3rd harmonic in Europe is 150Hz, in the USA this is 180Hz due to the 60Hz supply. The frequencies we are most concerned about are the 3rd, 5th and 7th and multiples of these.

In early lighting installations with resistive dimmers most electrical loads were linear with a direct relationship between voltage and current under Ohm's Law. Many current pieces of lighting equipment generate harmonics as a function of the type of device, the way it operates and the method used to create the arc or strike the lamp or control the power. One of the supposed greatest sources of harmonics is the dimmers. Dimmer harmonics are a function of the connected load, the method employed for power control and the actual level the dimmer is operating at. Equally, the modern office has many components used that are also major generators of harmonics such as computers, printers and photocopiers. The world around us is changing and harmonic distortion has become a major issue for the electrical supply authorities. Sometimes these distortions are making the supply waveform so poor that dimmers and motor controllers tied to a clean mains waveform are unable to 'lock' due to the waveform degradation.

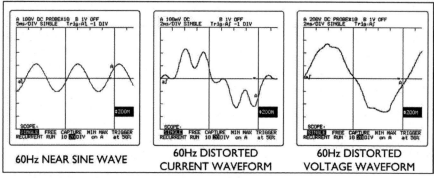

| 60Hz NEAR SINE WAVE | 60Hz DISTORTED CURRENT WAVEFORM | 60Hz DISTORTED VOLTAGE WAVEFORM |

Fig 2: Examples of Incoming 120 Volt 60 Hz electrical supply and what happens to voltage and current waveforms when distortion occurs, graphs: Fluke Inc.

This book does not go into the deep electrical theory of harmonics, however a little more explanation may help the reader to understand this subject better.

Any repeating waveform that appears to be non sinusoidal can be mathematically analysed and will be found to comprise of a single frequency sine wave. This is called the fundamental frequency. In Europe with a 50Hz supply we see multiple sine waves at 150Hz (third harmonic), 250Hz (5th harmonic) and 350Hz (7th harmonic). The harmonics are defined by name, frequency and sequence. The sequence describes the phase rotation with respect to the fundamental frequency. These sequences can be positive, negative or zero.

Phase rotation is best considered by thinking about how an AC power supply is generated. In simple terms this is achieved by rotating a coil of wire within a magnetic field between the poles of a magnet. When the wires travel perpendicularly across the magnetic field a voltage is generated. When rotated parallel to the magnetic field, the output voltage is zero. In other words the generated output voltage is a function of the sine of the angle at which the wires cross the magnetic field as the coil of wire is rotating.

Three phase power is produced by having three coils of wire offset by 120 degrees spinning within an outer case called an armature within a generating device. If one cycle is considered as 360 degrees then each sine wave is offset from the next by 120 degrees. If we apply this three phase supply to a three phase motor a rotating magnetic field is generated, which drags the armature round with it.

Relating this to the sequence it is now possible to see that a positive rotation sequence harmonic, if fed to the same three phase motor of the example above, would generate a magnetic field that is rotating in the same direction as the fundamental. A negative sequence harmonic creates a field that is rotating in the opposite direction to the fundamental. Zero sequence items have no rotation and no effect.

If we consider the effect of the 5th harmonic (250Hz) current (negative sequence), we can see that a substantial amount of power is used trying to turn the motor in the opposite direction. This would result in excessive heat being generated, potentially affecting the lifetime of the motor. A motor operating at 10 degrees Celsius above the rated temperature would reduce its operating life by as much as 50%.

These issues are important if we consider the effects on items such as standby generators or transformers. The same heating effects will occur in these devices as in the motor example above. Once harmonics occur they can render motor control circuits unstable. A 3rd harmonic occurs three times as often as the fundamental, consequently if items are tied to a zero crossing point instability can occur. In a generator this may result in three times as many zero crossing detections occurring, resulting in the motor slowing which in turn could damage equipment connected to it. I have often witnessed dimmers changing in intensity levels when harmonics are present.

Later in this chapter we look at circuit breaker technology, and here again harmonic effects can render this protection inadequate or cause nuisance tripping. One type of low cost breaker passes current through the coil of a solenoid pulling a plunger in when a predetermined current flows through the coil. This type of breaker is fine if the load is linear. If harmonic currents are flowing the peak current will be higher than the predetermined current, resulting in the breaker tripping, even though the linear load current has not been exceeded.

Better breakers for the lighting industry are true r.m.s. (root mean square) devices. Here r.m.s. is best understood as the heating value of a current or voltage waveform. A true r.m.s. breaker uses a bi-metallic trip mechanism which distorts when a current flows through it due to the heating effect. These breakers will trip at the true r.m.s. value of the current waveform and will therefore be immune to the peak tripping of the peak sensing breakers.

Within a dimmer, high instantaneous currents are generated at the point the dimmer is fired. This can be 15 to 20 times the normal running current and gives rise to very high spikes on the current waveform. To reduce this current a filter choke is connected in the output – see Chapter 5. This choke has the effect of 'tuning' the circuit and whilst reducing the amplitude of the current can itself create higher frequency currents, albeit at lower energy levels. All of these harmonics are radiated around the cabling system because the connection of the load to the dimmer completes the circuit, effectively connecting an 'aerial' to the dimmers. The effect on the power supply is a vector sum of all of the dimmers connected to the three electrical supply phases. As the load on the dimmers changes, depending on the intensity settings, so the harmonic distortion will vary moment by moment.

Another issue to be considered is power factor. This is a measure of how close to a perfectly resistive load the device behaves. For example, a tungsten halogen lamp behaves in an inductive fashion during the lamp burning cycle. Other devices behave more like a capacitor, such a device may be a motor. These actions result in the load lagging behind with an inductive load or leading with a capacitive load. *Fig 2* shows the result when measured inside a dimmer at the choke when a cold lamp is turned on. *Fig 3* shows the standard mains waveform and the effect when a non linear load, such as a capacitive or inductive load, is connected.

In the same way as harmonics change during the dimming process, so the power factor of the dimmer changes. It is worth noting that most dimmer manufacturers quote power factor figures of better than 0.95. These figures are given when the dimming is operating at full load and in full conduction i.e. when they are fully turned on and therefore not dimming! Early dimmer installations often used to fit large power factor correction capacitors on the walls of the dimmer room.

Many modern dimmers, fluorescent fittings and other devices have power factor correction fitted. This is important because the closer to unity the device the less power is wasted in the device.

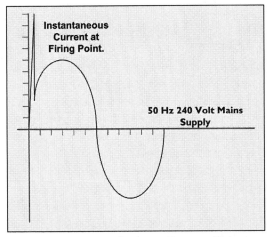

Fig 3: Instantaneous Current at Dimmer Firing Point.

Equally, less power is lost by the supply authority in heating and other energy inefficient symptoms.

Good equipment will minimise the harmonic pollution added to the network, indeed the EU is currently looking at legislation to control this which may result in considerable changes to the design of dimmers and allied equipment. Harmonic pollution of this type benefits no-one and ultimately we all pay for it via increased electrical supply costs. Ultimately this will have to be reduced in all pieces of equipment; some have expressed concern that this will make conventional dimming systems redundant and that new techniques to dim loads will be required. This may be true, but the normal replacement cycle on dimming equipment will surely survive the bureaucrats, so it is unlikely that equipment purchased now will require replacement when and if harmonic legislation is put into everyday standards. Power factor correction has become normal procedure and many theatre cabinet dimmers and motorised fixtures already include corrective devices.

8.4   Electrical Protection and Distribution Boards

At the point the electrical supply arrives in the building a central distribution board will be provided. This will contain the supply authority's mandatory protective devices together with their required measuring devices. Large users will now find that the supply authorities will install a telephone line so that, via a modem, they can monitor the power demand, measure usage and gain a historic view on maximum demand helping users to manage their maximum demand.

Within this intake room a large distribution board will be sited. This will probably be a factory built unit containing all of the major supply protection prior to being fed to local distribution and sub distribution boards.

In some large venues management may decide that they will provide emergency power supplies. This may comprise a Uninterrupted Power Supply (UPS) system for low power demand venues or a standby generator for large users. These devices need to be connected into the internal electrical network together with sensing and changeover devices to switch in the back-up supplies when required. These must be linked into the network 'upstream' of the power demand but 'downstream' of the primary supply inputs. It is important to understand and consider these requirements before planning such a network. It is equally important to consider what items should be powered in a back-up situation. It is really no use placing a UPS on the lighting control room supply if the dimmers are not receiving back-up power. Within the UK it is rare indeed for venues to have any form of back-up whilst in Europe and other parts of the world back-up systems are more commonplace. For any back-up system to be effective it must have the capacity to handle a substantial portion of the lighting load as well as other technical systems. Remember also that to be effective the geographic location of the outlets must be considered so that whatever proportion of the load is backed up the area of the performance can still be illuminated.

Switchgear choice is very important as is the way that the high power feeds are routed around the building. Ideally switchgear should be selected, installed and forgotten, save for the annual inspection. Reliability and accurate protection are the key requirements coupled with a good quality annual inspection to check for arcing contacts, loose connections and corrosion.

With a very large complex it may be easier to have a number of substations running high voltage power around the complex like a ring main. Installing changeover switches would allow different feeders to be routed to different transformers providing facilities to switch out areas from the network for maintenance. With one venue a single substation feeding the building is quite commonplace. In the UK high grade transformers tend to be the norm with good current regulation ensuring that the on and off load voltages are very similar. In other parts of the world lower grade transformers are used with quite high off load voltages. With very small systems such as a school hall a single supply is provided derived from the school's general electrical distribution system.

In all cases the quality of the electrical system is really a function of the system design, installation and selected switchgear. There are a number of good quality suppliers of these items within the UK including MEM, Merlin Gerin, Proteus, Siemens, Square D and others. Choosing equipment from a well known brand can help to source spare parts quickly should problems develop.

The production lighting power requirements are often one of the biggest loads placed on the building system, and each venue should be provided with its own lighting supply. In each case a main supply protective device should be provided. This could be a set of fuses, a moulded case circuit breaker (MCCB), an air circuit breaker (ACB) or a miniature circuit breaker (MCB) in smaller venues. To save venue staff having to visit the dimmer room at the end of a working day it is often worth installing a contactor with a remote on off switch.

From the primary production lighting primary protective device, such as an air circuit breaker (ACB) or moulded case circuit breaker (MCCB), a number of sub protective devices will be required. These provide two levels of use, one is clearly to sub protect the supply to a piece of equipment such as a dimmer cabinet. The second is to allow the piece of equipment to be isolated so that maintenance work can be carried out whilst the remainder of the system is still powered.

It is sensible to locate all of these protective devices into one panel type distribution board similar to that shown in *Fig 4*. Here the outgoing supplies for the dimmer

Fig 4: Typical Main Distribution Board
photo: the author.

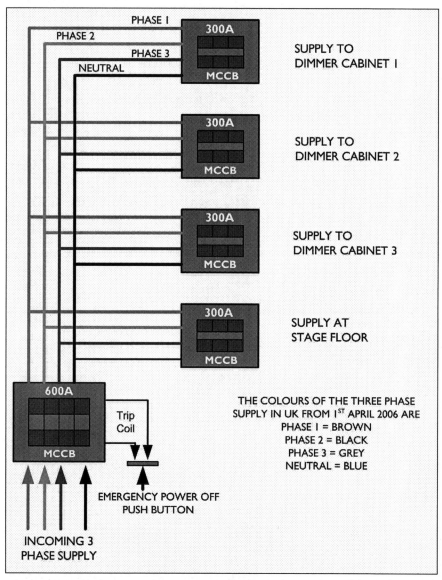

Fig 5: Simple Theatre Production Lighting Electrical Distribution.

cabinets, stage temporary power other lighting related supplies all have their own protective devices and or isolators. In addition, the primary protective device is located in the same cabinet together with the emergency tripping coils or contactor.

This makes operation easy, understanding simpler and thus electrical safety easier to enforce. When choosing the switchgear make sure that obvious items like facilities to insert padlocks to keep supplies isolated are provided, doors to separate isolators shut properly and that adequate labelling is provided. The layout of the switchboard should be logical, for instance having the dimmer cabinet isolator number 1 located first on the left moving right for isolators protecting higher number dimmer cabinets.

In essence a production lighting electrical distribution system should be designed to deal with the following electrical requirements:

- An incoming protective device with an optional means to isolate this supply in emergencies from the performance area.
- Protective and isolation device for each Production Lighting dimmer cabinet.
- Protective and isolation device for any Houselight supplies or dimmers.
- Protective and isolation device for any Working Light supplies.
- Protective and isolation device for each Non-dimmed distribution board.
- Protective and isolation device for any large electrical supplies sited on the stage (stage temporary dimmer power), these to be further backed up by local isolation at the connection point.
- Protective and isolation devices for any production lighting supplies located on socket boxes or for dedicated items such as followspots.
- Safety devices to suit the venue installation and the end user capabilities.
- Any required changeover systems if the production lighting is to be fed from a back-up supply as well as a standard supply.

Fig 5 details a typical small theatre installation with an incoming supply protective MCCB with a remote tripping coil so that the emergency stop button can trip the entire supply off. Three smaller 200 Amp MCCB's are provided to power dimmer cabinets. A further 125 Amp MCCB is provided for a stage temporary supply together with a 100 Amp MCCB for the Non-dim cabinet. All of the above would be housed into a panel board, typically shown in *Fig 8* used for internal power distribution. Such units are available from many

Fig 6: Simple 6 way European three phase MCCB board, photo: Merlin Gerin Ltd. UK.

suppliers. A typical example of a much larger Form 4 distribution board is shown in *Fig 9* from Nulec Switchgear in the UK. Many countries have different regulations, some requiring disconnection of the supply phases and neutral, some only the phases. I favour Neutral (2 pole) disconnection as this provides a completely safe method of isolation for maintenance works to be undertaken.

The individual protective devices for the dimmer cabinets need consideration of a number of issues. Primarily, the protection of the dimmer cabinet, however the electrical supply rupture current ratings need also to be considered – what does this mean? Typically, a very large capacity electrical supply needs to be provided for a performance venue. This supply is often derived from an on-site transformer. This means that it is conceivable that many thousands of Amps could be delivered under short circuit or fault conditions. When such a fault develops all switchgear must be specified so that it will break the supply and thus provide suitable levels of electrical protection. Many installers seem unaware of these requirements and most manufacturers miss off the rupture current ratings of their dimmer cabinets in technical data sheets!

With a typical medium-size theatre supply of 600 Amp Three Phase we may have a rupture current of potentially 25kA (25,000 Amps). A typical circuit breaker fitted on the output of a dimmer will only reliably protect up to 6kA (6000 Amps). So if a major fault develops it is possible for the dimmer breaker contacts to weld 'on' resulting in 25,000 Amps flowing through the system unless additional measures are taken.

Typical MCCB devices can provide ratings of 10 to 16kA but again this is insufficient protection. One way around this problem is to provide some high rupture current rating devices in the system. Standard high capacity electrical fuses have very high rupture current ratings, typically figures of 20 to 25kA are common. Some dimmer manufacturers install fuses within the dimmer cabinets to guarantee protection. Alternatively, these can be provided within a switchfuse feeding each dimmer or Form 4 switchgear can incorporate HRC fuses within each dimmer supply line rather than MCCBs. Rupture current rating calculations should always be undertaken by qualified personnel and are a serious consideration in planning any electrical system within a venue due to the size of the lighting supply.

Fig 7: Typical Form 4 Distribution Board
photo: MEM/Delta Electrical Ltd.

Another important consideration is electrical discrimination. If miniature circuit breakers (MCBs) are provided on the dimmer output it is always a good idea to use fuses upstream to ensure that 'a degree of difference' (discrimination) in the characteristics of the protective devices is provided. Again, some manufacturers fit HRC fuses within dimmer cabinets to sub fuse the intake supply down into groups feeding crates of modules. This provides excellent discrimination as well as providing proper levels of rupture current rating.

MCBs used in lighting systems have a thermal and magnetic detection for overload and over current protection. One such unit from Crabtree Electrical is shown in *Fig 8*.

With an MCB the long term protection, typically one second after energising, is defined as the thermal protection. When deflection of the bi-metallic blade occurs, due to the heating effect of the overload current, it moves the trip lever, actuating the latching mechanism. This separates the main contacts due to the action of the spring.

Short term protection, typically one second after energising, is defined as the magnetic operation. The magnetic component is dealt with by the electro-magnetic coil. The coil under heavy short-circuit conditions creates an electro-magnetic field which causes the latch mechanism to force the contacts apart. These contacts are usually forced apart in less than one millisecond, effectively preventing the contacts from welding on. When the contacts are forced apart a high intensity arc is produced across the contacts. The resultant arc is dispersed rapidly, under the influence of electro magnetic forces, between the deflector plate and into the arc runner.

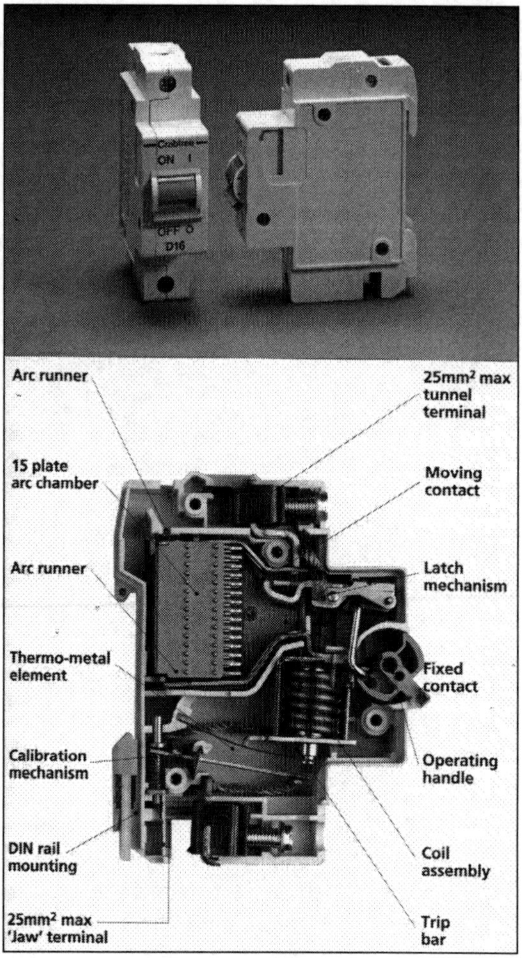

The arc runner splits this arc into smaller arcs generating a

Fig 8: Cutaway view of MCB photo: Crabtree/Electrium Sales Ltd.

very high arc voltage and quickly reducing the current to zero. In worst case conditions the tripping action takes around 6 milliseconds.

MCB's are produced in a number of different classes. The selection of the right class is very important to avoid un-wanted tripping on power-ups or flashing through dimmer channels.

B class MCB's trip between 3 and 5 times their rated current

C class MCB's trip between 5 and 10 times their rated current

D class MCB's trip between 10 and 20 times their rated current. In lighting systems C class breakers are typically used as these have the necessary inductive rating characteristics to resist tripping with cold lamps and yet still provide adequate protection.

8.5 Residual Current and Earth leakage Issues

The other prime design consideration is electrical safety for personnel. Often these considerations are driven by insurance companies but every planner should consider these issues and has to accept responsibility for their design! Typically the question relates to use of Residual Current Devices (RCD) - are these required or not? Any electrical system or piece of equipment can develop a fault, and current Electricity At Work Regulations reduce this risk by requiring regular inspections and tests. However, accidents still occur and equipment fails, hence the need for automatic protection systems. Residual Current Devices detect leakage currents flowing between the supply and earth even when these currents are very low, as might be the case when insulation breakdown has started before a complete failure occurs. Automatic devices, as their name implies, detect a fault and automatically isolate the supply. It is this automatic isolation that can give rise to problems with venue personnel and typical remarks like "what do we need these for" are common amongst some theatre electricians who have yet to be trained to current standards!

The big issue with RCD devices is when they trip out during a show and plunge parts of the stage or performance space into darkness. Electricians will argue that they are not required and one cannot take the risk of tripping problems during a live show. This argument is important but should a lamp fail in a major 'special', one could argue that this equally affects the show lighting. Safety must be the primary issue so this must be seriously considered. The ever changing labour situation of using more and more casual staff should also not be forgotten. Neither should the touring nature of the performance venue business involving crew working in a different building day after day. These personnel are usually unfamiliar with a venue, not completely acquainted with procedure, and want to finish the job as fast as possible. They are perfect cases for providing additional protection for their own safety as well as the venue owners no-claims insurance policy!

System design requires a considerable amount of thought and consideration must be given to keeping a show going along with being electrically safe. In any venues used for teaching or used by inexperienced personnel or children there is no doubt that RCD protection is an essential part of the electrical installation. This rule should apply to professional organisations as well as to colleges and universities. Often professional organisations think that they are immune to fault conditions developing.

I firmly believe that using these devices is essential in almost all performance venues. Everyone can make a mistake and all pieces of equipment can fail. Furthermore, this adds additional protection should rented equipment, that may not have been properly tested and maintained, be connected to a system that is otherwise in prefect condition.

Unfortunately some of the early earth leakage devices, such as the Earth Circuit Breaker (ECB) and the Earth Leakage Circuit Breaker (ELCB) were not very tolerant of distorted mains waveforms such as those created by dimmers or discharge luminaires. This resulted in nuisance tripping at a vital moment in a performance, and as the electricians could not explain the reason they lost confidence in the devices. RCD's produced today have a higher tolerance to distorted waveforms and companies such as Merlin Gerin produce devices specifically for use with dimmers and other lighting equipment. Such a device costs around £60 ($100), a small sum to pay when this may save a life!

The recently published Association of British Theatre Technicians *Technical Standards for Places of Public Entertainment* suggests applying RCD protection to dimmers, general power and lighting power outlets. Sensibly they recommend that not every dimmer should be provided with an RCD, and to save cost they propose that a maximum of 8 x 2.5kW or 3kW or 4 x 5kW dimmers could be protected by one RCD. Should a fault develop then this group of dimmers will trip leaving the remainder operational, allowing the show to continue. When designing a scheme that includes RCD's it is essential to consider the number of dimmers being used and therefore the maximum number that could be lost safely whilst still allowing the show to continue. Putting one RCD on the whole supply is electrically very safe, but causes major problems when one silly fault trips the entire system off during a show.

The UK Institute of Electrical Engineers 16th Edition regulations, current as this book goes to press, define two types of electrical contact – indirect and direct. Indirect refers to "contact of persons with exposed conductive parts made live by a fault which may result in an electric shock" – as shown in *Fig 9*. Proper earthing is always the front line defence system for an electrical installation. A low resistance path back to the over-current protective device will ensure that the device will trip and disconnect the fault before damage occurs. The 16th Edition requires the use of an RCD where the earth loop impedance (this is the impedance between the supply and back via the earth connection typically being a very low value) is too high to ensure automatic disconnection in the specified time by the operation of the over current protection device. In these circumstances the product of the RCD sensitivity in amperes and the earth fault loop impedance in ohms shall not exceed 50. Typically, with a 30mA sensitivity RCD the maximum permissible earth loop impedance shall not exceed 1667 Ohms.

Direct contact is defined as "contacts of persons with live parts which may result in electric shock" – as shown in *Fig 9*. The 16th Edition recognises only two main means of affording protection from direct contacts namely to erect barriers and to insulate cables. RCD's must never be used to provide the sole means of offering direct contact protection. They must only ever be used as a supplementary protection device against direct contact where damage may occur such as trailing socket outlets, equipment used outside, equipment used in wet areas or areas of high risk.

Fig 10 shows the levels of protection afforded by RCD devices together with the physiological effects. 30mA devices offer a high degree of protection against electrocution in an accidental shock situation. Typically a current of between 80mA and 240mA will flow through the human body depending on the voltage across it. A 30mA RCD will typically trip in less than 30 milliseconds at these fault currents cutting off the current flow well within the specified regulation requirements.

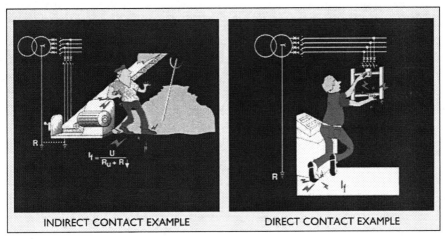

| INDIRECT CONTACT EXAMPLE | DIRECT CONTACT EXAMPLE |

Fig 9: Indirect and Direct Contact, pictures: Schneider Electric/Merlin Gerin.

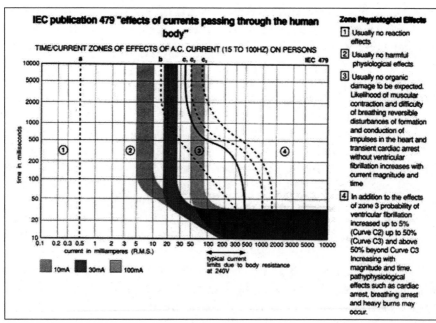

Fig 10: Effects of Currents Passing Through Human Body, drawing: IEC.

Certainly at the very minimum RCD protection should be provided for all sockets at stage level. Floor level equipment can comprise musical instruments, effects equipment such as smoke machines, show electrical equipment like cookers or 'practicals' and set pieces made of metal and containing electrical items. These tend to be used by performers as well as technicians and thus insurance companies quite rightly take the view that they wish to minimise their risk where highly insured performers are concerned.

RCD protection within dimmers has long been a discussion subject. When ELCB's, then early RCD's were first launched they were very poor at coping with waveforms suffering from harmonic distortion or a degradation of a pure 50 or 60Hz waveform. Consequently, severe nuisance tripping problems occurred and electricians hated the problems they created.

Dimmer manufacturers have traditionally balanced the cost of adding RCD devices with the overall cost safety issue. Many manufacturers offer optional RCD protection by fitting one RCD per group of dimmers. A typical 24 channel hard wired wall mount dimmer might have three RCD's for the 24 dimmers – one RCD per eight dimmers. This solution, being structured around the 3 phase electrical supply, provides eight dimmers per supply phase. With a large number of dimmers losing eight channels may not present a problem. With a system of only 24 dimmers to lose eight removes some 33% of the dimmers and is not so acceptable. Locating the RCD within the dimmer cabinet prior to the power control device helps to reduce the problems associated with waveform distortion and helps to protect the system from nuisance tripping. Adding an RCD to such a cabinet adds around £500 ($900) per group of eight dimmers at current UK list prices.

Recent developments have seen dimmer manufacturers offering protection per dimmer rather than per group of dimmers. Adding such protection adds more than £100 ($170) per channel at list price. With, say, 600 dimmers this adds a considerable capital cost to the system. These devices are fitted prior to the power device or afterwards depending on the manufacturer of the dimmer. Those fitted on the dimmer output may not be true RCD's – more an electronic leakage current detector circuit.

A further recent development has been the fitting of Residual Current Circuit Breaker (RCBO) devices. These offer the benefit of detecting earth leakage currents, overload conditions and short circuit conditions with a reasonable level of rupture current protection. They are available with a C class rating suitable for highly inductive heavy industrial applications and are very suitable for lighting installations. They have a further advantage that many of them are the same physical size as an MCB, so fitting them into a dimmer module instead of an MCB becomes an easily fitted factory option. These units are

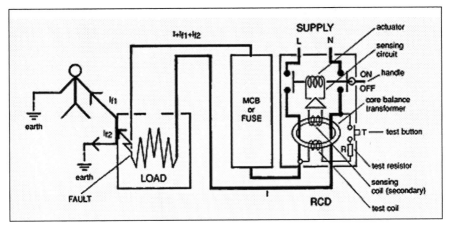

Fig 11: Schematic Diagram of RCD Operation, drawing: MEM Low Voltage Products.

more competitively priced than a separate MCB and RCD combination. A number of manufacturers have already started to use these devices, and more will undoubtedly follow shortly.

One manufacturer of RCD's is Merlin Gerin. They produce a very wide range of these devices and have a range of products called their A series designed specifically to be fitted on the output of a phase controlled circuit. They have high levels of immunity to nuisance tripping on distorted waveforms. The devices are also produced by other manufacturers and are classified as A Class. The standard unit is classified as AC Standard. If devices are to be fitted on stage adjacent to dimmer outputs then make sure the A Series units are specified. If direct or non-dimmed supplies are being protected the AC standard version will be acceptable.

My view is always to fit RCD's on groups of dimmers if the performance space is contained within an educational establishment, is a training venue or a space where there is no resident electrical staff to look after, re-lamp and focus the lighting. If the performance space is located within a professional environment with trained electrical staff, a grouped RCD system for grid (high) level circuits with RCD protection on floor level circuits is proposed. Where electrical equipment is used within the venue and then taken outside for use in other spaces it would be highly desirable to fit RCD protection on dimmers and electrical distribution units. *Fig 11* shows a schematic diagram of an RCD connected to an earth fault showing the principal parts of the installation.

8.6 Phasing Performance Venue Electrical Installations

An issue of great discussion between electrical engineers and lighting designers relates to how to decide what production lighting elements are connected to what electrical phase. Electrical engineers always try and design a balanced installation as this ensures nice balanced neutral currents, helps to control peak demand and helps to keep the entire complex power systems balanced. Lighting designers work in reverse; they use whatever dimmers and circuits most suit the set being illuminated from the best located lighting angle and position.

In a performance venue we always tend to have a fixed size of area to illuminate although the venue might be such that theatre-in-the-round, end stage, flat floor or conference mode may all end up with different sizes of stage areas. With a complex comprising a number of venues one could conceive of one phase only being used in each of two or three venues resulting in a major imbalance on the complex electrical system. So how do we deal with this problem?

There is really no hard and fast rule and it very much depends on the stage lighting layout. Looking at several examples may help to address this issue and offer some ways of dealing with this in other designs.

8.6.1 Example 1: European Black Box Drama Studio

Equipped with 24 dimmers used for educational applications with no fixed seating and a lighting grid over the whole area.

Proposal: *Use a single phase 63 or 100 Amp supply.*

Why Single Phase?

Simply that a single phase supply is inherently electrically safer than a 3 phase one and within an educational environment safety is paramount. So here we would also use RCD protection per dimmer or per group of dimmers.

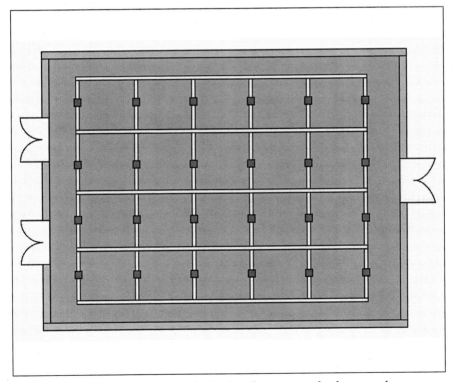

Fig 12: Example 1 showing layout of school grid using a single phase supply.

8.6.2 Example 2: Large College Stage in the UK

Equipped with 54 dimmers used for teaching drama and dance applications and school productions as well as being used by the music department for concerts. Performances can be staged using the conventional proscenium or within the body of the hall

Fig 13 details the lighting bars after considering the different performance modes, such as:

Conventional Stage: Uses Side Bars 5 and 6, Front of House
Bars 3 and 4 and Over Stage Bars 7, 8 and 9.

Hall End Stage: Uses Over Stage Bars 1 and 2 and Front of House
Bars 3 and 4 and Side Bars 5 and 6.

Theatre-in-Round: Uses Over Stage Bars 2 and 3, Front of House Bars
1, 4, 5 and 6.

In all cases each bar has been placed on a different electrical phase to minimise the likelihood of a three phase electric shock. The warning label fitted by the installer in the hall will stipulate that extension cables cannot be run from one lighting bar to another. All of the 54 circuits are wired back to a dimmer system. *Fig 13* shows a simple layout of the bars and sockets

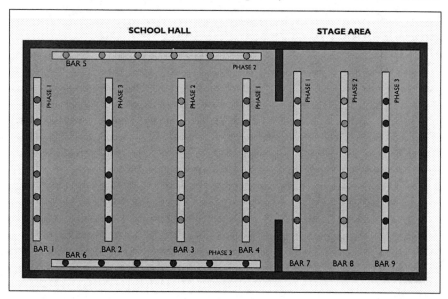

Fig 13: Example 2 showing phasing layout of lighting bars.

with the sockets coloured to correspond to the supply phase to which they are connected.

An alternative solution to the fixed outlets wired back to a centralised dimming system is to consider using distributed dimming. Currently a number of different distributed solutions exist from a number of manufacturers. These can comprise a powered unit with dimmers and outlets housed in a bar-like format that can hang from the lighting bar. Another solution is to use a portable pack that can be mounted at the end of the bar with loose cables then run along the bar to the pack.

In these cases the electrical system is considerably revised with a significant reduction in electrical cost. This is shown on *Fig 14* where a single phase 63 Amp outlet is provided centrally on the bar. The distributed dimmer is then plugged into the power outlet as required. This would allow less dimmer bars to be purchased as it is very unlikely that all of the different performance formats would be used simultaneously.

The bars would be connected to a 4 way 3 phase distribution board with slots to accept 12 x 63 Amp single phase MCB's with three un-used slots. This solution also removes the necessity of a dimmer room, often saving valuable space in education establishments and multi-purpose venues together with a

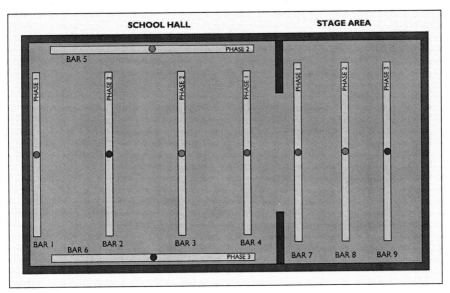

Fig 14: Example 2 showing UK phasing layout of distributed dimmers.

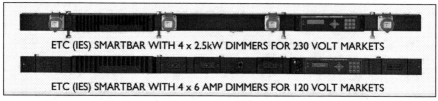

ETC (IES) SMARTBAR WITH 4 x 2.5kW DIMMERS FOR 230 VOLT MARKETS

ETC (IES) SMARTBAR WITH 4 x 6 AMP DIMMERS FOR 120 VOLT MARKETS

Fig 15: Selection of ETC Powerbar Distributed Dimmers for world markets
photos: ETC Europe Ltd.

reduced initial capital cost. Distributed dimmer bars and packs are currently available from ETC in both USA and European ratings and Entertainment Technology in USA with their Intelligent Power Strips (see Chapter 7) in 110 and 240V and their Raceway system in 110 and 240 volt versions.

It should be noted that if readers are located in parts of the world other than the UK the phase separation shown in Fig 20 can be disregarded as many local regulations requiring balanced phases over-ride the safety issues adopted in the UK. In this case with a 220/240 volt supply we would typically see *Fig 14* replaced with *Fig 16*, where each outlet is a three phase 32 Amp socket wired back individually to a 32 Amp three phase MCB.

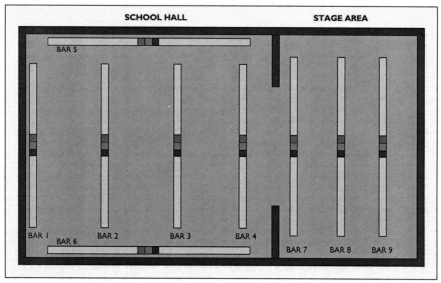

Fig 16: Example 2 showing European phasing layout of distributed dimmers, socket is
connected to all three electrical phases.

What size of electrical supply is required for Example 2?
Solution 1 with 54 channels of installed 10 Amp (2.5kW) rated dimmers connected via 3 phases requires a 540 Amp capacity supply. This equates to a 180 Amp 3 phase supply if no diversity is considered. Diversity is explained later in this chapter but in essence this means, in lighting terms, what lights are going to be used at the same time. With Example 2 we are unlikely to use all of the hall circuits at the same time as the stage. If the stage is used then we will probably place luminaires on Bars 3 and 4 for front of house lighting and Bars 7, 8 and 9 for over-stage lighting. We may also apply a few cross lights onto Bars 5 and 6. Effectively three of the nine bars will not be used so we could consider reducing the supply capacity by 30%. We could consider further reductions due to 650W or 1kW lamps being loaded onto a 2.5kW dimmer channel then a reduction of 50% could be considered. For this example of a school the author would suggest that, after diversity, a supply sized at 100 Amp three phase should cover all requirements with fixed dimming. The same argument also applies to the distributed dimming solution.

8.6.3 Example 3: Hotel Ballroom used as a Performance Space with Three Partitioned Areas

The hotel requires a permanent installation to avoid damage to the ballroom caused by repeated use of trussing, access provided by means of catwalks in roof void.

In the UK lighting bars would be provided attached to the access catwalks with slots cut into the ceiling to allow lighting to be pointed in any direction allowing performances and events to be staged in each of the rooms or in combinations of rooms. This is shown in *Fig 17* where three bars are provided in each of the divided rooms.

Each bar contains 12 dimmed outlets connected back to a central dimmer and non-dim system. The alternative to this solution would be to again use distributed dimmers or to allow event companies to place local dimmer packs up on the access catwalks. This is shown in *Fig 18* where 32 Amp 3 phase outlets are provided. In larger rooms this could be increased to 2, 3 or 4 three phase 32 Amp outlets, allowing more distributed bars or packs to be accommodated.

What size of electrical supply is required for Example 3?
For such an installation the total load equates to 108 x 2.5kW rated dimming

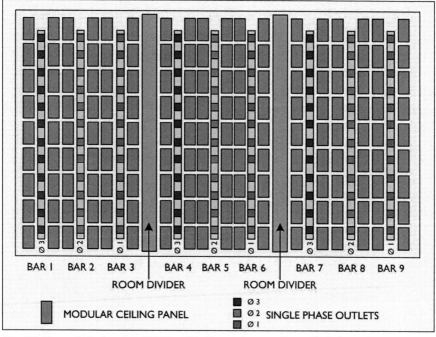

BAR 1 BAR 2 BAR 3 | BAR 4 BAR 5 BAR 6 | BAR 7 BAR 8 BAR 9

ROOM DIVIDER　　　ROOM DIVIDER

MODULAR CEILING PANEL

Ø3
Ø2　SINGLE PHASE OUTLETS
Ø1

Fig 17: Example 3 showing UK Hotel Ballroom layout of installed dimmed outlets.

which correlates to a total potential load of 270kW equal at 230 volts to 1171.80 Amps or a 400 Amp 3 phase supply before any diversity is applied. Once again diversity can be considered; with this system it is possible that the hotel operator may wish to use at least two or the three rooms simultaneously. So again, a 30% reduction can be immediately considered, further reductions down to a total of 50% seem acceptable as again it is unlikely that all channels would be used simultaneously. This would suggest that a suitable supply would be 225 Amp 3 phase.

The other method by which some event organisers might wish to use the ballroom would be to rig a ground supported truss. It would therefore be sensible to provide an easily accessible power supply into which a temporary lighting and sound rig could be connected. For this reason it would be sensible to provide a three phase temporary lighting supply of say 225 Amp three phase at a convenient location to allow access into any of the three rooms. A 63 Amp three phase supply should also be provided for the sound system, again in a convenient location to all 3 rooms.

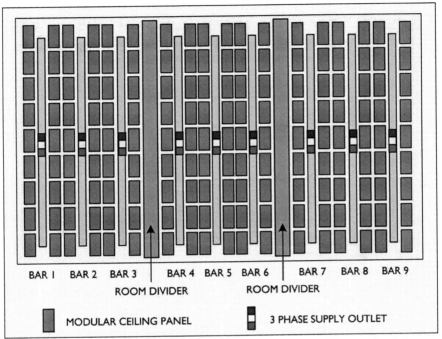

| BAR 1 | BAR 2 | BAR 3 | BAR 4 | BAR 5 | BAR 6 | BAR 7 | BAR 8 | BAR 9 |

ROOM DIVIDER   ROOM DIVIDER

■ MODULAR CEILING PANEL   ▯ 3 PHASE SUPPLY OUTLET

Fig 18: Example 3 showing Hotel Ballroom layout for distributed dimmers with 3 phase outlets.

8.6.4 Example 4: 600-seat Repertory Theatre

Equipped with Front of House Lighting Rig and Flown Over Stage Lighting Bars with stage level dip sockets

This is a fairly standard theatre application used throughout the world. In such an installation today we may well see some 240 to 360 channels of dimming distributed over the stage and auditorium. In many parts of the world there would be no consideration of phase segregation, and each adjacent outlet could be on a different phase. In the UK historically the format widely adopted was to use one phase for front of house, one phase for over the stage and one phase for the stage floor and under stage areas. This never achieved a phase balance but can any design ever achieve this? The answer is 'no' as the lighting designer must not be restricted as to where they hang and connect the luminaires used to illuminate a subject. For this reason each production scene may be widely out of balance one to the next. I would argue that mixing 3 phases everywhere stands a substantially better chance of being balanced than running single

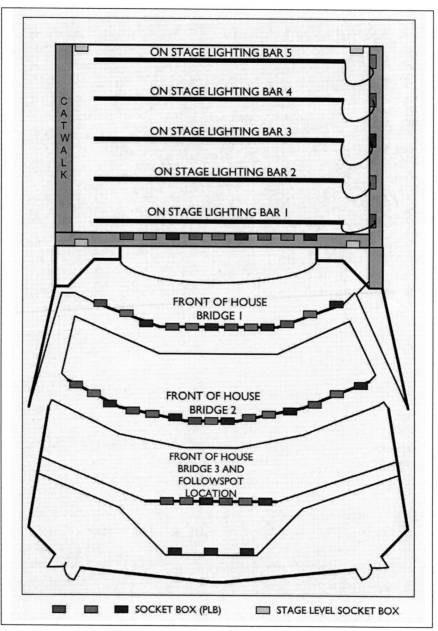

ON STAGE LIGHTING BAR 5

ON STAGE LIGHTING BAR 4

ON STAGE LIGHTING BAR 3

ON STAGE LIGHTING BAR 2

ON STAGE LIGHTING BAR I

C A T W A L K

FRONT OF HOUSE
BRIDGE I

FRONT OF HOUSE
BRIDGE 2

FRONT OF HOUSE
BRIDGE 3 AND
FOLLOWSPOT
LOCATION

SOCKET BOX (PLB)   STAGE LEVEL SOCKET BOX

Fig 19: Example 4 showing Repertory Theatre layout of production lighting outlets.

phases to geographically split areas. For example it may be possible to run a phase to each of the lighting bars over the stage on the basis that extension cables will not be run between the bars. Similarly, in front of house (FOH) locations we can split them to being Stage Left, (SL) Centre and Stage Right (SR). With modern dimming a lower total dimmer cost is achieved as most large density cabinets are designed to operate with an equal number of dimmers per phase.

Fig 19 shows a typical layout where the phases have been balanced by use of production lighting socket boxes. These are wall, bar or catwalk mounted boxes onto which socket outlets are mounted on the front

Fig 20: Production Lighting Socket Box, photo: the author.

panel. *Fig 20* shows a typical theatre socket box with Cee 17 16 Amp (2P+E) outlets for 2.5/3kW and Cee 17 32 Amp (2P+E) outlets for 5kW dimmers and non-dims. *Fig 20* also shows multi-way 'Socapex' type connectors used to feed groups of 6 channels to remote lighting bars or breakout boxes. The box in the photograph is exactly the type that would be located on the stage catwalk into which the over stage bars are connected. Multi-way cables feeding these bars may be manually raised and lowered or they may be subject to an automatic cable management system such as a windlass or cable reeler.

What size of electrical supply is required for Example 4?

If we assume that 360 channels are to be installed of which 346 are 3kW and 24 are 5kW this gives us a theoretical total load of 346 x 3 = 1038kW plus 24 x 5 = 120kW producing a total load of 1158kW. Converting this at the rate of 1000 Watts/230 volts = 4.34 Amps per kilowatt gives us a total theoretical current of 5025 Amps; dividing this by 3 gives 1675.00 Amps per phase. Theatre diversity is a subject on which many consultants have different views. Historically a typical theatre would use a "warm" and "cool" wash with some "open white" wash and some specials. Modern lighting has become more complex with a greater number of fixtures being used but the lamp load being reduced as 575, 600 and 800 watt fixtures replace the 1000, 1200 and 2000 watt fixtures. The author's view about theatre diversity is that it is safe to reduce the supply by a factor of 40%, and in some cases this can be increased to 50%. For this repertory theatre this would produce a power supply of 1000 Amps per phase giving a working load of 691kWs.

8.6.5 Example 5: Performance Space within Shopping Mall

This is quite a common occurrence throughout the world where large retail outlets are now provided with spaces that can be used to stage shows, maybe to have a Christmas ice show or to stage a fashion show. These venues often have audiences at different levels and very often on all four sides so they are similar to lighting for a theatre-in-the-round format. *Fig 21* shows a typical layout where we have the performance area on the ground floor (1st floor in other parts of the world) and audience viewing from the first, second and third floors. To light correctly such an area the luminaires need to be angled from all four sides unless the cost effective 120 degree rule is applied. This example provides lighting on four sides allowing for a 'stage set' to be located at any of the four edges of the performance space. To assist with rigging it has been envisaged that motorised lighting bars fixed to the underside of the mall upper ceiling have been provided. Additional 'front' lighting is provided at the first floor as this provides an ideal 45 degree lighting angle. These positions are fixed to the front of the first floor balcony rail, making the fittings remote from the public but easy to rig and focus for the technicians. *Fig 21* shows the layout of the outlets and lighting positions.

Once again phase segregation has been maintained in order to achieve a balanced load. With lighting coming from three sides it should be relatively easy to achieve a balance as three luminaires will always be needed to light any area in any colour.

What size of electrical supply is required for Example 5?

With 80 channels of 3kW dimming this would give a total theoretical load of 80 x 3 = 320kW; this equates to a total current of 320 x 4.34 = 1388 Amps or 463 Amp per phase with a 3 phase supply. Lighting from three sides for each area ensures that the normal diversity rules have to be discarded as a greater

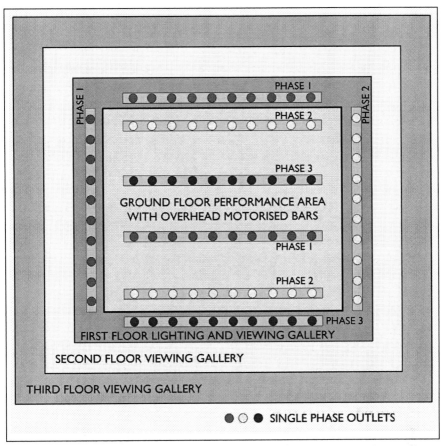

Fig 21: Example 5 Shopping Mall 'Theatre in the Round' format showing layout of production lighting outlets.

load will be ever present due to 3 lamps being used always to light what one or two might have done in a more conventional venue.

Therefore the maximum diversity the author would suggest in an in-the-round type venue would be 30%. This would reduce the supply to 325 Amp 3 phase.

Some designers are concerned about phase separation and try to maintain a safe distance between outlets on the basis that it will not be possible for an individual to touch equipment connected to two different electrical phases. This is often possible and whilst electrically safer is much less likely to produce a phase balanced solution. The five examples provided show how phase balancing can be achieved and where the author considers electrical safety to be of a higher priority than electrical balance.

Phase balance and phase separation are both important issues. The UK IEE 16th Edition regulations do not preclude mixing phases on a lighting bar or a an overhead flown lighting structure providing the user is notified, by means of a visible warning label, that 415 volts are present. In Europe and the rest of the world 3 phase installations are commonplace. This solution provides a substantially better balanced system at the design stage, but during operation there is absolutely no chance that the system will remain balanced. Good lighting designers will consider this once their design is finished, however this is always low on the design priority scale. If the luxury of current meters were more readily available then more people would watch the load and manage this within the peak demand.

With larger venues it becomes much more important to achieve a balance as out of balance neutral currents can climb to very high levels. In fact this is a most important part of any production lighting electrical system. Due to the high probability of high neutral currents, made even larger due to harmonics, it is essential that the neutral conductor, within the lighting system, is at least the same size as the phase conductor. If continuous periods of high imbalances are forecast it would be wise to use an even larger sized neutral conductor. Equally, never be tempted to reduce the amount of neutral conductor travelling from the dimmer to the load circuits even where groups of sockets are sited in the same location. Here is a good reason for considering the use of sine wave dimmers discussed in Chapter 7!

So the golden rules, when balancing phases, are to ensure that the phases are well geographically distributed over the venue in case one phase fails. Where a number of sockets are sited in the same location feed these from different phases, perhaps keeping one phase to each socket box. Given a choice try not to allocate one dimmer cabinet to the same physical area as this may cause problems should a dimmer processor fail. All the time we are trying to think about failure; think about balance and think about the geographic socket distribution over the venue.

Another point worth mentioning concerns socket outlets at stage or venue floor level. Here there is a possibility that other equipment connected to other supplies will also be present on the stage or studio floor. Some designers do not like the idea of having three phases present in areas where an audience or performers will be sited. As long as adequate precautions are taken, ideally fitting RCD's on these supplies, there should not be a problem. These outlets tend to be specified for groundrow lighting or for plugging in specials. They are distributed around the floor area to suit different production requirements with very few of them used at the same time. It is often possible to wire the floor level outlets to a single supply phase, and this could be the same phase as other technical or direct supplies. This helps to restrict 415 volt problems at floor level. Either way both solutions are acceptable and both require care in operation from the venue lighting crew.

Finally, labelling is critical. The new European colour regulations for cabling make it more difficult to identify phase colours. The old UK phase colours of red, yellow and blue to identify Phase one, Phase two and Phase three are replaced from April 1st 2006 with Brown, Black and Grey for Phases 1 to 3 respectively with Blue now neutral. With the phase colours no longer so visible in the darkness of performance venues the method of identifying phases has to change. Historically boxes could be painted the colour of the source phase or could have the channel number engraved on a phase colour background label. With the new cable colours of Brown, Black and Grey they will all merge together in the gloom of a stage area. I believe the best way forward now is to use the following as the phase identification methods. Everything connected to phase one should be labelled L1, to phase 2 it should be L2 and L3 for phase 3.

8.7 Socket Outlets and Wall Boxes

All lighting systems require connections to be made between power sources, dimmers, luminaires and extension cables on a very regular basis. This requires the selected connector to be highly reliable, easy to use, should mate together and stay together once connected, should have a reliable cable grip, be easy to wire up correctly and should stand up to being bashed, dropped, stood on and pulled in all directions. Historically in the UK we have seen a number of different connectors used for school and theatre lighting systems, and in recent years these have been the 5 Amp round 3 pin and the 15 Amp round 3 pin. Some venues still continue with the 15 Amp round pin. I believe that it makes sense to replace this thinking with standardisation. As previously mentioned, Europe has a similar problem with different connectors in many countries. Even the USA has three standard connectors!

Standardisation has not been adopted anywhere. However there is one connector range that does span the globe. This is the CEE 17 range of connectors originally developed by a Swedish Company called Ceeform. These connectors are detailed in *Fig 4* in Chapter 6 showing the many types available. The prime advantage is they are available in 110V, 230V and 415V versions with single and three phase versions. Each version use a phase coloured plugtop cover with yellow used for 110V, blue for 240V and red for 415V versions.

The sockets feature a lift up cover protecting the socket pins from dust ingress as well as providing electrical safety protection. A pip on the side of the plug mates with the lift up flap to provide a simple locking mechanism.

1: PANEL WITH 8 x 16 AMP 240V SOCKETS WIRED TO 4 x 3kW DIMMERS

2: PANEL WITH 4 x 16 AMP 240V SOCKETS WIRED TO 2 x 3kW DIMMERS (On Left) and 4 x 16 AMP 240V SOCKETS WIRED TO 2 x 3kW NON DIMS (On Right)

3: PANEL WITH 1 x 32 AMP 240V SOCKET WIRED TO 1 x 6kW DIMMER (On Left) SPLIT DOWN INTO 2 PAIRS OF 2 x 16 AMP 240V SOCKETS EACH PROTECTED VIA MCB's TO 2 x 3kW NON DIMS (On Right)

4: PANEL WITH 1 x SOCAPEX 19 PIN 25 AMP 240V SOCKET WIRED TO 6 x 3kW DIMMERS

5: PANEL WITH DMX 5 PIN XLR INLETS AND OUTLETS, ETHERCON FOR ETHERNET AND XLR FOR CABLE RIGGERS CONTROL CONNECTION

Fig 22: Typical Venue Wall Box with mixed lighting services, photo: the author.

Many versions of the sockets are provided including conventional flat units, 45 degree units and right angle versions. All of these versions can be ideal when used on production lighting boxes (PLB's).

PLB's are a very important part of any lighting installation, and their facilities, location and type of construction all need careful consideration. A PLB is basically a socket box or facility panel located around the venue at a convenient height for items to be connected to. *Fig 22* shows a large format box designed to use 19 inch panels. With larger panels it makes sense to hinge these panels, allowing much easier wiring terminations and longer term easy maintenance access. The hinges can be of the piano continuous type or industrial single hinges at the top and bottom of the panel. PLB's can come in many different sizes and shapes as well as being in different colours if they are visible to the public.

PLB's should be designed so that they do not block catwalks and walkways, and when fixed on stage make sure the location does not block fire escape routes because of extension cables connecting into the box. This is particularly important on catwalks. I recently witnessed socket boxes being located on the opposite side of a catwalk to the lighting bars, resulting in cables running across the catwalk creating a significant tripping hazard. Common sense should prevail, as lighting technicians need to access these boxes during performances and rehearsals. Locate them carefully. Importantly lay them out logically and consistently around the venue. The boxes should be constructed from at least 4mm thick steel to provide sufficient rigidity to withstand the constant insertion and extraction of plugtops. Panels could have returns comprising of the edges being folded through 90 degrees to add rigidity or ribs added to the back box.

Also remember that the front panels are a final finish item left in the venue for many years after the installation has been completed. Contractors must be instructed to take care with them during the installation works. For this reason they are usually manufactured in a two part set as 'First Fix' and 'Second Fix' items. First Fix means items that are installed during the infra-structure containment installation. This means the back box should be delivered separately from the front panels so they can be linked to cable tray, trunking or conduit. Once the feeder cables have been run in then the second fix works can commence. Typically this means terminating the cables and fixing the front panels in place after testing has been completed. This requires the front panels to be delivered at this point allowing wiring to be terminated. Alternatively, I am a great believer in getting the electrical contractor to terminate the installed wiring into terminals housed in the back box. This allows the specialist to deliver fully wired and tested front panels that can quickly be terminated into the back box terminals. Good practice here requires ferrules to be crimped onto the end of installed cables and also onto the front panel wiring looms. This considerably improves termination reliability and should be specified in the electrical contractor work specification. Numbering of cables is equally important, but more of this later.

One method of PLB construction that works very well is to use the standard 19 inch equipment rack style of construction. The outer carcase is manufactured from a heavy gauge metal folded and welded to produce a rigid construction. Down both internal vertical sides a notched racking strip is provided into which captive nuts can be inserted. The racking strips should be constructed to match a fixed number of U. This allows standard 19 inch width panels to be fixed as detailed in *Figs 20 and 22*. With any venue it makes sense to design a set of basic socket type modules so that they can be used in various boxes around the venue. Typical European socket combinations include 16A for up to 3kW supplies, 32A for up to 6kW and 63A for the occassionaly used 10kW supplies. In some instances breaking the 5kW supplies down into twin 16A outlets can be useful as this enables 5kW dimmers to be used with 16A connectors and therefore become more usable on a day-to-day basis. To suit the theatre requirement of trying to make everything black, some manufacturers of CEE 17 connectors now offer these with black bodies and colour coded lift up flaps. These can be used, as shown in *Fig 22*, to differentiate between dimmed and non-dimmed supplies. The photograph shows the non-dimmed outlets using black-bodied 16 Amp whilst the 3kW outlets have blue-bodied connectors. This provides a quick reference for the technicians as to which service they are connecting into.

Always remember the installer and the longer term maintenance requirements. Behind the panels the necessary electrical and data connections need to be made. Consequently, behind these panels terminals should be provided into which the hard-wired cabling can be terminated and tested by the installer. From here a pre-made wiring loom carries the connections to the front panels. With simple PLB's, with a few sockets, installed wiring can be taken to the PLB front panel. As with all parts of a lighting system cost becomes a key issue; contractors like to cut corners and too often an item that lasts for many many years suffers from cost decisions that ultimately result in poor reliability and early replacement. The same holds true for the choice of connector; these are available at different price levels with imported versions being some 40% less in cost than European manufactured items. Check the screw terminals and make sure adequately sized cables can be terminated into the connector's terminals. Check the method by which the lift up flap is hinged, as poor quality units are known to break off with repeated use. Where it has been decided that lighting services will be collected together in a lighting PLB this necessitates mixing low voltage and high voltage cables. *Figs 20 and 22* show examples of this. Where this occurs the PLB design must allow for the power and the data cable access to be separate in order to comply with electrical regulations and also to maintain a degree of screening between the data and potential dimmer noise.

Access for electrical cabling is always a major issue to be considered early on in the venue design. All too often the architect, interior designer and even the acoustician will have resolved their requirements with construction proceeding only to find that lighting and other technical services have no suitable access. Remember that not only lighting will have PLB cabling access requirements but audio, video, intercom, and computers/IT will all need segregated cable access. On stage, other services such as water may also need to be found homes on the stage walls.

As explained before, dimmers generate a reasonable amount of harmonics, and these can show up as audible noise in the audio chain or as visible hum bars in the video chain. Consequently great care should be taken to keep the electrical system cabling as far as possible from the technical cabling. If there is no route that allows them to be separated by at least 200mm and if they must cross one another, always cross at 90 degrees to minimise induced noise. Good system design always tries to achieve the maximum segregation as possible between lighting and technical services. In a venue this might be best explained by running technical cables on the left hand side and running lighting on the right. Where they cross over on-stage, run one at the front and one at the back. A typical layout system is shown in diagramatical format in *Fig 23*. This shows two dimmer rooms to primarily provoke thought about cable lengths and also to consider distributing the dimmers around the venue.

The containment used to carry lighting cables varies across the world from cable tray, trunking and conduit. Cable tray is widely used to carry cables around buildings used for entertainment. This often means that there will be separate trays for technical cables, lighting and other electrical services.

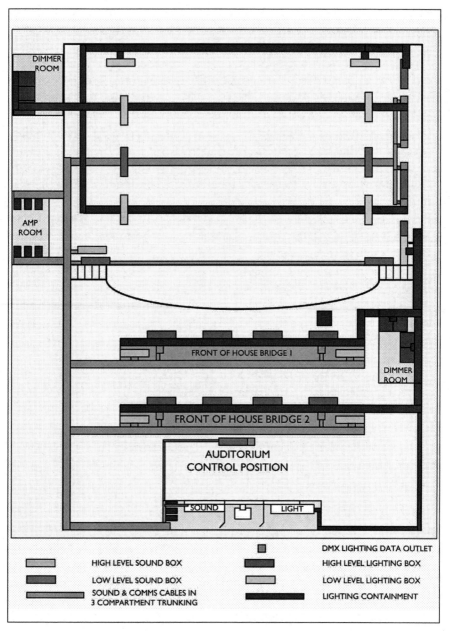

Fig 23: Layout of Typical Theatre Technical Cabling System – Light and Sound.

DIMMER ROOM

AMP ROOM

FRONT OF HOUSE BRIDGE 1

DIMMER ROOM

FRONT OF HOUSE BRIDGE 2

AUDITORIUM CONTROL POSITION

SOUND | LIGHT

HIGH LEVEL SOUND BOX

LOW LEVEL SOUND BOX

SOUND & COMMS CABLES IN
3 COMPARTMENT TRUNKING

DMX LIGHTING DATA OUTLET

HIGH LEVEL LIGHTING BOX

LOW LEVEL LIGHTING BOX

LIGHTING CONTAINMENT

Vertical trays are used to link from the main feeder routes down into the PLB's, and horizontal trays then link between technical facility boxes. With lighting PLB's similar cable systems can be employed. At all times the sound/AV/video facility boxes and the lighting PLB's are physically separated to reduce noise induction between the systems. This requires vertical riser and horizontal feeder trays to be kept separate for the different systems. Ideally a clearance of at least 600mm should be maintained to ensure no induction or cross coupling takes place.

Metal electrical trunking offers better electrical screening properties than open cable tray, although adding covers can help to improve tray screening properties. Trays and trunking can be surface mounted, hidden in false ceilings, mounted on catwalks or suspended at high level in technical areas. Wherever they are located remember that another contractor may need to re-wire the system in 20 or 30 years time – so never bury this without allowing good cable pulling access.

Cable tray has one advantage over trunking in that the cables tied to the tray are open to the atmosphere. Cables installed in trunking are bunched together with one warm cable heating up the adjacent cable. This would not normally be an issue, however within a performance venue a lot of cables run at high level close to the luminaire grid. This is the hottest part of the lighting system and cables can often reach temperatures in excess of 80 degrees Celsius when contained in trunking. For this reason the author always specifies tri-rated type PVC covered single cables when trunking is used as the containment system. Tri-rated has a temperature rating of 120 degrees Celsius and is very flexible, allowing for an easy installation.

With power cabling from dimmers to socket outlets it is possible to hear a dimmer 'buzz'. For this reason it is often better to run these cables and their containment in spaces not exposed to the stage or audience. If trunking must be mounted within noise sensitive areas it is often sensible to mount it via an acoustic damping material. Noise can be reduced by making sure that the correct size of cable is used, the correct size of neutral cable has been installed, and that the cables are correctly supported in the containment to avoid standing waves being set up. I was recently surprised when visiting an installation where the end user was complaining that the trunking system was vibrating when the stage lighting was in use. Removing the trunking covers I was surprised to discover that the electrical contractor had run all the phase cables as one loom and the neutrals as another. This is not good practice and led to standing waves being set up in the trunking as there was no cancellation occurring as the phases were travelling separately to the neutrals. Always run phase, neutral and earth conductors as a set so as to avoid these problems.

8.8 Cable Sizes

An important part of a performance lighting system is being able to organise a system to consistently deliver the same output from each lighting outlet. If the voltage at the socket is inconsistent the intensity of the same type of luminaire connected in different sockets will vary and the colour temperature will be different. So not only will the intensity be different but any colour filter inserted in front of the lens will project a different hue to that of another luminaire. With a British 240 volt electrical system each volt equates to 5 degrees Kelvin of colour temperature. If we choose the wrong cable we can easily reduce the voltage at the socket without realising what has happened. This is always an issue as some electrical contractors like to save money on copper by going one size below on their cable selections! This also helps them to reduce the size of the containment system as well!

Under the current Institute of Electrical Engineers 16th Edition Regulations there are clear specifications for each type of cable covering a voltage drop per metre length of cable. In addition, 'bunching factors' are provided where cables running together in an enclosed cable trunking system are given a de-rating factor. Running cables together reduces their current carrying capacities due to the heating effects.

Calculation of the voltage drop requires the use of Ohm's Law.

$$V = I R$$

Here

V = Voltage Drop

I = Current travelling through cable

R = Cable Resistance

Under the 16th Edition Electrical Regulations the voltage drop must not exceed 4% of the nominal supply voltage; this equates to 9.6 volts for a single phase 240 volt supply, 9.2 volts for single phase 230 volts and 16.6 volts for a 415V three phase supply. Under IEE 16th Edition Regulations 230 volts is now the UK nominal standard voltage.

In practice, calculation of the cable resistance is complex as it increases when the cable becomes hot. For this reason the IEE publish a list of tables detailing voltage drop per amp per metre for each type of cable. To demonstrate the voltage drop let's take a 5kW lamp working at a voltage of 240 volts. This 5kW lamp equates to a current of 5000W divided by 240 volts equals a current of 20.833 Amps. Using this we can then apply the current to the published cable figures to calculate the voltage drop at a given distance in metres.

To demonstrate these effects, calculations are shown for a typical 5kW dimmer circuit installed in a performance venue. Prior to calculating the size of cable required, we need to use the IEE cable specifications to check what size of cables may be considered based on using single PVC cables bunched together in a trunking containment system. Our cable route takes us 75 metres from the dimmer terminal to the luminaire socket located on Front of House Bridge 2.

Fig 24 immediately shows us that the 4mm and 6mm cables exceed the 9.6 volts allowed, forcing use of the 10 mm² sized cable. Even with this cable the actual voltage at the lamp will be 240 − 6.87 = 233.13V. These figures exclude any voltage drop between the supply and the dimmer, between the socket outlet and the luminaire together with any voltage drop associated with cables on cable management systems.

Some manufacturers produce dimming systems that are designed to accept a higher supply input to compensate for the voltage drop on the installation cables. In theory this may sound like a sensible idea. However, this can present a series of problems particularly when other supplies such as non-dims and temporary supplies are also derived from the same source as the dimmer feeds. Equally, when problems occur with the dimmer processing, exceptionally high voltages can reach the loads as they will if voltage spikes or transients pass through the system. Accordingly this practice is discouraged.

It should be noted that every cable within the lighting system will be subject to a voltage drop. Equally, any dimmer cable may radiate electrical interference, and for these reasons experienced electrical engineers should

CABLE SIZE	VOLT DROP PER METRE	VOLT DROP FOR 75m
4mm²	11.0 mV PER AMP PER METRE	17.18 VOLTS
6mm²	7.3 mV PER AMP PER METRE	11.40 VOLTS
10mm²	4.4 mV PER AMP PER METRE	6.87 VOLTS

Fig 24: Cable Volt Drop Specifications, data from IEE 16ᵗʰ Edition Regulations.

be employed to design a system to minimise these problems. Whilst many dimmers provide a neutral conductor as a busbar type connection, never be tempted to loop neutrals between cabinets or around socket outlets. Equally, never loop a large electrical supply through the dimmer cabinets even if the busbars are rated for the size of the supply.

In some parts of the world 3-core double insulated cables are used mounted on cable tray. This is an interesting standard and can lead to some very large cable trays and a very large volume of cables appearing in the dimmer room. *Figs 12 and 13* in Chapter 3 shows a 'before' and 'after' photograph of a relatively small dimmer room, with less than 160 dimmer load circuits using these type of cables.

8.9   Earthing

Earthing is a system-critical issue. Each socket outlet should be fed with a direct earth connection running with the phase and neutral conductor. It is, however, acceptable to use an earth conductor equal to half the conductor size of the phase. An important aspect of earthing is avoidance of circulating earth loops which have a severe impact on sound and vision equipment.

Any new installation should always be tested to ensure that the earth loop impedance is below acceptable levels. If RCD's are being used each circuit must be fed with its own neutral and earth to enable the RCD to operate correctly.

I prefer to maintain the same conductor size for earth as for the phase as this ensures, under fault conditions, the minimum earth loop impedance and thus the highest degree of protection.

One point often forgotten, due to different installation and contractual responsibilities, is that a lighting system contains a considerable number of metal parts. These include lighting bars, socket boxes, booms, trusses, cable reelers, luminaires, hanging clamps and much more. Riggers, technicians and electricians naturally touch these items continuously. Accordingly, it is essential that proper earth bonding of all of the relevant lighting structures and elements is carried out. This should be checked on a regular basis as should all items of loose equipment.

Items that move need particular care with earthing. Here it is highly desirable to ensure that each circuit is fed with its own full size earth conductor in case flexible cables break or are damaged. It is often sensible to run a separate and dedicated earth outside any flat form or multicore cables to provide a degree of additional protection, leaving these longer than the main cable cores means they are still connected when other cores have pulled out!

8.10 Geographic Layout

There are no hard and fast rules about how to physically lay out the electrical system – where is it best to site the dimmer room or the intake area? Clearly there are some important physical points. The intake room will contain large and heavy switchgear, and the dimmer room will have similarly large and weighty items. The lighting grid will be located high up in the venue and thus to keep dimmer cabling short perhaps the dimmers should be at a similar level?

Each building is different and therefore has a unique design best suited to that building. Basic principles apply to items like transformers, and these are best located on the ground floor in a room accessed directly from the outside allowing maintenance and replacement access. However, on a number of recent projects I have noticed that the transformers have been located on the roof of the building to improve the usable space allocation.

The dimmer room can be sited almost anywhere as long as that access is provided to bring in replacement cabinets. I have been involved with projects where the dimmer room has been at grid level in theatres and TV studios, off the stage at floor level, in the theatre basement and on intermediate building levels. Access is one governing factor but remember dimmer cabinets can weigh hundreds of kilograms, can be up to 2 metres tall, up to 800mm wide and very awkward to move about – even if access is available and the floor loading is large enough to carry the weight of the cabinets. Remember that the dimmer cabling length is an important issue in terms of containment and cable size and the overall cost of the installation. The shorter the cable run, the smaller the cable size and the smaller the size of the containment, all of which results in a reduced installation cost. If placing the dimmer room at grid level requires a lift to be installed then this is not an economic solution.

The dimmer room is a source of fire due to the large amount of electrical plant contained within it. The room may require cooling independent of the venue air conditioning, may need special fire extinguishing, should have one-hour fire doors and ideally should not exit into a fire escape corridor. The extracted air must not be linked into the venue's main air conditioning system as any smoke generated will then be spread throughout the building. The dimmer room should ideally be acoustically separated from the auditorium and stage areas or be located well away from the performance and public area. If they must be located close to these areas then make sure they are not backed up against the stage or auditorium walls so as to avoid noise transmission into the building structure.

As explained in Chapters 6 and 7, dimmers have become smaller and acoustically quieter, allowing small spaces to be turned into dimmer rooms. Electrical distribution systems have also reduced in size allowing dimmers to be installed in riser cupboards and small electrical rooms. Always remember that dimmers generate heat so any room housing them should be fitted with additional ventilation. Where a venue has lighting outlets located in different parts of the building it makes economic sense to locate the dimmers close to the outlets and then to link the dimmers via a control network to a centralised control system.

It should also be remembered that wherever the dimmers are sited power will be required with its associated cable feeders and outgoing cables from the dimmers to the luminaire socket outlets. Accommodating these cables and their containment often creates problems as the trunking or cable tray can become physically very large when many circuits are involved. When planning a system good practice dictates that at least 40% space should be left for future expansion. Cable ratings are de-rated due to bunching factors and with temperature as mentioned in this chapter. Leaving space helps to reduce these problems and prolong the operational life.

Alternatively, all of these load cable problems can virtually be forgotten when using distributed dimmers mounted on the bridges, trusses, lighting bars or motorised lighting structures. Here only a power supply and data feed are required into which the distributed dimmers or dimmer bars can be plugged. All the luminaires then plug directly into the dimmer. This saves considerable quantities of cabling and trunking and in some performance venues can provide an ideal alternative solution to fixed dimmers and cabling.

Theatres and performance spaces are very industrial environments as far as electrical systems are concerned. Much of the electrical equipment goes through rapid heating and cooling, has to withstand high temperatures continuously, and often has to be very flexible with moving parts. Therefore it is always wise to use high quality components, high temperature cables, good quality cable tray and trunking, and to allow space for additional cabling and access for future maintenance.

Always provide sufficient socket box locations to minimise the number of extension cables running along the catwalks, stage floor or crossing fire escapes routes. Small drama-type spaces might be able to cope with a socket box per wall to reduce the initial cost, however in use it is found that multiple floor cables are run adding to the rigging time and labour costs! For medium to large size venues the PLB location will be very much a function of where suspension points are provided and where luminaires can be rigged.

8.11 Electrical Diversity

Another issue requiring consideration relates to electrical diversity. In simple terms this means that even though we have 600 dimmers how many of them are we going to use at one time? This is an important issue because installing a large electrical supply, possibly with an associated transformer, is a high capital cost. This also results in standing charges based on the supply size. It is therefore essential to economically work out the supply requirements providing a sensibly sized solution to balance facilities versus running and capital costs.

Chapter 4 discussed how to estimate the number of dimmers and their suggested electrical supply size. Some venues are easy to calculate as they are designed to provide a dedicated role that rarely changes, such as a school hall or museum. Others are used for training and education and are often controlled more by budget than operational considerations. Others are designed to be general performance venues where many different forms of programming will be made with many different lighting requirements. It is these venues that need a more careful look. It is very rare that an entire venue area will need to be lit simultaneously. What is important is that the circuit distribution makes it possible to hang a luminaire in virtually any position and be able to connect this to a dimmer. For one show, such as a conference, it may only use one-third of a performance area, for another one half, for another the whole stage. In an Opera House we may have a number of lighting designs rigged to allow for rapid show changeover. Accordingly, the real question is how many lights will we use from the structured modular circuit distribution?

The principles of lighting and the need to use tints and colours to create mood and atmosphere, tends to require any area to be illuminated from a number of angles, in a number of colour washes as well as open white (no colour). In addition, the area under illumination may require special lighting effects like gobos, a moving light that itself may require to be in more than one colour, special effects like smoke, practicals as part of the set - in other words a whole series of different lighting types to create the final picture viewed by the audience.

Almost certainly we need to be able to cover 60 to 70% of the stage with at least 50% of the available circuits. It is therefore common to use what apparently looks like high levels of diversity. Looking at the use of a number of colours we could argue that not all colours will be used at the same time. However, if we were to equip a cyclorama with a four colour wash of light how many of these would we use at the same time? Probably at least two so here a lighting diversity of up to 50% might apply. If we look at front of house lighting then we know that for the forestage and area under the proscenium to be illuminated, to the required level, a specific number of units are required in each colour, unless a double rigged solution is adopted where one rig is without colour and the other is fitted with colour changers (scroller). Here we might want white and some percentage of colour so the diversity level would be much less, say 20%. On the other hand if we want to rapidly change colour then we might have a third rig with colour changers allowing cross-fading from one colour to the next. In this case we could increase the diversity factor to say 40%.

Over stage we will have area lighting, colour wash, specials, localised area lighting, back light, cyc lighting and specific show related items. Of course, not all of this will be used at once. Measuring the actual maximum load relative to the rigged load always produces fascinating results. In fact some years ago one control system manufacturer had software that could tell you once a show had been recorded which channels were not used. This showed quickly the items that were hired and rigged, even focused but ultimately were discarded by the designer! Actual measurements seem to universally show that for a rigged load the maximum load is likely to be only 60% of this. For this reason, in most performance venues, unless they are very small, the author works with a reduction factor of 40%, extending this in larger venues up to 50%. Recently one manufacturer, ETC, conducted a survey of end users to find out exactly the sort of usage levels for a given number of dimmers. To those of us working with dimmers everyday the survey revealed what we knew already – dimmers are now rarely loaded to capacity. Users prefer to feed one luminaire from a dimmer to provide better balance and control!

To try and put a gauge on the size of electrical supply, number of dimmers, number of non-dims, ratings of the dimmers and suggested diversity, a table has been provided in *Fig 25*. The figures quoted are from actual projects the author has been involved with and cover a number of different types of venue from an opera house, repertory theatre, arena, ballroom, amphitheatre, college hall, to a drama studio and so on. They are indicative only, as each venue will need to be designed for the intended purpose. Hopefully they will guide designers into the right area at the very least.

It should always be remembered that socket outlets fed from dimmers with associated luminaire rigging positions create the lighting flexibility. As set costs become ever more restricted lighting is used more and more to create atmosphere and colour. Effects luminaires also need power so do not forget that controllable supplies for non-dimmable fixtures should also be included and calculated into the maximum power supply demand and diversity calculations. For this reason a suggested number of non-dims have been included within *Fig 25*.

Lighting practices are constantly changing as new technology replaces old; as techniques change, style and design are ever evolving, fashions change, and designers are encourage to experiment and be different. More students than ever are passing through drama colleges - all keen to try out their ideas. Any building designed now must be able to cope with changes for possibly 25 years before the next opportunity comes for someone else to have a go at getting it right!

These changes and requirements suggest to the author that critically diversity issues are best addressed by firstly laying out the lighting plot, planning a modular layout of sockets for both dimmed and non-dimmed supplies, considering the venue usage and required turnaround time and finally considering the type of productions likely to be staged. The list below includes consideration of planning for the future.

Fig 25 shows guide levels only; practical considerations of what is actually available, the costs, available space for the distribution and other factors will also help make these decisions for you. One issue that always confuses

TYPE OF VENUE AND NO OF SEATS	NUMBER OF 2.5kW DIMMERS	NUMBER OF 2.5kW NON DIMS	NUMBER OF 5kW DIMMERS	NUMBER OF 5kW NON DIMS	TOTAL LOAD IN kW's	TOTAL CURRENT IN AMPS's	SUGGESTED CURRENT IN AMP's	DIVERSITY APPLIED IN %
SCHOOL DRAMA STUDIO FOR 50 PEOPLE	24	0	0	0	60	260	100 A SP	41.6
SCHOOL DRAMA STUDIO FOR 100 PEOPLE	36	4	0	0	100	434	63 A TPN	56.0
COMMUNITY THEATRE FOR 300 PEOPLE	72	12	0	0	210	911	150 A TPN	50.6
REPERTORY THEATRE FOR 1200 PEOPLE	192	24	12	8	640	2777	450 A TPN	51.3
THEATRE IN THE ROUND FOR 600 PEOPLE	240	30	0	0	675	2929	500 A TPN	48.7
LARGE SCALE REPERTORY THEATRE FOR 1400 PEOPLE	280	30	24	8	935	4935	750 A TPN	48.7
LARGE SCALE OPERA HOUSE FOR 1600 PEOPLE	360	60	60	24	1470	6380	1000 A TPN	52.9

Fig 25: Typical Venue Electrical Factors.

experienced electrical engineers, who have never worked in a performance environment, is that when calculating the likely load they never understand that only some luminaires are used at one time! "Why do you need so many lights?" is a constant question! Another question that I would ask is "why does the technical department always appear to take the brunt of the cutbacks when buildings are designed?"

8.12 Non-dimmed Supplies

As previously mentioned, there is now heavy usage of non-dimmable light sources such as moving lights and discharge lamps. These units need to be rigged in the same locations as conventional luminaires. Many older venues do not provide direct power in these locations, requiring large numbers of extension cables to be used often on moving bars and structures.

When planning a refurbishment or new installation serious consideration should be given to these requirements. The author was involved in a major refurbishment of a medium sized performance venue. The client's representative discussed these issues as considerable numbers of moving lights were regularly being used in the venue at the time of the refurbishment. The low cost solution here, as new dimmers were being installed, was to fit each dimmer channel with a direct and dim switch. This allowed direct power from the supply to be fed directly to the socket or for the dimmer to feed the socket.

If the dimmers do not provide this facility then good practice suggests that a direct outlet should always be provided for every 4 to 8 dimmed outlets depending on the size of the venue. A similar layout of outlets should be provided as structured for the dimmers. This should include outlets on the high level grid, on stage electrics gallery, front of house bridges, side lighting ladders and booms, at stage floor level, and under-stage. Each outlet should be fed from a separate distribution board or non-dim controlled cabinet. Each outlet should be wired as a radial circuit direct from the cabinet channel circuit breaker to a socket outlet. Floor level outlets may need to be protected by RCD devices. If residual current leakage detection systems are in use they should also cover these supplies as rental equipment tends to use these outlets on a regular basis. Where non-dimmed outlets are provided adjacent to dimmed outlets they should follow the same electrical phasing philosophy as defined for the dimmers.

When moving lights are used there is a requirement to use haze or smoke generation equipment so that the resulting light beams and colour washes become more visible to the audience. These units will require similar direct power, and devices like heavy fog machines and other effects may need large electrical supplies, as may stage practicals. For this reason it is sensible to provide direct larger single and three phase supplies around the stage area PLB's and in a few locations on the grid or catwalks.

Where 3 phase supplies are fitted onto PLB's I recommend that built into the socket or mounted adjacent to it, an isolator should be provided so that a local isolation device is available in case of emergencies or during rigging works. These can be simple rotary types which tend to be physically small and easily mounted on PLB front panels.

One subject where there seems to be an inconsistency is the control philospophy for the non-dims. Historically the non-dim circuits were turned on an off with a mains rated switch. This resulted in clicks and bangs on the sound systems. Later the switches were replaced with relays switched on and off via a DC control voltage. Whilst this avoided the clicks and bangs it required a separate non-dim control panel to turn them on and off. When the rehearsals and plotting sessions are in progress this often required another desk to be moved into the auditorium with consequent additional multicore cables.

When DMX control technology came along this allowed non-dims to be controlled from the lighting console as part of the lighting cues. The author believes this offers a sensible and beneficial facility to the end user, however some specifiers still insist on having dedicated controls. One system I approve of is to centralise lighting functions into a lighting control system that is in addition to the production lighting control console.

The next section looks at house and working lighting and deals with this in more detail. However *Fig 26* shows a typical screen from such a control touch selection screen. *Fig 27* details a typical conventional push button control panel.

8.13 Working Lights

Any performance venue needs some working or house lights to be installed that provide lighting when rigging lights, carrying out maintenance, building sets, cleaning and other requirements. Ideally, these lights need to be similar, in colour balance, to the production lighting so that sets can be painted and set up in similar conditions.

In smaller venues it is often possible to install fluorescent fittings with 3200^0K tubes. These can be fitted directly to the ceiling above a school or

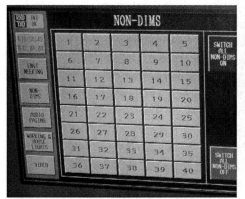
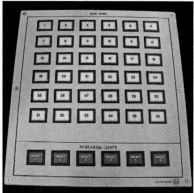

Fig 26: Touch screen non-dim selection
screen, photo: LSI Projects Ltd.

Fig 27: Conventional non-dim p0ush
button panel, photo: LSI Projects Ltd.

college lighting grid without impeding the hanging of luminaires. In larger venues trying to find positions to locate fittings can be difficult due to over stage flown bars and bridges, scenery flown sets, curtains, etc. Whatever fittings are selected these are likely to be left on for long periods of time and therefore should be energy efficient as well as producing sufficient 'task lighting' for the relevant works to be carried out. I have witnessed some appallingly bad working light installations where the stage crew need to turn on the production lighting to work!

Designing a working light system requires the same degree of care and consideration as that applied to the production lighting electrical system. Working lights, as their name implies, are lights that enable the technical crew in a venue to be able to carry out their duties during the day, whilst rehearsals are in progress and during a show. This will usually require a control that defines the operational status of the building – Day, Rehearsal, Show and Night. In these different modes the working lighting should be pre-configured so that lights that could affect a performance shall be controlled, for example, so that no stray white light can be visible to the audience when a show is in progress.

Consequently a working light system requires the following ideal facilities. These may never all be provided but at least they may give an understanding of the possibilities helps when designing these systems:

Day Mode: General white light of high intensity to enable stage and
              scenery works to be carried out such as cleaning, rigging, set
              painting, maintenance, get ins and get outs. This will cover

all of the technical areas such as: grid, catwalks, bridges, front of house technical areas, understage areas, orchestra pit, under elevators and lifts in the sub stage and access corridors.

Rehearsal Mode: Lighting that should be primarily colour matched to the production lighting so that costumes, scenery, make-up and other production related issues can be viewed in the same light conditions as they will have under production lighting.

Show Mode: In this mode lighting that enables technicians, performers, show crew, management and others to move around the technical areas in safety whilst a show is in progress. This typically means using low intensity blue light that is carefully positioned to light up walkways, access ladders, the back stage area, quick change spaces, operational positions like stage management, corridors leading to the stage, catwalks, front of house technical areas and the like.

Night Mode: Basically a security mode that allows technicians and security staff to make a safe exit from the building once all works have been completed or allow security staff to make patrols turning on sufficient light to walk safely around the building.

Special Mode: As this system controls substantial amounts of light around virtually all of the technical areas, special modes have been used to assist in building-wide facilities. For example, when the fire alarm sounds in the back stage areas it is sensible to allow a remote input from the fire alarm to turn on the white lighting throughout the area to assist everyone backstage to evacuate the area. Similarly, during a performance it would be useful to ensure that other systems cannot affect the performance. Examples here are the turning off the Page to Stage communication system and control of lights on music stands.

Typically the different modes need to be controlled from a logical system that has a simple and easy to operate 'user interface'. Historically we would

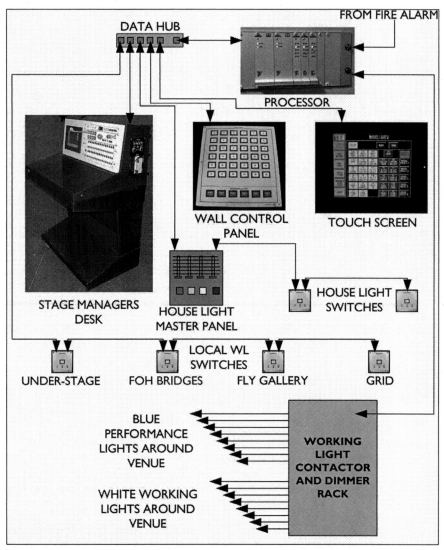

Fig 28: Example Of Integrated Control System, drawing: LSI Projects Ltd.

have seen mains rated switches located on large panels on stage that turned on and off the various circuits. These advanced to relay control systems with master controls for the states, progressing through to contactors controlled from logical control systems with software specifically written for a venue.

This had the disadvantage that the software was bespoke, had to be written external to the venue by a contractor, and required external support when the venue wished to change the programming.

In recent years facilities have been made available from a small number of suppliers that allow end-user programming modifications and allow day to day alterations to suit the production requirements. These systems are inherently more useful to the end user, cost around the same as a bespoke solution, and can add a significant number of user benefits by integrating many different control requirements into one system.

This type of technology can provide significant end-user benefits by looking at the multitude of separate control systems for which cabling and controls have to be implemented in a modern performance venue. Examples could include Working Lights, House Lights, Non-dims, Stage Management, Video switching, audio control of show relay and paging systems, control of curtains and masking – the list is almost endless. One might ask if it is wise to trust so many different systems to one controller. What happens if a failure occurs? Do all systems then fail? The answer is no because one can provide different processing with a main and back-up data network running around the building in the same way that an office computer network might be cabled. This book concentrates on the lighting requirements for performance venues so in *Fig 28* an example of a typical 'Integrated Control' is shown. This controls working lights from main panels located on stage, in the control room and in the auditorium rehearsal control position. In addition, local switches are provided to enable technicians to turn light on and off locally only if the master logic allows for this. The system controls non-dims allowing both the production lighting desk and the local panels to make selections. House lights are controlled and are selectable from the master panels, local panels and from the lighting desk. In addition the system allows house light intensity levels to be set by the production lighting desk and then recorded as memories on the control system. The system allows for remote security inputs with commands to turn the working lights to full and the house lights to full.

As a guide the following areas will probably benefit from controlled working lights:

    Orchestra Pit
    Under Stage Areas
    Fly Gallery
    Electrics Gallery

Grid
Over Stage Bridge(s)
Front of House Bridge(s)
Lobbies leading to stage area
Stage Area

One recent development is to consider dimmable blue performance lights. The cost of a DMX controlled dimmer is more or less the same as a DMX controlled contactor. Accordingly, it is often helpful to be able to set the intensity of the blue light to avoid visibility to the audience whilst maintaining operational safety. For example trying to adequately light the stage area for artists in blue light is always a subject of great debate. Fittings can be placed low down on walls to light the floor area but as soon as scenery is moved off stage they can become blocked. Alternatively, mounting them under a catwalk pointing downwards with barndoors carefully controlling the light output still does not solve the problem. Providing outlets into which blue lights can be plugged helps considerably to position the blue light where it is needed. Dimming them as well further controls the lighting levels, achieving a better balance.

Similarly, when planning note that working and rehearsal light provided from controlled sockets rather than fixed in position luminaires, can create the show flexibility the technicians need. This is sensible along over-stage

Fig 29: Stage illuminated for rehearsals using white light, photo: Sharp Theatre, Mahwah, New Jersey, USA

Fig 30: Same stage illuminated under blue light, photo: Sharp Theatre, Mahwah, New Jersey, USA

bridges, along catwalks, in stage socket boxes (PLB) and along the fly gallery so the flyman can position light around the sets they are using.

8.14 House Lights

House light systems tend to fall within the domain of a separate design package to performance lighting systems. However, it is important that the basic requirements and the methods by which these should be controlled relative to the other lighting systems are understood. House lights should provide sufficient light for the audience to make their way to their seats safely. In some venues, such as those used for conferences and symposiums, the audience may also require sufficient light to read from notes or to make notes. Schemes may be required so that in a multi-purpose venue different lighting configurations are provided for (say) cinema, theatre, music and conference.

These requirements can be easily achieved by wiring all fittings back to a house light dimming system. The control system may then select the required channels, set their intensity and then store these into memories that can easily be recalled. These are usually called presets. There are many proprietary systems available but care should be taken in selection of these solutions.

From the end-user point of view it makes much more sense to standardise on one type of dimmer for the entire complex. This simplifies maintenance as only one set of spare parts need to be held in stock, makes interfacing between the different systems easier and it generally provides the technical staff with an easier to manage installation. One of the critical parts of any house lighting system is the choice of fittings and the maintenance of the required lighting levels throughout the auditorium. Lighting levels can be a function of the décor, of the aisles, the purpose of the auditorium, the height of the fittings relative to the public, or the interior décor. Often lighting is added for decorative purposes as shown in *Fig 31*.

One major element in terms of the system that has to be considered is that of acoustic noise. Some fittings use lamps with relatively long filaments. When these are dimmed standing waves can be set up in the filament resulting in the filaments 'singing' producing an annoying buzzing sound when maintained at an intensity level below 90% on a dimmer. Lamps such as the higher number PAR's - Par 46, 56 and 64 – all exhibit large amounts of lamp 'singing' unless they are connected to a good quality dimmer with good quality wiring and cable laying between the fixture and the dimmer. Mounting them in an acoustic mounting helps to stop high density ceiling panels such as wood resonating

Fig 31: Example of Audiorium using Lighting for Effect, photo: Andrew Nu.

with the 'singing'. Often it is possible to use the MR range of dichroic lamps as a downlighter solution. These tend to be low wattage lamps and require the use of dimmable transformers if they are to be connected to a dimmer. Experience shows that each fitting should be separately equipped with a suitable electronic dimmable transformer. Excellent solutions are available from Multiform Ltd in the UK to dim most of the MR range but do check the compatability of transformer to dimmer.

One unpleasant way to light auditoria is to leave it in the hands of an electrical engineer without any training in auditoria design. The author has witnessed a number of these designs that are based on using fluorescent fittings, probably to save energy and to shed electrical load. These produce poor colour rendering in auditoria, lack the warmth and lustre of a tungsten carefully designed solution and never dim smoothly from 0 to 100% intensity. There is absolutely nothing wrong with dimmed fluorescent lighting in many applications but they do not work well in a public auditorium. Energy efficient tungsten solutions can be found that work well. Also LED lighting is finding its way into decorative lighting within auditoria. Whilst this currently cannot replace the conventional light source it can provide high levels of very long life highly efficient lighting that can easily change colour.

With house lighting the best solution is to employ an architectural lighting practice to design a complete solution, suggest to them that the dimming system has already been decided and to specify the level of control or preset configurations that are required. Remember to define the specific requirements, the types of presets that you require and how these should function within the auditorium. For example you may require specific lighting or separate control for:

Cinema
Orchestral and music recitals including the forestage area
Theatre style
Conference mode
Separate control of seating blocks to adjust the size of the
    auditorium
Ability to turn off some lights when stage thrust or catwalk is
    added

These different requirements can be easily recorded onto the different presets that the houselight control system can provide. For example in *Fig 14* Example 3 we showed a typical hotel ballroom. In this ballroom we have two partitions allowing the room to be subdivided. It should be simple for the control system to receive inputs from the partitions to confirm which are open and which are closed, immediately configuring the system to match the partion positions. The integrated control system shown in *Fig 28* could be programmed to deal with these different configurations whilst allowing local control plates to address user programmed presets. The end-user would be provided with simple push button wall plates in locations allowing cleaners, front of house manager, lighting control operator, stage manager, projectionist and other locations to all have access to the houselights, albeit in a structured way allowing for different levels of priority.

As noted previously, the dimmers specified should ideally be the same as the production lighting dimmers to ensure no interference is created on the audio and video systems and to reduce the acoustic and filament noise from linear or long filament lamps. As many of these dimmers have built-in facilities to store memories and for these memories to be remotely accessed, very simple control systems can be provided. These can simply be push button closing contact switches connected to analogue input ports on the dimmer memory control lines. This provides a very low cost preset solution for the small to medium sized venues.

8.15 Conclusions on Electrical Systems

The list below provides some simple reminders of the items that have been covered within this lengthy chapter:

Sizing of an electrical supply

Decision on whether to use technical or general mains earthing

Consideration of the harmonic effects of motors and dimmers

What type of electrical distribution and protection are required

Use of residual current protective devices – where and how many

How to phase balance and allocate electrical phases

Design of Production Lighting Boxes and their location

Sizing of load and supply cables

Allocation of dimmers and non-dims and their associated electrical supplies.

Working Light – type and integrated control system requirements.

House Lighting – type and integrated and local control requirements.

Useful information electrical distribution, cables, containment, protective devices and other related issues may be obtained from:

Allied Tubes Inc (USA)	www.alliedtibe.com
Andolite Ltd. (UK)	www.andolite.co.uk
Eaton MEM Ltd. (UK)	www.memonline.com
Hager Ltd. (UK)	www.hager.co.uk
Kopex Ltd. (UK)	www.kopex.co.uk
Merlin Gerin (UK)	www.scheider.co.uk
Mita Cable Management	www.mita.co.uk
Moeller Electric Ltd. (UK)	www.moeller.co.uk
RS Components Ltd. (UK)	www.rs-components.co.uk
Siemens Worldwide	www.siemens.com
Square D (UK)	www.scheider.co.uk
Telemecanique UK	www.scheider.co.uk

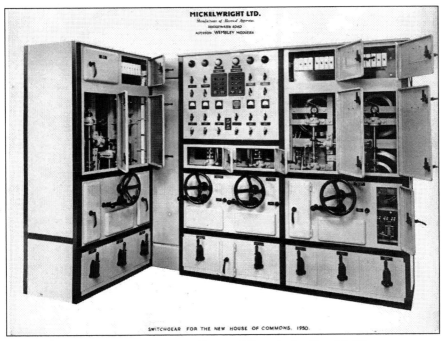

Fig 32: UK House of Commons Main Electrical Distribution Panel 1950 photo: The STLD Archive.

Fig 33: Modern Distribution Board with 1200 Amp incoming supply protected via an air circuit breaker, photo: Electrical Control Systems NI Ltd.

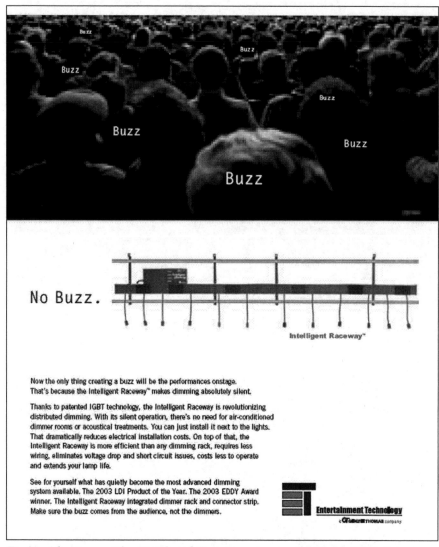

Fig 34: Advertisement for Distributed Containment system fitted with IGBT dimmers – called raceway, advertisement: Entertainment Technology, Inc.

9
SETTING UP A SYSTEM AND FAULT FINDING

The Sage Concert Hall, Newcastle Upon Tyne viewed from the overhead technical area, photo: Theatre Projects Consultants UK.

Contents:
- Introduction
- Routine Maintenance on all dimmer types
- Commissioning an Existing Dimmer System
- Commissioning a new Dimmer Installation
- Commissioning a Temporary Installation
- Conclusions

9.1 Introduction

This chapter looks at the sort of problems which can occur with a dimmer or with a dimming system. Space does not allow specific solutions with a particular product, but here are some general ideas about how to diagnose problems and how to at least narrow down the issues before attempting a fix or calling the service engineer.

It must be stressed that dimming equipment is connected to heavy current electrical supplies and is not to be tampered with by unqualified personnel. It is not the intention of this chapter to fault find down to component level, on say a printed circuit card, and indeed this should never be attempted by anyone other than those fully trained in dimmer servicing. The aim is to suggest solutions to typical problems that one might experience.

Time is also taken in considering how to commission a new system or how to take over a previously installed system when perhaps you move to a new position or want to check the performance of the dimming in a venue your show is moving to.

Firstly I would like to cover the very thorny subject of maintenance and what will help to prolong the life of the dimmers when often they are in the dimmer room and only get visited when a breaker 'pops'.

9.2 Routine Maintenance

Dimmers are complicated pieces of equipment and the components within them go through considerable stress cycles due to the rapid heating and cooling they go through on a daily basis. Some of them contain fans, all of them emit hot air and most have points at which heat emerges from the dimmer. As the requirements for each type of dimmer are slightly different I have listed my recommendations under different dimmer types. I have also included mention of older equipment – aware that some of these items are still in use. In all cases these checks should be carried out with the electrical supply removed or isolated. Experience here suggests that this is a two-person job unless the power supply can be padlocked off, to prevent someone else turning on the supply, unaware that someone is working on it. Always fix a label to the supply confirming that it is turned off due to work being carried out on the system. Also, always advise others who may use the system that you are carrying out work.

9.2.1 Portable Packs in Small Systems

The simple 4 or 6 pack dimmers really need no servicing save that they should be looked at perhaps once a year, the dust wiped off them and all the plugs and sockets checked to make sure they are mating correctly and not arcing due to be being half out of the socket. This type of dimmer is best left turned off when not in use. The law requires that these shall be subject to an annual electrical safety inspection, that shall be carried out by a qualified contractor. This test should also include other equipment connected to the dimmer so that the whole system is checked. This is essential in venues such as schools and colleges where inexperienced personnel are using the equipment. Experience has shown me that one source of problems can occur with the fuse holders. For some reason people never seem to tighten them up, so before you use the system make sure that if your turn them clockwise they are tight. Another point about fuses is that as they are not so easily available there is a tendency to put in 'what looks right'. Often these are not quite the right size or the correct rating. This can be dangerous, can lead to arcing and overheating in the fuse holder and if the current rating is too high will result in damage to the dimmer channel. So again, it is worth a regular check!

9.2.2 Rack Mounted Packs

This type of dimmer tends to be built into relatively small packages and consequently often features forced cooling using a fan or fans. These need to be checked on a regular basis as items can get pushed or drop into the fans and they get blocked with dust – and if they are not working efficiently the dimmer can overheat. One simple procedure that seems to work well, with the pack electrical supply turned off, is to use a vacuum cleaner and to point the nozzle into the fan grille and any extraction ventilation slots and suck up any dust. Once you have completed this use a ball point pen or pencil and gently check that the fan blades rotate in case someone has stuffed something into the fan. I recently found someone had pushed a piece of chalk into a dimmer pack fan at a school! Again this type of pack may have fuses or circuit breaker protection. As with the portable packs it is worth checking the fuses and the fuse holders. Some of these packs use standard connectors for each output channel – again make sure that these are pushed fully into the sockets. Others use multipin connectors, and these should be checked as sometimes they get 'cross threaded' and do not mate completely. Again, this can result in a poor connection.

9.2.3 Wall Mounted Dimmer Racks

Here I am talking about the 12, 24 and 36 way racks used across the world in the small to medium scale application. Some of these are convection cooled, some have forced cooling. With this type of cabinet it is sensible to remove the front cover and to vacuum out the entire rack as often the ventilation grille is at the bottom and the fan at the top. This draws dust through the entire rack and deposits it across all the surfaces and can clog up heat sinks as well as the fan. Another area where problems can occur is with the terminals used to connect the dimmer to the load circuits and for the incoming power. Sometimes during the heating and cooling cycle these can become loose, equally as these terminals compress the wires after some time the compression becomes permanent and they can work loose. Using a screwdriver check that they are really tight, making sure the screwdriver is the correct size for the terminals otherwise the terminals can crack or the screw heads become damaged.

9.2.4 Flight Cased Dimmers

As these dimmers move around they need to be regularly checked to ensure that connectors, printed circuit cards and all items are firmly fixed inside the packs. Again, clean out the fans and ventilation slots and check for damage where connectors may have been forced. Also remember that these tend to get heavy use so take a good look at the inside of the packs to make sure no wiring is showing signs of overheating. This usually shows up by the wire suffering some discolouration or darkened areas on printed circuit cards. Flick the circuit breakers on and off to make sure that none of them are damaged. This type of dimmer should go through a much more regular set of electrical tests, which should include testing the RCD devices by using their front mounted test buttons.

9.2.5 High Density Cabinet Dimmers

These really need a combination of all of the previously related items. Many of these feature air filters that should be cleaned out or replaced depending on the type of filters employed. There are many more wiring terminations so checking the terminals to ensure the wires are terminated tightly is essential. Some years ago I was called in to look at a fire which had occurred in a UK venue in the dimmer room. Even in all of the blackened remains it was possible to see that wires within the terminals were loose and that arcing had occurred, overheating the terminals with the wiring then burning due to the excessive heat generated.

Where plug-in modules are provided it is a sensible precaution to annually pull out each module and check the connectors at the rear. Sometimes the modules are not pushed completely home creating a poor contact and potential damage to the connectors on the module. Sometimes the modules have been pushed in with too much force and in some units they crack and again make a poor connection. If the unit has facilities to test the fans it is a wise precaution to do this – particularly if the rack has more than one fan in case one of them is stuck or failed. Once again check the breakers, any fitted RCD's and also the tightness of the power feeders, particularly the neutral. This can sometimes become loose due to the harmonic currents travelling along the cable. Some years ago I was inspecting an installation prior to commencing work on laying a new larger supply cable. On going to the main intake and opening the main supply isolator I was horrified to see that the neutral cable was resting in an old style soldered lug as all of the solder had dropped out due to overheating. Looking at the rest of the isolator internals there was considerable burning behind the isolator. This had not been picked up by the theatre staff or the annual insurance inspection, as the intake was accessed from outside the building no-one had smelt any overheating! As part of any electrical inspection, covers should be opened in all the electrical protection and isolation equipment. A good inspector will check terminals, blades on the isolators and the action of the ACB or MCCB.

9.2.6 Distributed Dimmer Bars and Packs

These are somewhat more complex to maintain simply because they are often sealed into small packages with complete heat sinks. This often results in a visual only inspection being possible. So again check that RCD's operate when the test button is pushed, check that the circuit breakers operate and check the supply cables into the unit.

9.2.7 Other Tests for all Types of Dimmers

One of the other tests that is sensible to carry out before using the system after some time or as part of the annual 'check up' is to plug in a DMX tester and check that the DMX inputs work correctly. To do this you need a simple DMX tester that can output DMX. Connect this to the input of the dimmer and make sure that the power to the dimmer is turned on. Then check channel by channel by plugging in a lamp to each channel and setting the DMX channel to the correct address. Check channel by channel to verify that each channel operates correctly.

9.3 Commissioning an Existing System

If you are taking over an existing system it is reasonable to assume that it should be in good order and free of wiring problems. Before undertaking any of these procedures check that there is no tape over breakers or if fuses have been removed as this often points towards a historic problem that has not been rectified. Leave these channels until the very end of any tests as they need a very careful approach.

Firstly I have assumed that you have carried out the routine maintenance checks and that you are satisfied that all the racks are clean, have the correct fuses or the breakers can be opened and closed, that the connectors are all plugged in or hard wired terminals are all correctly tightened down. Carry out a final visual check and once you are satisfied that everything is satisfactory apply power to the first pack, wall dimmer or cabinet. Using either two people with an intercom or radio 'walkie talkie' or a local DMX tester or rigger's control turn on each channel and verify that if a lamp is plugged in locally to a pack or at the remote socket outlet that the dimmer operates correctly. The quick check here is to select the dimmer at say 50% and 0% - this can be done by using the control desk, alternatively use the riggers control or a DMX tester. You need to make sure that you understand the channel patching that may have been applied to the dimmers. As explained in earlier chapters, sometimes the dimmer numbering is not sequential in the rack to accommodate geographic socket location or electrical phasing. Hopefully the original installer will have carefully marked the channel numbers on the dimmers so that this is easy. Alternatively you may need to use the DMX address function on the dimmer to check how this has been set. Some dimmers are easy to test because a local test facility is built into their operator programming menu. This enables each channel to be turned on and off, enabling the second person to walk around the venue plugging in fixtures to the appropriate outlets.

Testing each channel at percentage below full (100% intensity) helps provide some protection to the device if there is a wiring fault as only around half the output voltage will be sent to the load. This also helps to avoid large pops and bangs as fuses fail or breakers trip out if a fault is discovered. It is important to check the channel at an intensity setting and at zero to ensure that the dimmer is actually dimming and not stuck switched on, potentially indicating power control device failure.

Once all of the channels have been checked and a list made of potentially failed channels you can then consider whether you feel comfortable to check the channels marked with tape or whether you wish to leave this for others. If there is a fault this may be within the dimmer or with the connected cabling. Before applying power you could check the cabling with a simple insulation tester. To do this the connector needs to be unplugged or the wiring removed from the terminals. This should be done with the power turned off. Connect the insulation tester to the phase and neutral conductor and make sure that a high impedance is measured. This should run into M Ohm's or millions of Ohms indicating an 'open circuit'. Any reading below a M Ohm suggests that insulation failure is occurring. When Ohms are measured this indicates a short circuit on the cable or a problem in the connector or socket outlet box. These may be looked at by yourself or by a qualified electrician. Sometimes a simple visual inspection can find a problem quickly, at other times an electrical engineer is required to trace the problem.

Visual inspections can be simple and often the problem can be found quickly. With a portable dimmer the problem can often lie with the extension cables. These often get pulled tightly, resulting in wires pulling out of the plugtops or trailing sockets. When they pull out they can touch adjacent terminals and short out. So a wise technician regularly checks extension cables, particularly if they are heavily used and pulled around a rig.

With socket boxes, cables can drop out of terminals caused by the regular insertion and extraction of plug tops. Remove the cover of the box, making absolutely certain that all electrical supplies within the box have been isolated. By this I mean some boxes might have direct technical supplies, non-dims, general power and other supplies. These are usually fed from their own breakers in different distribution boards or racks from the dimmers and these MUST be isolated before attempting to check socket boxes. If you are in any doubt then you must call a qualified electrician. If you are satisfied that the supplies are isolated and will not be turned on by others, using a voltmeter first check that there is no voltages present on any of the connectors. If you are sure that all is correct remove the screws from the front of the box and carefully remove this. Some boxes have hinges making this procedure simple. Once the box is opened locate the circuit which apparently has the problem and check that the wires are correctly terminated into the socket. Sometimes there is a loom that allows installed and box wiring to be joined together. This often comprises another set of terminals that are prone to the same problems as those reported inside dimmer racks. So again check these for tightness. If everything appears to be in order maybe you are not looking at the right circuit. By this I mean the socket might be mis-numbered or perhaps the dimmer patch is incorrect. To check you have found the right pair of wires a simple continuity check can be carried out. Apply a shorting plug to the socket and back at the dimmer room use a continuity checker to verify that with the plug inserted a short circuit is detected and when removed the circuit is open circuit. If all of this checks out as being correct, re-assemble the socket box and do not forget to REMOVE THE SHORTING PLUG.

At this stage power can be applied to the dimmer and the channel faded up to 50% and then faded down again. If the channel remains on irrespective of the intensity setting the problems lies within the dimmer and is probably the power control device – a thyristor or triac has been damaged and should be replaced. This requires replacement of the faulty device and with thyristors it is always best to replace these as pairs in case one has failed and the offer has been 'stressed' but has yet to fail. If everything appears to be satisfactory but the dimmer is still not working then a service engineer is definitely required.

9.4 Commissioning a New System

This section has been included as a guide only, as the process can be dangerous and requires the correct test gear, an understanding of heavy current electricity, and is provided for everyone to understand the correct procedure to check the dimming system.

9.4.1 Installed System

This procedure applies to a simple 24 way system through to a 360 channel solution. Prior to any powered testing you must be sure that the electrical system has been tested and inspected and that the appropriate test certificates with results have been handed over. Even then problems can occur. Testing an installation in Greece some six years ago I was handed all the relevant test results circuit by circuit, the electrical test certificate to confirm the system was safe for use and unusually, due to a time pressure from the client, I instructed the power to be applied to the main switchboard without my usual visual checks. This powered up correctly with the voltmeters showing the correct phase to phase and phase to neutral voltages. Normally before I carry out any live power testing I go around each cabinet and carry out a visual inspection as this can often find the obvious problem. On this day I had not! Instructing the local electrical contractor to apply power to the first cabinet there was a loud explosion and the front cover blew off the cabinet and hit the wall opposite prior to the MCCB tripping.

Later inspection confirmed that when the electrical contractor had inserted wires into the European style bus-bars he had stripped back too much of the insulation and all three phases and neutral were touching one another producing a direct short circuit. At this point the electrical energy available through the protection system was many thousands of Amps. The MCCB device was of local manufacture and delivered thousands of Amps before tripping. This completely blew apart the dimmer cabinet busbar which hit the flimsy front cover held on with short self tapping screws. This parted company with the main cabinet, blowing it across the room. Having turned off the supply and then visually inspected each other cabinet the same wiring mistake was found. So how could the system have been tested? At this point I handed the keys of the distribution panel back to the electrical contractor saying: "sorry no testing today. Tomorrow you come back and I witness your electrical tests before we turn on any more power". So beware, never trust anyone, always check and check again as you can never be too careful where electricity is concerned.

I must just add another experience on this same installation. Some two days later, having commissioned everything, the audience was arriving in the auditorium for the first performance. As one does, I walked around the building and into the auditorium and noticed that there was some flicker on the houselights. Going back into the dimmer room there was that 'never to be forgotten' smell of electrical burning! Reaching the houselight dimmer cabinet everything seemed fine but following the smell I reached a home made metal box containing a 63 Amp MCCB device feeding the dimmer cabinet. Opening the door the smell hit me (remember at this time the houselights are on and the panel is live). Looking at the MCCB I could see that the neutral wire was literally smouldering. As the show was starting shortly I decided to wait to attack the problem. However as I moved away from the panel I received an electric shock on my left arm. Well this was Greece, this was a home made distribution board and normal sensible practises did not apply. I received a shock because the indicators fitted to confirm that power was present on each phase have live terminals on the rear of the indicators. In the UK we would normally use transformer fed indicators where feeder cables would be insulated but on this project none had been fitted. Again, my error for not checking! I had been drawn to a serious problem and forgot my own safety procedures. So I repeat: check and check again.

So if you are sure about proceeding, my suggestion is to carry out a visual inspection with the electrical contractor who installed the system. Ask him to go through each cabinet with both of you visually inspecting the cabling, checking phase colours and the neutral for the correct termination – without shorts, looking at the load wiring, checking for tightness and carrying out a thorough visual inspection. These days I also ask that they random test the incoming supplies into a couple of packs or cabinets to ensure there are not short circuits, not so much in the UK but in more far away locations where contracting can be, shall we say, variable! My rule is never to trust anyone - least of all a local electrician, and to always check and check again. Always carry a voltmeter and check that off really does mean off and always padlock or lock off the supply feeding equipment you are working on. Of course, fit a label, but as I know well labels can get removed!

Having satisfied yourself, and the contractor, that all looks well and with all of the individual dimmer supplies turned off, apply power to the production lighting switchboard. This might be an isolator on the wall, a simple MCB type distribution board or a large floor standing cabinet of the types shown in Chapter 8. Using a voltmeter, ensure that the correct supply voltage is present on each of the phases and between phase and neutral at the distribution board. Larger distribution boards may have panel mounted meters making this an easy process, others may have indicators but beware these might be mis-wired giving false readings.

Go to the first dimmer pack or cabinet and with all of the load breakers fitted to each dimmer channel turned off or the fuses removed apply power to the unit. Check that the pack or rack has powered up. This might be shown on phase indicators on the front panel or a front panel LCD or LED type display becoming illuminated with a welcome message. Almost all dimmers need to go through a set up procedure even if this is only to set the DMX address. Set the address by following the manufacturer's instructions; other facilities may need to be programmed such as:

- Dimmer Law
- Set maximum output voltage
- Set default instruction on loss of DMX
- Set response speed
- Number of dimmers within cabinet (some diagnostic systems require this)
- Rating of dimmers/non-dims within cabinet
- Set threshold voltages for automatic voltage compensation systems
- Set up of any provided user preferences

Some manufacturers include a built-in dimmer cabinet diagnostic system which checks out the cabinet prior to connecting the loads. If this is provided it is well worth carrying out these tests and this will primarily check out the processing systems prior to commencing load checking, avoiding any confusing potential faults later on.

One test that you should do, and now is as good a time as any, is to verify that all of the data that you have programmed is retained by the dimmer cabinet.

Having checked the cabinets and set up the correct cabinet information you can then commence the load checking. This process will check that the dimmer is responding to the correct DMX setting and also checks that the contractor has wired the correct outlet to the correct dimmer channel. As voltages are now going to be applied to the connected wiring, any short circuits or wiring errors will show up. To minimise any problems I like to check dimmer by dimmer with only the selected dimmer fuse or breaker turned on.

If the dimmer has a local test facility you can use this to check channel by channel through the system. If a series of six channel packs is being set up then the easiest method is to connect a known load, such as a 500 Watt fixture, into each pack output socket and verify that the dimmer dims up and down by adjusting the test intensity.

If the dimmer has hard-wired outputs then this will involve a second person walking around the venue to the appropriate output socket and plugging in a known working load. Again check each channel one by one and verify that the dimmer operates correctly from 0 to the test intensity. If the channel does not come on record this as a failure and proceed to the next. If the dimmer module is fitted with an RCD, press the local module or rack mounted RCD test switch to verify that it operates correctly. This can help to identify problems with neutral wiring that can often happen if the contractor's bits of masking tape with their circuit numbers have fallen off!

Once all channels have been tested you will have a list of a completely working system or, hopefully, only a couple of channels that are not working. These now need to be investigated to see what might be causing the problem.

If no output has been found at a socket go back to the offending circuit on the local test facility and turn the dimmer on. Most dimmers have front panel mounted indicators to confirm that the dimmer is working or is receiving voltage; some have indicators to confirm current flow – in other words that a lamp is connected. Check that the dimmer 'on' light is illuminated. If it is it may be the contractor may have mis-wired a circuit. Looking through the list of faults you may find that dimmer 66 and 69 are not working. This may be caused by the contractor mis-reading the cable marking when terminating cables if you plug into socket 69 and turn on channel 66 you may find it works! You might see that two adjacent circuits are not working - often this can be caused by the neutral wires being crossed over at the dimmer during final termination. If RCD's are fitted you may find that the circuit does not work but the RCD trips. Again this may indicate a mis-wired neutral so look for other circuits close by or with possible numbering errors. You will be surprised how often this problem occurs.

If the circuit breaker or fuse fails when the circuit is turned on then this probably indicates a short circuit during the wiring phase. Take a look at the terminals in the dimmer rack; with the cabinet power turned off, you are checking to see if wire strands are touching. This can occur with multi-stranded cable where a few strands miss going into the terminal and touch the adjacent conductors. Also take a look at the termination into the socket box and also if there are intermediate connection points. For example, it may be that the circuit appears on an over-stage bar that has a cable management system to allow cables to rise and fall when the bar is moved. These tend to have additional connection points at the top and bottom of the rise and fall cable. It may be that multiway connectors are in use at the connection points for the bars, and sometimes loose strands of wire here can short between connector pins. It is therefore advisable firstly to take a physical look; sometimes a torch or hand lamp can reveal clearly the problem that the naked eye cannot see.

Occasionally the problem is within the dimmer pack or rack, or sometimes your programming has created a problem - so do check that the DMX patch you have entered is correct otherwise you can chase your own tail for a long time! With packs it is easy to check the pack itself because if there is no output on one socket then the problem is found. With installed dimmers it is more difficult because some of them have wiring terminals behind the modules and these cannot be reached unless a module extender is used. What you are trying to do is to check that there is an output voltage. Be warned here that it is no use using one of the voltage sticks or one of the low cost high impedance voltmeters as these can show there is a voltage present when there is leakage across the power device. You need to use a proper, ideally true r.m.s. meter as this will indicate true voltage at the output terminals. If you can safely attach meter probes you should see zero volts when the dimmer is turned off and approximately half the supply voltage when you fade the dimmer up to 50% intensity. If no voltage is measured check that you are addressing the correct channel, check that the fuse or breaker are okay, and that the module is pushed fully home if a plug-in system is being tested. One area where I have been caught out on a number of occasions is to assume that if there is a tested label on the equipment that it has in fact been tested. I can think of two recent circumstances where I spent far too long looking for installed faults only to eventually find that there were internal dimmer rack faults! Therefore never assume anything – check and double check.

9.4.2 Temporary System

The real difference between a permanently installed system and one rigged on a temporary basis is that the dimmers should have been checked before they left the store or rental company. So should the cabling, and in theory all that has to be done is to plug up and off you go! Well we have all been there at three o'clock in the morning and it is all plugged up only to find some parts work and others just will not.

In these circumstances, as well as a multi-meter it is also wise to have a multipin connector tester suitable for the multicore formats being used. These are often a proprietary box or even hand made device with an appropriate connector to mate with the end of a multicore fitted with neon or led indicators. Turning each channel on and off in turn should result in the appropriate indicator confirming the presence of a voltage on the correct pin. This can check multi-cores very quickly and saves hours of time trying to prod around with a pair of multi-meter probes trying to find the right pin!

So my usual route is to check out the dimmer end first, to make sure that the mains feeds have been correctly plugged into the flight cased dimmer. You would be amazed how often these are plugged up incorrectly with costly results! Once the 'mains' is set up and the racks correctly powered set up the DMX address on each pack or each case. Check this is correct with a lighting desk or a DMX tester. Some racks have indicators per channel to act like a channel mimic. Where these are fitted you can quickly flick through each channel and check the dimmers are okay. Where not fitted a quick 'whiz' through with a known working lamp per channel produces the same result

Another tip is to have a set of made-up leads to enable you to plug directly into the flight case. This might require a patch lead to lamp connector, a multi-way adaptor from the rack outputs to your test box and so on. Like all test leads they are only of any use if they are wired correctly and they have been checked regularly, otherwise further problems occur.

Having checked the flight cases are okay and are providing output, checking the feeds at the bar end is more difficult as these are often in the air. Well maybe not. I always like to flash out on the deck before the bars or trusses are flown as this saves so much time if faults occur. One of my biggest moans is about rental companies and their cables. So often the fault is with the cable and it seems across the world in general that cables are never properly checked and inspected. So often looking at the cable shows the problem. In the UK the theatre industry has for years used a 3 pin round plug called a 15 Amp. For whatever reason, the neutral pin works loose and often opening the plug shows the neutral wire pulled out of the terminal. Maybe one day we can all move to a sensible connector, like the CEE 17 unit favoured by film and TV! Enough of my moaning, suffice it to say that cables are often the problem, so apply your tester to the ends of each multi-core in turn and check correct operation. I have to admit here to finding all sorts of problems; one recent one was 'multi's' were rented from two small rental companies with clearly different views on pin out's. How such a thing can happen in this day and age is beyond me! Clearly one of these companies had invented their own code and therefore within their own systems everything worked, and mixing with another company who had followed the rest of the world convention did not work!

Electrical safety on touring systems is paramount and having spent a long time travelling the world you get to see some sights which are quite frankly astounding in their stupidity. Electrical standards organisations exist throughout the world to ensure that electrical installations are safe, and these guys do not invent rules just for something to do. Being a Member of the Institute of Electrical Engineers in the UK means that I have a responsibility to all, in terms of safety and compliance with regulations. Yes, of course the show has to go on but we do not want a fire or someone injured or even killed. So always think safety, never be tempted to botch a quick solution. When there are problems with cables cutting them open and joining them with a terminal block is perhaps not the best solution! I have seen cables taped together, wires twisted together without insulation and burnt cables and flight cased racks as the result of some 'quick fixes'. So when problems do occur on outgoing cables or multi's the only safe way is to use a new cable. Indeed, when running multiway cables or singles in 'tripes' it is sensible to include a spare multi or a few spare cables.

Where problems can develop with both installed and temporary dimming installations is where some form of earth leakage detection equipment is installed. These are becoming more prevalent in many systems either on the supply or within the dimmer or flight cases. When they trip the usual problem is to find out why? When this happens during a show not only is this annoying but fault finding can be difficult. For that reason it is advisable to look at the dimming system when designing the show, allocating lamps with different functions to the same RCD in a way that if an RCD trips out geographic areas of the performance space are not plunged into darkness. In TV this often means rigging a main key light to one protected dimmer with the back-up key light fed from another protected dimmer.

When an RCD trips the fault needs to be isolated. If one RCD is fitted per channel this is easy; if one RCD is protecting a group of dimmers it is necessary to find which circuit is creating the problem. The quickest way is to turn off all the dimmer breakers and then to reset the RCD. Turning on each channel one by one should show which channel is creating the problem. Sometimes, if a group of channels all trip out, you may find it is a fault with a multi-way cable often with incorrect terminations. Common causes of tripped RCD's are neutral to earth shorts – common in Par Cans – neutrals from one circuit mixed with a phase of another circuit, bad lamp holder, damaged cable or a damaged connector. Most of these faults are found easily by visual inspection and perhaps should have been found during proper maintenance periods. However, maintenance periods are being reduced, rental companies move equipment in and out of the store without checking so inevitably problems occur that could often be found had time been allowed. RCD faults should be found like other faults by trying the simple things first – a visual inspection often finds the problem quickly!

9.5 Conclusions

I hope that by now you have found the answers to the dimming questions or information that you were looking for. Over the course of the past nine chapters I have tried to provide a brief history of the different formats of dimming, how, why and when the major changes came about and how this led to the formats now available.

Included were a lot of details about the current formats and the products that are available around the world including guide prices to try and help you choose a solution that matches your requirements or plan systems for others to use.

The different formats were explained showing how they might be applied in different typical applications.

A simple rule of thumb guide showing how to calculate quantities of dimmer and non-dim channels was provided together with examples of using this guide.

Practical Dimming has looked at the different application of dimmers studying residential, architectural, entertainment and television applications. Wherever possible I have tried to cover products and solutions that match these different market requirements in both the 230 and the 110 volt world.

Up-to-date technological changes in the styles of dimming have been discussed and considered with some time being spent in suggesting that distributing the dimmers around an installation can provide significant benefits. This has been proved to be ever more worthwhile in the early part of 2006 where the price of copper is climbing at an alarming rate. No longer can the installation costs be ignored; they are now a significant portion of an installed dimmer system cost and therefore solutions that reduce the installation cost and yet maintain the system integrity and flexibility have to be considered seriously. You will no doubt have realised that I am a fan of distributed solutions. I firmly believe that we will see a much greater uptake of the distributed solution in years to come throughout the world in years to come as the cost argument is primarily the same.

The latest form of sine wave dimming has been considered and explained. This format is already being installed in many technical entertainment buildings where acoustic and electrical noise pollution are considered important aspects in the dimmer system design. Whether this solution becomes the norm or remains used in areas where noise is a major consideration will, I suspect, depend heavily on whether the standards institutions and energy providers win the argument about harmonic distortion. This will also affect the cost as currently there are a significant number of expensive components within a sine wave dimmer; if volumes were to significantly increase then there may well be some cost reduction benefits. However, a sine wave dimmer is an inherently more expensive dimmer so there will always be a cost penalty to pay. Having used sine wave dimmers one has to be amazed at the improved performance and their almost silent operation. Here again I am a convert and I am sure that use of this technology will increase dramatically as more and more manufacturers go down this path. Attending Pro Light + Sound in Frankfurt in Spring 2006 I saw more manufacturers offering this technology, and even now it is being utilised by some of the smaller manufacturers – a sure sign, sorry about the pun, that sine wave is on the increase. So take a look – do not just ignore this on cost, as again there are installed and distributed solutions available, and mixing and matching is a solution well worth considering.

Electrical considerations were discussed as those designing dimming systems often need to provide advice or design on the complete system. Protection of the dimming system and individual dimmers was discussed together with the trend towards use of residual current leakage detecting devices and the problems these can create within the dimming environment. The different types of power distribution were reviewed and the different methods needed for the installed and distributed systems were considered.

Hopefully *Practical Dimming* has covered the subjects that you were searching for information about, and contact details of many of the world's dimmer manufacturers has been provided. Do contact them as they are involved in dimming every day, they are very approachable and many helped provide information for this book for which I am very grateful. As with all technology, things can change very quickly so their websites can update data faster than the printed word.

Maybe some of the mystery has been removed? Maybe some new concepts or ideas about your next dimming system have been provoked. I certainly hope so!

I really hope that you found the book interesting and should you wish to make any comments or seek some further information do not hesitate to contact me via the email address provided. Thank you for buying *Practical Dimming*.

USEFUL CONTACT ADDRESSES

The following companies produce Dimming products or products that link to dimming equipment. The data is correct at the time of going to press.

A.C. Lighting Ltd.
Centauri House, Hillbottom Road, High Wycombe, Buckinghamshire HP12 4HQ, UK
Tel: +44 1494 446000 Fax: +44 1494 461024
www.aclighting.com

ADB-TTV Technologies SA.
Leuvensesteenweg 585, B – 1930 Zaventem, BELGIUM
Tel: +32 2 709 3211 Fax: +32 2 709 3280
www.adblighting.com

ADB UK.
15 Woking Business Park, Albert Drive, Woking, Surrey GU21 5JY, UK
Tel: +44 1483 764646 Fax: +44 1483 769955
www.lsiprojects.com

American DJ Supply, Inc.
4295 Charter Street, Los Angeles, CA 90058, USA
Tel: +1 323 582 2650 Fax: +1 323 582 2610
www.americandj.com

Andolite Ltd.
Unit 21 Hopkinson Way, West Portway, Andover, Hampshire, SP10 3LF, UK
Tel: +44 1264 356445 Fax: +44 1264 334401
www.andolite.co.uk

Anytronics Ltd.
Units 5-6 Hillside Industrial Estate, London Road, Horndean, Hants, PO8 0BL, UK
Tel: +44 2392 599410 Fax: +44 2392 598723
www.anytronics.com

Artistic Licence (UK) Ltd.
24 Forward Drive, Christchurch Avenue, Harrow, Middlesex, HA3 8NT, UK
Tel: +44 208 863 4515 Fax: +44 208 426 0551
www.artisticlicence.com

Avolites Ltd.
184 Park Avenue, Park Royal, London NW10 7XL, UK
Tel: +44 208 965 8522 Fax: +44 208 965 0290
www.avolites.org.uk

Belden Wire Inc.
(Belden CDT Electronics Division), 2200 U.S. 27 South, Richmond, IN 47374, USA
Tel: +1 765 983 5200 Fax: +1 765 983 5294
www.belden-wire.com

Colortran Inc (Part of Leviton Group)
PO Box 2210, Tualatin, OR 97062, USA
Tel: +1 503 404 5500 Fax: +1 503 404 5600
www.colortran.com

Compulite Systems (2000) Ltd.
9 Hanagar Street, Neve Ne'eman, B Industrial Zone, Hod Hasharon, 45421
ISRAEL
Tel: + 972 9 7446555 Fax: + 972 9 7466515
www.compulite.com

Creative Stage Lighting Co, Inc.
P.O. Box 567, 149 Route 28N, North Creek, NY 12853, USA
Tel: +1 518 251 3302 Fax: +1 518 251 2908
www.dura-flex.com

Crestron Electronics, Inc.
15 Volvo Drive, Rockleigh, NJ 07647, USA
Tel: +1 201 767 3400 Fax: +1 201 767 7576
www.crestron.com

Delmatic Ltd.
The Powerhouse, Power Road, Chiswick, London W4 5PY, UK
Tel: +44 20 8987 5900 Fax: +44 20 8987 5957
www.delmatic.com

Eaton MEM Ltd.
Reddings Lane, Birmingham, B11 3EZ, UK
Tel: +44 8700 545 333 Fax: +44 8700 540 333
www.memonline.com

Elation Professional, Inc.
4295 Charter Street, Los Angeles, CA 90058, USA
Tel: +1 323 582 3322 Fax: +1 323 582 3108
www.elationlighting.com

ELC (Anima Lighting Ltd.)
Route du Stand, Le Bouveret, CH-1897, SWITZERLAND
Tel: + 41 21 967 2001 Fax: + 41 860 79210 4613
www.elclighting.com

Electrical Control Systems NI Ltd
34.36 Sydney Street, Aughnacloy, Co Tyrone, BT69 6AE. UK
Tel: +353 48855 028855 Fax: +353 48855 028855.
Web: www.monelectrical.com

Electron SA.
68, Antiohias Street ,143 41, Nea Philadelphia, Athens, GREECE.
Tel: + 30 210 2584240 Fax: +30 210 2584245
www.electron.gr

Electronic Industries Alliance (EIA)
2001 Eye Street, NW, Washington D.C.20006, USA
www.eia.org

Electronic Theatre Controls Europe
5 Victoria Industrial Estate, Victoria Road, London W3 6UU, UK
Tel: +44 208 896 1000 Fax: +44 208 896 2000
www.etcconnect.com

Electronic Theatre Controls USA
3031 Pleasant View Road, PO Box 620979, Middleton WI 535620979, USA
Tel: +1 608 831 4116 Fax: +1 608 836 1736
www.etcconnect.com

Electronics Diversified, Inc.
1675 NW Cornelius Pass Rd, Hillsboro, OR 97124, USA
Tel: +1 503 645 5533 Fax: +1 503 629 9877
www.edionline.com

Entertainment Technology Inc.
10911 Petal Street, Dallas, Texas 75238, USA
Tel: +1 214 647 7880 Fax: +1 214 647 8032
www.etdimming.com

ESTA
875 Sixth Avenue, Suite 1005 New York, NY 10001, USA
Tel: +1 212 244 1505 Fax: +1 212 244 1502
www.esta.org

Ex-Or Ltd.
Haydock Lane, Haydock, Merseyside. WA11 9UJ, UK
Tel: +44 1942 719229 Fax +44 1942 272767
www.ex-or.com

Guangzhou HeDong Electronics Co. Ltd.
No.24 Jianzhong Road,
Tianhe Development Zone of High & New Technology Estate,
Guangzhou,510665, CHINA
Tel: +86 20 85530079 Fax: +86 20 85532325
www.hldchina.com.cn

Hager Ltd.
(Ashley, Klik, Tehalit) Hortonwood 50, Telford, Shropshire, TF1 7FT, UK
Tel: +44 1952 675615 Fax: +44 1952 675626

Hamilton Litestat
(R. Hamilton & Co Ltd.) Quarry Industrial Estate, Mere, Wiltshire. BA12 6LA, UK
Tel: +44 1747 860088 Fax: +44 1747 861032
www.hamilton-litestat.com

Helvar Lighting Control Ltd.,
Hawley Mill, Hawley Road, Dartford, Kent. DA2 7SY, UK
Tel: +44 1322 222211 Fax: +44 1322 282216
www.helvar.com

Howard Eaton Lighting Ltd.
Winterlands, Resting Oak Hill, Cooksbridge, Nr Lewes, East Sussex. BN8 4PR, UK
Tel: +44 1273 400670 Fax: +44 1273 400890
www.helluk.com

IEC - International Electrotechnical Commission
PO Box 131, 3 Rue de Varembe, 1211 Geneva 20, SWITZERLAND
Tel: +41 22 919 02 11
www.iec.ch

i Light Ltd.
Unit 4, Enterprise Centre, Penshurst, Tonbridge, Kent, TN11 8BG, UK
Tel: +44 1892 870072 Fax: +44 1892 870074
www.ilight.co.uk

Interactive Technologies Inc.
723 Sandringham Drive. Alpharetta, GA 30004, USA
Tel: +1 678 566 0365 Fax: +1 678 566 0366
www.interactive-online.com

ISO - International Organisation for Standardisation
1, Rue de Varembe, Case Postale 56, CH-1211 Geneva 20, SWITZERLAND
Tel: +41 22 74 901 11
www.iso.ch

Jands Pty Limited.
Locked Bag 15, 40 Kent Road, Mascot, NSW 2020, AUSTRALIA
Phone: +61 02 9582 0909 Fax: +61 02 9582 0999
www.jands.com.au

Kelsey Acoustics Ltd.
9 Lyon Road, Walton on Thames, Surrey, KT12 3PU, UK
Tel: +44 1932 886060 Fax: +44 1932 885565
www.kelseyweb.co.uk

Leviton Lighting Control Division
9013 Tuscany Way, Building 100, Austin, Texas 78754, USA
Tel: +1 512 927 7711 Fax: +1 512 927 7799
www.leviton.com

Light Processor Ltd.
20 Greenhill Crescent, Watford Business Park, Watford, Hertfordshire.
WD18 8JA UK
Tel: +44 1923 698080 Fax: +44 1923 698081
www.lightfactor.co.uk

Leprecon LLC.
P.O. Box 430, Hamburg, MI 48139, USA
Tel: +1 810 231 9373 Fax: +1 810 231 1631
www.leprecon.com

Lightronics Inc.
509 Central DR, Virginia Beach, VA 23454; USA
Tel: +1 757 486 3588 Fax: +1 757 486 3391
www.lightronics.com

Lite-Puter Enterprise Co., Ltd.
9F No 196, Sec.3 Ta Tung Road, His Chih, Taipei County, TAIWAN
Tel: +886 2 2648 6545 Fax: +886 2 2648 6546
www.liteputer.com.tw

LSC Lighting Systems (Aust) Pty Ltd.
7 University Place, Clayton 3168, Victoria, AUSTRALIA
Phone: +613 9561 5255 Fax: +613 9561 5277
www.lsclighting.com.au

LSI Projects Ltd.
15 Woking Business Park, Albert Drive, Woking, Surrey GU21 5JY, UK
Tel: +44 1483 764646 Fax: +44 1483 769955
www.lsiprojects.com

Lutron EA Ltd. - London
Lutron House, 6 Sovereign Close, Wapping, London. E1W 3JF, UK
Tel: +44.207.702.0657 Fax: +44.207.480.6899
www.lutron.com

Lutron USA
7200 Suter Road, Coopersburg, PA 18036-1299, USA
Tel: +1 610.282.3800
www.lutron.com

MK Electric Ltd.,
The Arnold Centre, Paycocke Road, Basildon, Essex. SS14 3EA, UK
Tel: +44 1268 563000 Fax: +441268 563563
www.mkelectric.co.uk

Moeller Electric Ltd.
Gatehouse Close, Aylesbury, Buckinghamshire, HP19 8DH, UK
Tel: +44 1296 393322 Fax: +44 1296 421854

Multiform Technology Ltd.
Station Road, Hellingly, Hailsham, East Sussex, BN27 4EU, UK
Tel: +44 1323 848117 Fax: +44 (0)1323 441906
www.multiform-uk.com

NSI Corp – Division of Leviton
P.O. Box 2210, Tualatin, Oregon 97062, USA
Tel: +1 503 404 5500 Fax: +1 503 404 5600
www.nsicorp.com

PLASA
38 St Leonards Road, Eastbourne, East Sussex, BN21 3UT, UK
Tel: +44 1323 418400 Fax: +44 1323 646905
www.plasa.org

Polaron Controls Ltd.
26 Greenhill Crescent, Watford Business Park, Watford, Hertfordshire
WD18 8XG, UK
Tel: +44 1923 495495 Fax: +44 1923 228796
www.polaron.co.uk

PRG Europe – Entertainment Technology Europe
20-22 Fairway Drive, Greenford, Middlesex, UB6 8PW, UK
Tel: +44 208 575 6666 Fax: +44 208 575 0424
www.prgeurope.com

Profibus International
Support Centre, Haid und Neu Strasse. 7, 76131 Karlsruhe, GERMANY
Tel: +49 721 9658 590 Fax: +49 721 9658 589
www.profibus.com

Osram GmbH
Hellabrunner Strasse 1, 81543 München, GERMANY
Tel.: +49 89 62 13 0 Fax: +49 89 62 13 20 20
www.osram.com

Pulsar Light Of Cambridge Ltd.
3 Coldhams Business Park, Norman Way, Cambridge CB1 3LH, UK
Tel: +44 1223 403500 Fax: +44 1223 403501
www.pulsarlight.com

Rako Controls Ltd.
Slip 7, The Historic Dockyard, Chatham, Kent. ME4 4TE, UK
Tel: +44 870 043 3905 Fax: +44 870 043 3906
www.rakocontrols.com

Robert Juliat S.A.S.
Route de Beaumont, F60530 Fresnoy-en-Thelle, FRANCE
Tel: + 33 344 265189 Fax: +33 344 269079
www.robertjuliat.fr

Schneider Electric Ltd
(Merlin Gerin, Square D and Telemecanique)
Stafford Park 5, Telford, Shropshire, TF3 3BL, UK
Tel: +44 1952 290029 Fax: +44 1952 290534
www.schneider.co.uk

Stagetec Distribution Ltd. (Compulite UK)
16 Tawfield, Bracknell, Berkshire, RG12 8YU, UK
Tel: +44 1344 440507 Fax: +44 1344 642018
www.stagetec.co.uk

Strand Lighting Ltd.
Unit 3, Hammersmith Studios, Yeldham Road, Hammersmith, London, W6 8JF, UK
Tel: +44 1592 656400 Fax: +44 208 735 9799
www.strandlighting.com

Strand Lighting, Inc.
6603 Darin Way, Cypress, CA 90630, USA
Tel: +1 714 230 8200 Fax: +1 714 899 0042
www.strandlighting.com

TMB UK
2 Commerce Road, Brentford, Middx. TW8 8LR, UK
Tel: +44 208 560 9652 Fax: +44 208 560 1064
www.tmb.com

TMB USA
10643 Glenoaks Boulevard, Pacoima, CA 91331, USA
Tel: +1 818 899 8818 Fax: +1 818 899 8813
www.tmb.com

USITT
Suite 5A, 10 West 19th Street, New York, NY 10011-4206, USA
Tel : +1 212 924 9088 Fax : +1 212 924 9343
www.usitt.org

Vari-Lite Inc.
10911 Petal Street, Dallas, Texas 75238, USA
Tel: +1 214 647 7880 Fax: +1 214 647 8038
www.vari-lite.com

XTBA Ltd.
Unit B, 443 Holloway Road, London N7 6LJ, UK
Tel: +44 207 281 7766 Fax: +44 207 272 1600
www.xtba.co.uk

Zero 88 Lighting Ltd.
Usk House, Lakeside, Llantarnam Park, Cwmbran NP44 3HD, UK
Tel: +44 1633 838088 Fax: +44 1633 867880
www.zero88.com

GLOSSARY

The following is a list of words and terms used in the book that may require clarification or expansion. The list is by no means all-inclusive, but hopefully will aid understanding of some of the 'buzz words' used in the industry. This list has been compiled by the author for exclusive use in his existing and future books, and principally for his *Lighting Systems for TV Studios, Practical DMX* and *Practical Dimming* titles.

A
Abbreviation for an ampere

AC
Alternating Current defined as an electrical current reversing its polarity at regular intervals, e.g. 50Hz in Europe and 60Hz in USA.

ACB
Air Circuit Breaker.

AC Coupled
An electronic or electrical circuit capable of passing an AC signal but with a response that does not pass DC (direct current) e.g. transformer or capacitor coupled.

ACN
Abbreviation for Advanced Control Network. This is a proposed new lighting industry protocol allowing devices from many different manufacturers to coexist on the same computer type network.

Ampere (Amp, A)
Unit of electrical current.

Amplifier
A device for increasing the strength of the input signals (can be either current or voltage) to provide greater 'power' for subsequent use. Widely used in DMX networks to increase the signal strength on line DMX lines.

Amplitude
Level or intensity of a signal.

Analogue
A signal continuously proportional to a physical parameter.

Anamorphic
In an optical system this describes a system having different vertical and horizontal magnifications.

AND Gate
A logic gate which gives an output of 1 (high) when all inputs are set to 1 (high).

Anti-phase
Out of phase by 180 degrees.

Array
A series of memory locations with a single name.

ArtNet
Trade name for freely available software to run Ethernet for lighting systems. Widely used by many manufacturers around the world.

Aspect Ratio
The ratio of the width to the height of a TV screen. Standard aspect ratio was 4:3; more recently wide-screen TV receivers offering 16:9 have become the standard format.

AutoCAD
Brand name of a range of computer software for design and drawings.

Autocue
Brand name of a teleprompter system.

AWG
American Wire Gauge.

Axial Profile
A hard edged luminaire where the lamp is placed concentrically within an ellipsoidal reflector. Also known as an ellipsoidal in the USA.

Backcloth
A painted background scenic cloth.

Backlight
A luminaire typically fixed directly behind a subject to improve separation of it from the backing, increasing the subject definition on camera.

Baffle
Louvered manual or motorised shutter that fits in front of a luminaire. Also term used to describe convection management plates which prevent light escaping from the body of a luminaire.

Bandwidth
The range of frequencies passed by a device or cable. This may be expressed as the range between the limits at which attenuation of -3dB below the maximum occurs.

Barndoor
A method of shuttering off unwanted light from a Fresnel spotlight comprising, usually, of four separately adjustable 'leaves' or doors. These doors may usually be rotated as one assembly to produce cuts to the light beam corresponding to the focus angle.

Baud
Unit of data transmission speed representing one change of data per second.

Baud Rate
Speed of data transmission; often but not necessarily equivalent to bits per second.

BBC PID
Abbreviation for the original British Broadcasting Corporation Planning and Installation Department. This has subsequently became part of BBC Resources as the Consultancy and Projects Division. Now owned by Siemens UK.

BCD
Binary Coded Decimal. Four bit or 4 wire system using weighted values of 1, 2, 4 and 8 to express numbers in the range of 0 to 9.

Bistable
An electronic circuit with two stable states, usually referring to 0 and 1. It is the basic element of counting in binary and of electronic memories.

Bit
A unit of data, a number of 'bits' make up a byte of data.

Blind
In lighting this refers to the creation or modification of a lighting cue without sending the information to the studio dimmers.

Blonde
Generic nme for a 2kW open-faced luminaire.

Boom
Vertical scaffolding pole (usually 48mm diameter) on which horizontal boom arms may be mounted, carrying luminaires (fixtures). Often used behind wings for side-lighting etc. Booms have a base plate (known in UK as a TANK TRAP) or stand at the bottom and are tied off to the grid or fly floor at the top (not always necessary for short booms). Booms can also be fixed to the rear of the proscenium arch (Pros. Boom) or hanging from the ends of lighting bars. Sometimes known in the US as a light tree. A light tree mounted upstage of a Tormentor is known as a Torm Tree.

Bps

Bits per second.

Braiding
A group of usually fine wires which are plaited together to form a flat cable or to act as a screen in co-axial or multicore cables.

Break
Time frame when data line is held off or 'low'.

Breakthrough
Unwanted signals appearing in a circuit from other circuits or devices.

Broad
A general illumination luminaire for fill applications traditionally 750 Watt now 500W, 800W or 1250 Watt.

Brown Out

A mains voltage reduction more common on 110 volt supplies, often leading to malfunctioning of mains powered equipment.

Buffer

1. Another name for a DMX distribution amplifier.
2. Electronic device in the signal path designed to pass or augment signals but to hold back unwanted or damaging signals.

Bug

A software error which causes an unintended result.

Bump Button

American term to describe a flash button where a channel or group of channels are instantly turned full on or off.

Byte

Number of bits of data, with DMX 8 bits of data equal one byte.

Cable Shield

This refers to the protective shield wound around data or other control cables. Typically this is connected to equipment ground at one or both ends to reduce interference.

Candela

Unit of luminous intensity.

CAT 5

Four twisted pair data cable with a typical bandwidth of 10 MHz.

CAT 5e

Four twisted pair data cable with a typical bandwidth of 100 MHz.

CAT 6

Four twisted pair data cable with a typical bandwidth of 200 MHz.

Catenary

In the lighting world this usually relates to an electrical feeder cable suspended at various points along its length allowing a connected object to be moved from one end to another without requiring disconnection. Another description used is festoon cabling to describe the same system. This is often used on track and barrel grid to link moveable bars to the central feeder trunking.

CDM Lamp

Trade name for a discharge lamp based on use of ceramic capsule metal halide technology.

Ceeform

The original manufacturer of a range of power connectors defined in England by the British Standard BS4343. The range has become an industry standard for 16A, 32A, 63A and 125 Amp single and three phase applications. Many manufacturers now produce such connectors including Ceeform, Garo, MK Electric, etc.

Channel
Best described as the control circuit on a lighting desk and its associated dimmer. These days this can be complicated if soft patching is employed. Here the control channel can be 'electronically patched' to control another dimmer or a group of dimmers.

Channel Controller
A set of controls specific to channel and intensity selection.

Channel Number
An identification number selected via a numeric keypad or via a specific fader.

Characteristic Impedance
Natural impedance in Ohms of an infinite length of cable.

Charge Coupled Device (CCD)
A semiconductor device along which stored information may be moved by charge transfer. Typically used in a TV camera as an image sensor in an array of elements in which charges are produced by light focused on its surface.

Checksum
A running binary addition producing a checksum digit at intervals. Used to check error in data, often for data received from storage devices.

Chip Camera
A video camera with a CCD image sensor.

Chocolate Block
A multi-pole strip connector.

Chroma
1. The component of a TV signal carrying the colour information.

2. Used to define the degree of colour saturation.

Chromakey
A television special effects technique in which areas of saturated blue or green in a foreground scene are replaced by a background picture from another source into which the foreground is electronically keyed.

CID Lamp
Abbreviation for a Compact Iodine Daylight discharge source with a colour temperature of 55000K.

Circuit Breaker
A re-settable electro-mechanical safety device used to replace the one-shot function of a fuse.

Class I
Electrical safety classification for a device that is connected to mains earth.

Class 2
Electrical safety classification for a device that is double insulated.

Clock (electronic)
A stable oscillator used for timing in digital systems

Closed Loop
In lighting, this definition is often applied to dimmers where it is defined as a feedback system in which the output result is fed back to be compared with the requirement defined by the input.

CMX
Digital protocol produced by Colortran in USA in 1980s.

Code
To transform information into a different form usually for more efficient storage or transmission e.g. BCD code.

Cold Mirror
A dichroic surface reflecting visible light but transmitting infra red radiation through

the glass so that it may be safely removed.

Colour Balance
The appearance of a colour image considered in terms of the ratio of its primary colour components.

Colour Bars
A video test waveform.

Colour Filter (filter, gel)
A transparent, usually plastic medium, that selectively absorbs defined areas of the visible spectrum.

Colour Frame
A metal or cardboard frame that slots into the front of a luminaire to carry a piece of colour filter or diffusion.

Colour Temperature
A method used to specify the colour of a source emitting light in a continuous spectrum. The temperature is defined in degrees Kelvin, with 1 degree Kelvin equal to absolute zero (-273oC). With TV lighting this is typically from 2600oK for a domestic tungsten lamp to 5700 oK for a discharge light source. The lower the temperature the more red the colour, the higher the temperature the greater percentage of blue colour.

Colour Wash
A group of soft-edged luminaires focused on a defined area with a specific colour.

Colour Wheel.
Early form of colour changer where 5 or 6 filters were inserted into a metal frame fitted into the colour runner of a luminaire. The 'wheel' was then rotated continuously by means of

motor. No facilities were provided to select a colour.

Common Mode Rejection
The ability of balanced or differential inputs to reject in-phase signals

Condenser Lens
A system of lenses and a reflector that enables light to be collected and concentrated into a defined beam. Similar to a lens system in a film or slide projector.

Cone
A circular tube placed in front of a Fresnel spotlight to reduce the size of the light beam. Also called a 'snoot'.

Console
A name given to a lighting or sound desk or the furniture into which control surfaces are mounted. Originally a Light Console was the first control instrument which permitted live artistic expression by a single person.

Contactor
An electro-mechanical switch operated by a coil. Used in lighting systems for remote control of dimmer power supplies, emergency power off systems and for console or switch operated direct supplies.

Continuity
The announcements made between programmes or the correct sequence and matching of actions and setting between successive scenes in a TV production. In lighting continuity (using a single camera) the matching of the 'look' from shot to shot.

Cool Light
Generic term to describe a light source where much of the projected heat of the lamp is removed by use of either a dichroic glass reflector for a tungsten or discharge source or by use of fluorescent light sources – ETC Source 4 and Strand SL are examples of cool lights.

Correction Filter
A piece of transparent material where the chemical composition is such that it will partially or entirely convert daylight to tungsten or tungsten to daylight by absorbing unwanted frequencies and passing the required frequencies.

Coving
A concave structure sited between the studio floor and the lower hem of a cyclorama cloth to give the impression of a seamless joint.

Crab
Shifting a camera sideways.

Cross Barrel
Used between lighting hoists or lighting bars to span between adjacent bars to provide a better luminaire position.

Crossfade
A change in lighting output where one lighting picture completely replaces another.

CSI Lamp
Compact Source Iodide, a particular metal halide lamp with a colour temperature of approximately 4300°K.

CSO
Colour Separation Overlay – see chromakey.

Cue
An identification given to a change in the lighting setup.

Cue Number
An identification given to a stored piece of data in a lighting console. Same as memory or file number.

Current Drive
Early analogue control format where the control desk sank current into dimmer channel usually in micro-amperes.

Cutaway
A non-critical, non dialogue shot used to link into principal action in scenes shot on a single camera.

Cyan
A secondary colour which is the complementary colour of red.

Cyclorama
A smooth and continuous opaque matt fabric or solid backing mounted around the periphery of a performance space to provide a surface onto which light can be directed to create different settings or the illusion of infinity.

D54
An analogue protocol created by Strand Lighting allowing 384 channels to be sent down a twisted pair cable

DALI
Stands for Digital Addressable Lighting Interface and is a digital data protocol lighting in buildings, widely used with fluorescent sources.

Data Complement
Negative half of the DMX signal often called DMX -, with DMX connected to pin 2 of a 5 pin XLR connector.

Datasafe
Trade name for a range of data cables.

Data True
Positive half of the DMX signal often called DMX +, with DMX connected to pin 3 of a 5 pin XLR connector.

Daylight
This is the illumination provided by natural sun and sky or by an artificial source with a

colour temperature of between 5000°K and 6000°K.

Daylight Filter
A correction blue glass or filter which will convert tungsten 3200°K light to daylight 5600°K.

DBO
Dead Black Out – usually fitted to a lighting console to provide instant switch off of the signal feeding all the dimmers.

DC (dc)
Direct Current.

Demultiplexer (demux)
In lighting terms a device which converts DMX data into an analogue signal.

Density
Measure of light attenuation.

Depth of Field
The range of object distances behind a camera within which objects remain in focus.

Depth of Focus
In an optical system this is defined as the range of distances behind the lens within which the image remains in focus.

Diaphragm
In lighting this usually refers to a variable iris accessory used to control the size of a light beam from a profile spotlight.

Dichroic
A device having selective reflection and transmission for radiation of certain wavelengths. A dichroic filter or mirror will transmit a given spectrum range and reflect others dependent upon the dichroic material and the angle at which light passes through it. Used to reflect away unwanted colours or heat, instead of absorbing it.

Diffraction
Interference effect produced as a result of light passing through very small spaces between opaque obstruction.

Diffuser
Spun glass fibre or woven textiles or sheets of frosted material that when inserted in front of a light source softens the beam, reducing potentially unwanted shadows.

Dimmer
An electrical device, usually electronic in operation, that controls the power reaching a lamp, thus allowing the intensity to be controlled.

Dimmer Curve
A means of controlling the relationship in a dimmer between output voltage and control input. Different curves are required for studio cameras or theatre.

DIN
German National Standards Organisation – Deutsches Institut für Normung.

Diode
Electronic component which allows transmission of data in one direction only.

Dip
Metal trap in the floor for electrical and data sockets

Dipless Crossfade
When the same channels are used at the same level in two different lighting states and

do not change as one set up is cross-faded into the next state.

Director
Generally the person responsible for the creative interpretation and look of a programme or theatre show. In TV the director usually sits in the production control room directing the technical operations staff, camera persons and generally managing the programme output.

Dispersion
Separation of light into its constituent parts such as white light passing through a prism.

DMX
A digital multiplexed protocol used to send large numbers of control channels over 2

pair data cable.

DMX512 1990
Was the current DMX standard until end of 2004. Most products purchased in 2004/2005 still contain this version of the protocol.

DMX512-A 2004
Now the current standard of DMX being issued as a world standard late in 2004.

Dock
Area used for temporary storage of scenery.

Dolly
Movable platform onto which a camera can be mounted to follow action.

Downstage Left
On the front of the stage, actor's left looking at the audience.

Downstage Right
On the front of the stage, actor's right looking at the audience.

Dowser
A mechanical shutter, usually on a followspot, to cut off the light beam.

Downstage
The area closest to the audience or to a camera in a TV studio.

Downtime
The time a piece of equipment is inoperative due to maintenance or the time a studio is out

of commission due to the previous show being removed prior to a new production being rigged.

Drapes
Another word for curtains.

Drop Arm
A piece of lighting hardware allowing a luminaire to be suspended from a lighting suspension point. They are available in various fixed lengths for adding together or in various adjustable lengths.

Duty Cycle
A method of defining the period of continuous operation a piece of equipment is designed to operate within. With lighting systems this can relate to dimmers, discharge lamps, telescopes and self-climbing hoists. This can be used to check the quality of the product and the suitability for use in lighting systems.

Earth Loop
A fault condition affecting signals passed between devices where circulating currents in multiple earth paths introduce unwanted currents. Often cured by use of isolated devices such as splitters in a DMX system.

EBU
Abbreviation for European Broadcasting Union, an international organisation of national broadcasters.

ECG
Abbreviation for electronic control gear usually running at high frequency widely used for control of fluorescent lamps.

Edge Triggered
A monostable or bistable which is triggered by a specific direction of change in the input state, rather than with the actual input 1 or 0. In other words triggered by the waveforms rising edge.

eDMX
Trade name for radio DMX system.

EIA
Electronic Industries Association, a US standards body.

EIB
European Installation Bus developed by Europe based companies primarily Siemens to enable networked control of lighting and other systems.

Eggcrate
A device used on a softlight to control the light by means of a lattice of cross baffles. The edge light is restricted by the baffles, enabling a degree of edge control to be provided particularly along the top and bottom edges. They tend to be used on tungsten softlights,

with honeycomb or parabolic V-blade louvers used on fluorescent softlights.

ELCB
Earth Leakage Circuit Breaker - early residual current protective device now replaced: see RCD.

ENG
Electronic News Gathering – recording of news events by means of lightweight battery-powered television cameras instead of film cameras.

EPROM
Erasable Programmable Read Only Memory.

EEPROM
Electrically Erasable Programmable Read Only Memory.

Error Checking
Method by which a control protocol can check the integrity of the data being sent down a line. Ethernet is an error checking protocol, DMX does not include this facility.

ESTA
Entertainment Services and Technology Association of USA. Trade association often leading with new standards and training programmes.

Ethernet
Ethernet was the name given to a manufacturers' specification developed by Digital Equipment Corporation, Intel Corporation and Xerox. The standard covering Ethernet technology was developed by the IEEE standards committee in 1983, later adopted as IEEE standard 802.3.

Exposure Meter
An instrument for measuring the brightness of surface or intensity of light incident upon a scene to be recorded by a camera.

Extension Bar
Typically comprises a length of barrel that can be pulled out from the end of the support barrel on a hoist to provide a small increase in distance for greater control of a luminaire suspension point.

Fade Up
Gradual increase in light intensity.

Fade Down
Gradual reduction in light intensity down to zero level.

Fader
A device used in lighting as a visual and physical means to control the light output from a dimmer. In reality this device usually comprises of a variable resistor where the change in resistance, as the fader is adjusted, is measured and used to control the dimmer power control circuitry.

Fade Time
The time taken from the beginning of a lighting change to the completion of the change.

Fag Packet Sketch
Jargon for a free hand sketch usually on a piece of paper to hand.

Fall Off
The gradual reduction in light intensity from the centre of a cyclorama cloth or screen to the corners and edges.

Fill Light
In TV a softlight that is used to 'fill in' the gaps and shadows created by keylights. Typical natural fill light is the sky. These sources help to reduce shadows created by key lights.

Flag (French)
In lighting this is a black metal plate usually mounted on the arm of the luminaire that is used to create a sharp cut-off of unwanted light in areas the barndoors cannot reach.

Flare
Scatter of light in a lens which creates an undesirable image on camera often caused by a back light or a light just out of the frame at the side of the picture.

Flat
A term to define a piece of scenery usually made by stretching fabric over a wooden frame.

Flip Flop
A mechanical system for carrying cables down onto a lighting structure or self -climbing hoist. Comprises a series of hinged trays that open out or close up as a suspension system. Can be used to feed control data to moveable lighting bars.

Floodlight (also called Flood)
A fixture where the light source and reflector combination are the only means of controlling the light output, usually produced in two versions – Symmetric and Asymmetric. The Symmetric units have the lamp mounted in the centre of the reflector with equal distribution above and below. The asymmetric versions have the lamp mounted towards one end of the reflector directing light in one direction. These units are typical for cyclorama or groundrow applications or for internally reflected softlights.

Floor Manager
The person in the studio responsible for organising the studio and performers – the equivalent of a stage manager in a theatre except that the floor manager is relaying the directors instructions (via talkback) to the artists.

Floor Paint
Special scenery paint that can be applied to studio floors with special rollers to artificially create scenic floors. The paint can be removed by application of a water-based cleaning machine. Floor paint can represent carpet, parquet flooring tiles or simply plain black, grey or any other solid colour.

Floor Plan
Scale drawing of studio floor showing layout of set pieces, access doors, cyclorama and other show or fixed items.

F number (f stop)
The relative aperture of a lens diaphragm calculated by dividing its focal length by its diameter.

Focal Length
The distance from the rear focal point of a lens to the point at which light rays, from an object an infinite distance from the lens, form the sharpest image.

FOH
Front of house – area occupied by audience.

Followspot
A high power profile spotlight with a narrow focusing angle enabling illumination of a performer from a long distance or at high intensity. Typically 5 to 15 degrees are the normal adjustment angles for theatre applications although wide angle versions, for shorter throw applications, are manufactured for TV applications. DMX controlled versions have been produced.

French Brace
A strut used to support pieces of scenery.

Fresnel Lens
A stepped lens formed of concentric rings producing a hard edged light in TV terms but a soft edge in Theatre terms. Named in 1820 after its inventor, Augustin Jean Fresnel.

Gaffer
Senior lighting electrician in a TV or film studio or on location.

Gallery
Studio control room usually comprising production, sound and lighting all housed in acoustically separated areas.

Gate
1.   Slot at focal point of profile spotlight that accepts irises, gobos and other focusable accessories.
2.   In electronics an element of digital logic, e.g. AND, OR, NAND, NOR or EXCLUSIVE-OR.

GHz
Gigahertz – a measure of frequency denoting it is measured in a factor of 10^9.

Gobo (USA - Pattern)
A metallic device that when inserted into the gate of a luminaire will shape the light output. Normally this means that a pattern is etched out of the metal to project a defined image. Alternatively, proprietary standard designs are produced to suit most manufacturers' profile luminaires.

Grade I
Very high quality CRT monitor provided for lighting director to balance camera pictures.

Grandmaster
The final control in a lighting console that controls the entire output from the console. Typically comprises a calibrated fader or digital control wheel.

Grey Scale Chart
A test chart showing graded scales from black to white used for line up of cameras and picture monitors.

Grid
Framework located above a stage or studio floor allowing lights and scenery to be suspended.

Ground
Electrical connection to mains earth.

Grounding
Another word to describe connecting a piece of powered or passive equipment to mains earth potential. Data signals are usually not grounded however the case of the equipment is connected to mains earth to comply with electrical standards.

Ground Loop
A fault condition affecting signals passed between devices where circulating currents in multiple ground paths introduce unwanted currents.

Groundrow
Luminaires mounted on the studio floor to uplight a cyclorama cloth or items of scenery.

Half Wave
An electronic circuit that operates on the positive or the negative cycle of an alternating current but not on both. Faulty dimmers often produce only half light intensity when the power control section fails in a Half Wave condition.

Harmonic
Frequencies that are a multiple of the fundamental frequency.

Harmonic Distortion
The unwanted generation of harmonics that show up in lighting systems due to the use of dimmers.

Hard Light
A type of light that produces shadows typified by the sun on a clear day. These luminaires are profile's in stage lighting and Fresnel's or profiles in terms of TV lighting.

HDTV
A new picture standard that produces very high quality pictures based on using more than 1000 lines of information per picture. Different standards are currently proposed in Europe, USA and Japan.

Heat Filter and Heat Glass
A clear glass used to absorb or reflect infra red radiation whilst passing visible light. Often used in followspots and moving lights to keep luminaire gates, shutters, dowsers and other devices cool.

Hexadecimal
Method of expressing the 16 possible states of 4 binary bits. These states are expressed a a single character 0,1,2,3,4,5,6,7,8,9,A,B,C,D,E or F. Eight-bit bytes are dealt with as two four bit quantities, e.g. A7 hex = 10100111 binary.

Highest Takes Precedence (HTP)
A term usually applied to control systems where the same channel is under control by more than one source with the resulting output level being the highest setting of the two controls. For example, if channel one is set at level 5 in fader 1 and channel one is set at level 7 in fader 2 the highest level set by fader 2 will take precedence.

HMI
A discharge lamp with a colour temperature equivalent to daylight, namely 5600°K. Trade name for a Metal Halide lamp.

Hot Spot
An area of excessive brightness in an otherwise balanced lighting state or the peak of excessive brightness seen in a Fresnel lens or any other light source.

House Light
Lights that provide illumination for the public area of a performance venue. In a TV studio these are often called Working lights.

HRC
High Rupture Capacity – usually applied to fuses. Particularly useful on dimmers as they handle large short-term surge currents without failing.

Hub
This is a mains powered unit with a number of ports used to connect several Ethernet cabled zones.

Hue
The attribute by which a colour may be defined within the visible spectrum.

IEC
International Electrotechnical Commission.

IEE
Institution of Electrical Engineers in the UK.

IEEE
Institute of Electrical and Electronic Engineers.

IGBT
Insulated Gate Bipolar Transistor.

Illumination
A measurement of the amount of light falling on a surface. It is measured in lux equating to lumens per square metre.

Impedance
Resistance to flow of current.

Insulation Displacement Connector (IDC)
A form of connecting system where wires are terminated without removing their insulation. The connector displaces the insulation to form a good electrical connection.

I/O
Abbreviation for Input/Output.

Iris – camera
A mechanical device that is used to control the amount of light passing through the camera lens onto the photo sensitive camera pick up devices.

Iris – spotlight
A mechanical device inserted into the gate of a profile luminaire comprising of a set of concentric leaves that can be opened or closed to vary the size of the light beam.

ISO
International Organisation for Standardisation.

Isolating Transformer
A transformer with separate primary and secondary windings to provide isolation and safety usually from the mains.

Isolated Splitter
Another name for a DMX distribution amplifier fitted with electrical isolation between the input DMX signal and each of the distribution amplifier outputs.

K96
Digital protocol for 480 control channels produced by Kliegl in USA.

Keylight
The principal light source revealing an object's shape.

Kicker
A luminaire used to produce a high light effect in back lighting applications from a shallow angle or even below.

kHz
Kilohertz – a measure of frequency denoting it is measured in a factor of 10^3.

kW - Kilowatt
Equal to 1000 watts.

kVA
Abbreviation for kilo Volt Amperes. Often used in lighting systems to define the ratings of transformers used to feed low voltage lamps.

Lamp
A hot light source that converts electrical energy into light energy, referred to as a 'bulb' in the UK and 'globe' in USA.

LAN
Local Area Network – a method of connecting computers together within a restricted area.

Lantern
A theatre term referring to a studio lighting unit, fixture or luminaire. In film and TV usually means a spherical fabric diffuser traditionally made of China silk or Japanese paper around a photoflood or other small source.

Latch
In electronics, a bistable used to hold a state from one sampling instant to the next.

Latest Takes Precedence (LTP)
On a lighting console where the latest action in time succeeds. For example, if we select channel 11 at 8 and then later we select channel 11 at 6 in another part of the console outputting to the dimmers, the output will be at intensity level 6. The opposite of highest takes precedence and the normal mode on most TV memory consoles.

LED
Light Emitting Diode Often used as indicator lamps on electronic equipment. Comprises of a semi-conductor junction which when conducting emits visible light.

Lighting Barrel and Lighting Bar
Usually a 48.3mm outside diameter bar (tube) from which luminaires are suspended.

Lighting Console
Device for controlling the intensity of luminaires by sending signals to dimmers.

Lighting Plot
Plan of the luminaire layout for a production drawn by the lighting director in television and lighting designer in theatrical lighting. In theatre it tabulates all the different successive lighting states that comprise the cues.

Lighting Rig
A design of lighting to light a production or the lighting system installed within a studio in its entirety.

Lime
Jargon for a followspot.

Limit
In terms of lighting, this is a facility often provided on dimmers whereby the upper and lower output voltages can be calibrated to prolong lamp life at the upper setting and to improve lamp turn-on times at the lower setting.

Live
1.   In TV a description for television pictures being broadcast as they are seen directly

by the camera as opposed to recorded.
2. Describes information processed as it occurs in real time.

Lock-up
In a micro-processor device this is when the processor gets stuck in a state or a loop of states and 'freezes'. The system usually needs to be reset to get out of this condition. With Ethernet this usually means de-powering.

Logarithm
Of a number, the power of a fixed number (called the 'base', usually 10) that equals the number.

Logic
In electronics an arrangement of gates and other circuit elements to perform a specified task.

Lumen
The unit of luminous flux or amount of light emitted per second from a lamp or projector.

Luminaire
Lighting unit in a studio giving some control of size, shape or colour of the lux from the lamp or lamps within it. Colloquially known as light, lantern, instrument (USA), fixture (USA), generic and fitting.

LUT
Look Up Table, fixed data or addresses used within a computer programme.

Lux
The metric unit of measurement of the incident light arriving on a defined surface. This replaced the old measuring system of foot candles (1 foot candle is equal to 10.76 lux).

LVCR
Lighting and Vision Control Room.

M & E
Mechanical and Electrical engineers.

Macro
A function on a lighting console allowing a collection of separate functions or key strokes to be grouped together to be controlled by one action.

Magenta
A secondary colour which is the complementary colour of green.

Manchester Code
A low speed data protocol often used to control office based lighting schemes.

Masking
Typically curtains or pieces of scenery used to hide unwanted areas of the stage or studio that might be seen by the audience or camera.

MCB
Abbreviation of Miniature Circuit Breaker used for protection of electrical circuits. Many types are available. Within the lighting world C class inductive rated MCBs are common due to the inductive nature of cold lamps.

MCCB
Moulded Case Circuit Breaker. Basically a higher capacity version of a miniature circuit breaker.

Merger
Electronic powered device to combine together two DMX signals into one composite DMX signal. Often fitted with offset to allow channel numbers to be 'added' together.

Metal Halide Lamp
A compact mercury arc with metal halide additions, enclosed in a quartz envelope.

MIDI
Musical Instrument Digital Interface. A protocol allowing musical instruments to be connected to lighting control equipment.

MHz
Megahertz – a measure of frequency denoting it is measured in a factor of 10^6.

Microsecond
One millionth part of a second, denoting a factor of 10^{-6}.

Millisecond
One thousandth part of a second, denoting a factor of 10^{-3}.

Mizar
A very small Fresnel of 300 or 500 Watt.

Monochrome
Picture without colour information (Black and White).

Monostable
An electronic circuit element, with one stable and one unstable state. If triggered into the unstable state it will regain the stable state after a defined period.

MOSFET
Metal Oxide Field Effect Transistor.

Movefade
A change from one lighting state to another where channels not present in the new state are unchanged, unlike a crossfade where such channels will fade out.

MSB
Most Significant Bit, in a digital word.

MSR Lamp.
Stands for Medium Source Rare Earth and is a discharge lamp widely used in all forms of

theatre and TV discharge powered lighting fixtures.

Multicores (multi's)
generic term for a cable with a large number of cores used to carry lighting control, audio signals and, with a suitable voltage rating, loads from dimmers to luminaires. Often may get called Socapex or Litton or Harting referring to the name of the connector fitted at either end.

Multiplexer (mux)
In lighting terms a device which converts from an analogue signal to a DMX signal.

NAND gate
A gate which gives an output of zero (low) when all of its inputs are set to 1 (high)

Nanosecond
One thousandth part of a microsecond, denoting a factor of 10^{-9}.

Netbus
Trade name for a remote programming and fault reporting system used with dimmers.

Ni-Cad
Trade name for Nickel Cadmium rechargeable cell or battery of cells.

Node
Any device communicating with another device on an Ethernet network. All nodes have a network address. Hubs, concentrators and repeaters are all part of the network but are not nodes. In a lighting system a typical node is a lighting console or remote video monitor.

Non-Dim
A direct supply circuit that is only switched on and off, usually controlled via a relay or contactor. Some can also be controlled from the lighting console with a suitable interface.

NOR gate
A gate which will produce an output state of zero (low) when any of its inputs are set to logic 1 (high).

North Light
Hot, heavy and large soft light source.

NTSC
National Television Standards Committee – TV standard for the USA and Japan based on 525 lines, 60 fields and 30 frames per second.

OB
Outside Broadcast.

Offset
Name given in DMX merge units to a programming function allowing one of the two input channels to be re-numbered relative to their original numbering allowing channels to be 'added' together.

Ohm - Ω
Unit of electrical resistance defined by Ohms Law: Volts = Amperes (current) x Ohms (resistance).

Opto-isolator
A combination of a Light Emitting Diode (LED) and a phototransistor in a sealed electronic type package.

OR gate
A gate where an output of 1 (high) is produced if any input is set to 1 (high).

Oscilloscope
A cathode ray tube device used to display and measure signals, typically gives a graphical display of voltage versus time.

PAL
Phase Alternate Line – TV standard for most of Europe with 625 lines.

Pan
A term used to define horizontal movement - typical on a pole operated luminaire allowing the luminaires horizontal position to be adjusted remotely.

Pantograph
A mechanical device for raising and lowering luminaires from the grid or lighting structure. Made up of a number of (usually) aluminium members joined together in a cross arm format working on the lazy tongs principle. The central pivot point allows the cross arms to open and close. Units are usually of the manual pull down type, although motorised versions are also available.

PAT
Portable Appliance Test. Mandatory periodic test of all portable electrical equipment.

Patch Panel
Generally a wall or equipment bay mounted facility where the user can select which input is connected to which output. These are used in lighting systems for DMX and Ethernet distribution using signal connectors. Other versions are produced rated at mains voltages allowing dimmer outputs to be patched to lighting grid outlets connected to luminaires.

Pathpoint®
Trade name for an active Ethernet connection point.

PCR
Production Control Room – the workplace of the Secretary or Production Assistant, the Director, the Vision Mixer and texter and the Technical Manager.

Phase Control
Method used by most types of dimmer to alter the point at which a power control semiconductor, such as a thyristor or triac, switch on. The switching is relative to the phase of the incoming power supply.

Phase Shift
Movement in time resulting in points of a waveform being earlier or later than the corresponding points of a reference waveform.

Photometer
Measuring device for luminous intensity of luminaires.

Phototransistor
Transistor able to convert light into an electrical signal.

Picosecond
One thousandth part of a nanosecond, denoting a factor of 10^{-12}.

Pile Wind
A type of winding mechanisms found on winches where the suspension cable is wound on top of itself via cable guides.

PLA
Programmable Logic Array.

PLASA
Professional Lighting and Sound Association of UK

Playback
Part of a lighting console where a previously stored memory, cue or file can be controlled and fed into the output of the console.

Plumbicon
A trade name for an obsolete vidicon camera tube using lead oxide.

Polarity
A positive or negative electrical state.

Pole Operation
A remote control mechanism for controlling the electrical and mechanical controls, such as pan, tilt and focus of luminaires by means of a operating pole.

Potentiometer
A variable resistor where the wiper and the two ends are employed as a potential divider.

Power Factor
The phase relationship between voltage and current in an alternating current circuit. Ideally this should be unity with this representing a non reactive load. Often power factor correction capacitors are added to dimmer installations to produce a near unity power factor.

Practical
Any light source or electrical equipment provided by the scenic designer which is safe enough to be used by the performer as part of the lighting design. Normally only ovens, hobs and vacuum cleaners are controlled by performers.

Preset
A facility provided on lighting consoles whereby a lighting picture can be created

internally within the console, and can be adjusted and previewed by the operator before connecting this to the dimmers for control of lighting levels. Normally under the control of a fader lever. A console may have only 1 or 2 playbacks but many presets. Another word for this in modern consoles is Submasters.

Primary Colours
The essential components in a colour reproduction system from which all available hues can be produced by mixing. In a three colour additive process, such as a colour TV tube, they are red, green and blue. In a subtractive process such as colour film they are cyan, magenta and yellow (CMY).

Producer
The person in overall charge of planning, artistic content and financial control of a production or TV programme.

Profile
A hard-edged light source where the beam size is governed by the luminaire gate and the diameter of the projection lens. Fixed focus and zoom focus versions exist. In all cases the resultant image is a function of the lens or relationship between the two lenses. The resulting beam may be shaped by insertion of metal plates or shutters into the luminaire gate to interrupt the light output. Condenser Optic profiles offer the sharpest edges and cleanest projection possibilities.

PROM
Programmable Read-Only Memory.

Protocol
A procedure agreed upon, ideally by agencies or standards bodies, wishing to communicate.

Pull up
A component in an electronic circuit to ensure a 'high' state in the absence of any active device dictating a 'low; condition, is usually a resistor.

Pup
A small Fresnel, typically rated at 1000 or 1200 watts.

PVC
Polyvinyl Chloride

Quartz Halogen – Quartz Iodine
The definition of a lamp manufactured using a quartz glass envelope containing a tungsten filament surrounded by halogen gas. Most TV studio luminaires are fitted with these types of lamp. As the quartz glass absorbs perspiration the envelope should not be touched by the human hand.

RAM
Random Access Memory – memory that can have any byte of its data written in, or read out in any order.

Redhead
Generic name for 800 or 1000 Watt simple open faced focusing floodlight with rotating barndoors.

RCD
Residual Current Device, a safety device which disconnects line power if a residual current flow occurs to earth.

RDM
Abbreviation for Remote Device Management officially an ANSI standard from August 2006. ANSI E1.20 (RDM) is an extension to DMX512 that allows for Bi-directional communication on the primary pair of a DMX512 link. This allows for a controller or piece of test equipment to intelligently discover other RDM enabled devices on the link such as moving lights or dimmer racks and manage them remotely. This includes the ability to remotely set the DMX512 Starting Address, querying the devices for Error or Stats Messages, and access to most any configuration setting that would normally be accomplished from the front panel of the device itself.

Reflector
Silvered mirror or polished metal surface used to collect and bounce light usually through a lens.

Refraction
Deflection of a beam of light on passing through one medium to the next.

Retriggerable
Describes a monostable which can additionally be triggered to remain in its unstable state for a further time period.

Return
A 'return' describes data being sent to a patch bay from a remote location.

RGB
Primary colours and format of a television system waveform – Red, Green and Blue.

Rigging
The setting up of lighting equipment in a studio or exterior location.

Risetime
The time taken for the leading edge of the output current waveform to rise from 10% to 90% conduction angle with a fully-rated load connected to the output.

RJ45
8 pin data connector widely used in the computer and telecommunications industry. Standard lighting connector for Ethernet connection.

r.m.s
Abbreviation of root mean square – is an effective way of measuring an alternating current or voltage taking the waveform into account. r.m.s. values are used when the waveform has become distorted and is a measurement of its ability to produce the same heating effect in a resistance as a direct current and directly relates to the power in watts.

ROM
Read Only Memory used for storing non-varying data or instructions.

Rostra or Rostrum
A platform used in a studio or in the theatre to provide elevation of performers, audience or equipment above floor level.

Rostrum Camera
Typically a still or video camera mounted on a vertical camera bench with highly calibrated controls for focus and zooming in on objects located on the camera bench. The bench is manually moved or motorised without affecting the geometry or camera focus. Method used to take video pictures from newspaper cuttings, still photographs etc.

RS232 – EIA232
An Electronic Industries Association, a US standards body, specification for interchange of data normally between a computer and a peripheral device close by.

RS422, RS423
Codings defining the control signals and types of connector required to provide common interfaces between electronic units. **RS422** is a differential 5 volt system on two wires. **RS432** allows for a high impedance state to allow more than one sending device to be on circuit.

Rupture Current
The current at which a device will completely fail and no longer operate correctly. Typically relates to electrical protective devices and is a measure of their capacity to deal with major electrical fault conditions.

RX
Abbreviation for a receiver.

S20
Analogue multiplexing protocol

Safety Bond
A steel wire rope bond that is attached around a luminaire and the suspension bar to provide complete protection should the hanging clamp or bracket fail. Some users require these bonds to be permanently attached to the luminaire body rather than be simply passed through the yoke.

Sample and Hold
A circuit element which samples the instantaneous amplitude of an electrical waveform and retains (holds) the value.

Saturated Rig
A term given to a lighting system where a uniform distribution of luminaires are provided on a square metre basis across the working area thus reducing the need to physically move luminaires around.

Sawtooth
An electrical waveform which has a slow change in amplitude followed by a rapid return or visa versa.

Scanner
Outside broadcast production vehicle.

Scene Dock or Dock
Area adjoining the stage or studio where scenery is temporarily stored.

Scoop
A general fill lighting luminaire shaped like a scoop, typically used in the USA in twos and fours.

SCR
Silicon Controlled Rectifier - thyristor

Screened Cable
A central conductor, or a number of conductors, insulated from an external screen formed by copper braiding or lapping or flexible metal.

Scrim
A wire mesh placed in front of a luminaire to reduce the resulting intensity of the whole or selected portion of the light beam.

Scroller
Jargon for a motorised colour changer controlled by DMX where motors are used to drive rolls of colour filter across an open aperture.

Scroll Wind
A type of winding mechanism where the suspension cable is wound on around a large spirally grooved drum side by side.

SECAM
Séquence Couleur avec Mémoire – TV standard from France and the USSR.

Semaphore Colour Changer.
Early form of selecting colour by remote control. Usually comprised of four motorised plates with colour filter inserted into a frame. Remote switch box could select any one of the four colours by low voltage control. Manufactured by CCT, Furse and Strand Lighting in the UK.

Send
An abbreviation in patching to define a circuit that sends data from a patch panel.

Serial Communication.
A data communication scheme needing only one wire (and return) where data is sent one bit at a time.

Set
The stage or studio floor area with scenery where the production is to be staged.

Sightlines / Sight Lines
A series of lines drawn on plan and section to show how much of the stage can be seen by the extreme seating positions in the auditorium.

Sine Wave
A simple waveform varying in a harmonic fashion.

Slave
A unit designed to function only as ordered by a 'master' unit.

Slew Rate
Rate of change of voltage.

SMX
Digital lighting protocol produced by Strand Lighting Ltd, never universally adopted.

S/N
Abbreviation for signal to noise ratio.

Softlight
A luminaire designed to produce a very soft and diffused light without creating hard shadows. Used in conjunction with Key lights to produce a balanced picture. The sky would be defined as a good softlight.

Software
The programme of instructions which the hardware of a computer or micro-processor obeys.

Sparks
Jargon for an electrician.

Spider
Jargon for an adapter converting from a Multiway connector to a number of single connectors.

Spike
A short pulse superimposed on another electrical signal such as a switching transient carried through the mains supply,

Splitter
Another name for a DMX distribution amplifier.

Spotlight
A traditional name for a profile luminaire or any light producing a narrow beam with a defined edge.

Square Wave
Electrical waveform switching virtually instantaneously between two voltage levels, with the on-off 'ratio' not necessarily of equal duration.

Stage Left
On the actor's left looking at the audience.

Stage Right
On the actor's right looking at the audience.

Stage Weight
Stackable heavy weight with hand grip used for stabilising scenery braces and flats or at the base of cyclorama cloths to provide tension.

Stand
A device usually comprising of a tripod base with fixed feet or wheeled castors on to which a luminaire can be fixed to raise it above floor level.

Start Bit
The first element in serial communication preceding the first data bit.

Stepper Motor
A type of motor which rotates in small but fixed teps at any of which its position can be held.

Stop Bit(s)
In serial data transmission, the period or periods of equal duration to the data element which terminate a block of data. They ensure enough time is provided to be ready for the next start bit.

STP
Shielded twisted pair cable, usually a Category cable with an outer shield.

Strike
1.   To dismantle and remove set or props.
2.   To light an arc lamp

Strobe
Electronically controlled flash light widely used in theatre and entertainment complexes. To be used with care and warnings if the public are invited to the performance.

Supertrooper
Trade name for a very large followspot produced by Strong Entertainment Lighting in USA.

SWC
Trade name for a system-wide control system for a network dimming system.

SWG
Abbreviation for Standard Wire Gauge

SWL
Abbreviation for Safe Working Load - defining the capacity that a lighting barrel or hoist or other suspension device can safely be supported by the specified structure.

Telescope
A suspension device made from a steel wire rope suspension cable passing through retractable tubes that when manually wound or motorised can be used to raise or lower a luminaire.

Terminator
A load inserted at the end of a transmission line to prevent the signal from bouncing back.

Three Phase
A three or four wire means of distributing AC electricity power supplies with the waveform in each of the three wires 120° out of phase. The fourth wire is the neutral in a star system

TIA
Telecommunications Industry Association – USA based trade association responsible for cable specification and standards.

Tilt
A term used to define rotational movement on a horizontal axis typically on a pole operated luminaire, allowing the luminaires vertical aim to be adjusted remotely.

Tormentors
Narrow masking flats adjacent and sometimes at right angles to the proscenium arch. Named because they mask the audience from being able to see into the wings. Often used in addition to a teaser, this being the first border behind the pros.

Toroidal Transformer
High efficiency transformer characterised by its circular shape and immunity to, and low production of, external magnetic fields.

Transmitter
A device which sends information.

Tungsten Halogen Lamp
A lamp consisting of a tungsten filament in usually a quartz glass envelope containing halogen gas to stop internal blackening of the envelope due to migration of tungsten from the filament. This type of lamp offers a higher degree of efficiency compared to other types.

Trunion
The primary suspension arm of the luminaire, also called the yoke or stirrup.

Truss
An alloy framework made up in a latticework with cross bracing to form a structure from which lighting equipment can be rigged.

Turnkey
Supplying a complete system, self contained and ready to use.

TX
Abbreviation for a transmitter.

UART
Universal Asynchronous Receiver-Transmitter. An integrated circuit for serial/parallel signal conversion and visa versa.

Unbalanced
Referring to a two-wire circuit one side of which is operating at or near ground potential.

Up stage
Performing area furthest from the audience or camera.

Upstage Left
At the rear of the stage, actor's left looking at the audience.

Upstage Right
At the rear of the stage, actor's right looking at the audience.

UPS
Abbreviation for an Uninterruptible Power Supply.

USITT
United States Institute of Theatre Technology, a well respected organisation that has made a significant impact on the entertainment industry world-wide through its working practice and standards committees.

UTP
Abbreviation for Unshielded Twisted Pair cable used in Ethernet network systems.

V
Abbreviation for a volt

VAR
Vision Apparatus Room.

Vectorscope
A piece of electronic test equipment displaying chrominance in a polar form such that saturated complimentary colours appear diametrically opposite, with white in the centre.

Vidicon
Camera tube operating on the photo resistive principle. These types of cameras have now been replaced with charge coupled device (CCD) cameras.

Vision Mixer
1. Electronic device for mixing and cutting together video pictures. Often contain a wide variety of special effects that may be added or superimposed on to the picture.
2. The person operating the mixer.

Voltage Drop
The loss of electrical energy when a current flows along a cable or through a device, when measured between the input and the output.

Voltage Insertion Loss
Typically the voltage difference between the input voltage to a dimmer or other piece of lighting control equipment and the output voltage when measured with a true root mean square voltmeter – similar to Voltage Drop.

VPLT
The Professional Lighting and Sound Association of Germany.

VTR
Video Tape Recorder.

W
Abbreviation for a watt, unit of electrical power.

Waveform
A presentation of the varying amplitude of a signal in relation to time.

White Balance
Normally an automatic system that ensures the correct colour rendition of the camera achieved by pointing the camera at a white surface illuminated by a typical light.

Wings
1.   The out of view areas usually to the sides of the acting area.
2.   Scenery standing where the acting area joins these technical areas.

Working Light (Workers)
Term given to identify task lighting within a theatre or technical area totally separate from the house or production lighting. Working light should be energy efficient as these lights remain on for long periods of time. Modern systems may include passive infra red or proximity detection to turn off luminaires when personnel are not present.

WYSIWYG
Piece of proprietary software enable lighting designs and visualisations in 3D. Acronym of "What You See Is What You Get". Mainly used by lighting designers and console operators as a tool for lighting design and production administration. Capable of 3D rendering of lighting states, and direct connection to a lighting control desk. Provides accurate pre-visualisation of lighting designs and greatly increases the understanding between the production team of the likely lighting results. Produced by Cast Lighting in Canada.

Xenon Lamp
A high intensity discharge lamp found in high power followspots and projectors with a colour temperature of approximately 65000K. In film Xenon lamps are used for hitting long distance reflectors. These lamps are also used in 'searchlights'.

XLR
A professional range of connectors widely used in TV systems. Range from 3 to 7 pins. Audio systems use 3 pin, Cue lights and power supplies 4 pin, DMX lighting data use 5 pin, 6 pin tend to be used for Riggers and Designers remote lighting controls and 7 pin for other lighting data connections.

Yellow
A secondary colour which is the complementary colour of blue.

Zero Crossing
The point on an AC waveform where the voltage crosses the X axis.

INDEX

+ve 5 volt dc 41
+ 10 volts dc 41
1.5 metre (5 feet) rule 92
10A radial circuit 132
120 degree rule 91
120 volt market 115
15 Amp connector 72
19 inch type equipment rack 134
19 inch type pack 144
1kW rated channel 47
24 channel cabinet 51
2N3055 power transistor 40
30A ring system 132
3rd harmonic 223, 225
3 Phase Patching System 44
3 phase patch panel 43
3 pin XLR connector 143, 146
45 degree lighting angle 88
5th harmonic 224
5 Amp 3 pin round plugtop 72
5 pin XLR 146
5 pin XLR connector 143
5 pin XLR Male Termination Wiring 146
6 channel pack 90
6 pack 133
7th harmonic 224
80 volt lamp 219
900 firing angle 63

Abbs, Terry 34
Acoustic 52
Acoustic damping 79
Acoustic damping material 259
Acoustic damping mount 161
Acoustic emission 59
Acoustic filament noise 147
Acoustic noise 75, 184, 185, 188, 198,
    202, 203, 205, 208, 210, 212, 214
Acoustic noise level 205
Acoustic shell 214
Acting area 99
AC Lighting Ltd. 46

ADB Eurodim 3 51, 173, 193
ADB Eurodim 3 sine wave 194
ADB Eurorack 49, 50, 162
ADB Eurorack 50 164
ADB Memopack 147
ADB Memorack 147
ADB TTV Technologies SA. 46, 136, 142,
    148, 149, 152, 156, 158, 167,
    168, 171, 174, 189, 194
AEG Germany 35
Air circuit breaker 229
Aldeham Ltd. 46
Altman Shakespeare 215, 219
Amateur theatre 48, 91
American DJ 137
Amsterdam Opera 215
Analogue 0 to 10 volt 126
Analogue dimmer 26, 46, 120
Analogue input unit dimmer 118
Analogue mode of transistor 185
Analysis of dimmer requirements - school
    hall 89
Annual inspection 178
Anytronics Contractor 164
Anytronics Contractor rack 50
Anytronics Ltd. 38, 50, 113, 115, 148,
    150, 167, 172
Architect 87, 95, 102
Architectural control 121
Architectural dimmer 58, 120
Architectural dimming 20, 86, 112, 115
Armature 225
Armstrong, Sir William 28
Arri GB Ltd. 25, 48, 50
Arri SmartPack dimmer 48
Arri SmartRack 49, 50
Audience lighting 100
Audio amplifier 26, 182
Audio chain 257
Audio mixer 45
Audio signal 221
Auditorium 95, 263

Auditorium side lighting 98
Auto-transformer 18, 26
Automatic fire extinguishing 71
AVAB 46
Average city theatre system 95
Average multi-purpose college system 91
Average school system 88
Average TV studio system 105
Avolites Art 2000 touring dimmer 45
Avolites flight cased dimmer 85
Avolites Ltd. 46, 147, 152, 153, 156, 157, 159, 163, 169
Avolite dimmer rack 45
A class device 240

Back lighting 87
Ballet 95
Band touring 45
Barbizon Lighting 46
Barndoors 18
Bar mountable pack 52
BBC PID /171 Draft Edition 6, March 1992 64
BBC PID Dimmer Specification 63
BBC Riverside Studios 31
Bentham, Fred 29, 30
Bi-polar transistor 182
Bijou Theatre Boston 29
Bleed through 41
BMS - Building Management Systems 121
Boom 101
Box labelling and identification 253
Breakout box 249
Brigham Young University 54
BS4343 connector 47
Building-wide 218
Building earth 221
Building regulations 207
Building structure 263
Burnham, Tim 130
Busbar 262
Busbar chamber 153
Bytecraft 189, 214
B class MCB 234

Cable containment 165
Cable management system 198
Cable reeler 211, 212, 249, 262
Cable segregation 221
Cable size 189
Cable volt drop specification 261
Cable winder 212
Cable windlass 212, 249
Camera 74, 87
Camlock connector 153, 155
Capacitive load 226
Capital cost 152, 193, 196, 265
Carlson, Steve 194
CCT Freedom 219
CCT Theatre Lighting 130
CEE 17 connector 73, 135, 153, 155, 209, 210, 254, 256
Celco Ltd. 46, 147, 152
Centralised dimming 121, 212, 243
Central processor 161
Century Lighting 37
Changeover switch 228
Channel patch 149
Choke 59, 113, 161, 177, 184
Chopping action 62
Cinema houselights 112
Circuit distribution 218
Circulating earth loop 262
City Theatre 101
Classical teaching 87
Climatic condition 71
Close-talk microphone 202
Closed loop control system 22
Clutch operated dimmer 29
Cold cathode 193, 195
Cold lamp start 187
College 47, 48, 65, 203
Colortran ENR dimmer 51
Colortran i96 range 173
Colortran Inc. 38, 46, 49, 113, 152, 160, 169
Colour balance 269
Colour changer 205
Colour scroller 100
Colour spectrum 18

Colour temperature 18, 43, 67
Colour wash 75, 97, 105
Compulite 46, 152, 156
Concert hall 88, 173, 185, 199
Concert lighting 102
Conduction angle 62
Conduit 165
Conference 95
Conference centre 101, 102, 104, 199
Conference room 121
Connaught Theatre Worthing 44
Connector provision 48
Contactor 100
Contactor controlled non dim 173
Continuous duty cycle 132
Continuous operation 147
Control channels 43
Control circuit inversion 41
Control desk 131
Control gate pulse 61
Control input to light output relationship 66
Control protocol 120, 121
Conventional electronic dimmer 82
Convention centre 102
Cooling cycle - luminaire 206
Cooling fan 153, 163
Cool colour 88
Cord patch panel 90
Cord patch unit 48
Cost of dimmer installation 104
Cost per dimmer channel 54
Counter-weighted bar 102
Counter-weighted flying 95
Crabtree 113
Crabtree/Electrium Ltd. 233, 234
Cragside 28
Crestron Inc. 118
Crimp ferrule 166
Critically diversity issues 267
Cross stage curtain 95
Cruise ship 20, 112
Cruise ship industry 20
Current meter 154, 155, 252
Current rating 149
Current waveform 186

Cyclorama 88, 94, 97
Cyclorama cloth 87, 94, 103
Cyclorama light 208
C class MCB 234
C class rating 239

D'Oyly Carte, Richard 28
DALI Digital Addressable Lighting Interface
    121
DALI node 121
DALI protocol 127, 128
Danish Opera House 214
Data network 46
Data protocol 46
Day mode 270
Dedicated earth 262
Degrees Celsius 71
Degrees Kelvin 67
Delmatic Ltd. 111, 113
Demultiplexing 46
Depth of field 107
Design phase 102
DEW Ltd. 41
de Jonge, Jan 186, 209
Diagnostic fault report 175
Diagnostic measuring device 157
Digital control protocol 46
Digital dimmer 49
Digital technology 46
Dimmable ballast 120
Dimmed outlet 218
Dimmed power 100
Dimmer 18
Dimmer bar 130, 196, 198, 200, 213
Dimmer box 202
Dimmer buzz 26, 59, 259
Dimmer cabling length 263
Dimmer channel combination 104
Dimmer designer 66
Dimmer diagnostics 80, 195
Dimmer efficiency 58
Dimmer harmonics 224
Dimmer heat dissipation 184
Dimmer law 66, 175
Dimmer noise 257

Dimmer on the wall 20
Dimmer outlet 108
Dimmer packaging 104
Dimmer processor 252
Dimmer rating 50, 82, 94
Dimmer repeatability 65
Dimmer response speed 69
Dimmer room 21, 78, 101, 143, 164, 174, 199, 207, 211, 227, 243, 257, 263
Dimmer room floor 79
Dimmer strip 196
Dimming fluorescent tubes 126
Dimming technology 72
Dines, Rick 212
Dip trap 99
Direct contact 236
Direct power 100, 268
Discharge ballast 193
Discharge lamp 223
Discharge source 100
Discrimination 233
Distributed bar 245
Distributed dimmer 130, 200, 243, 264
Distributed dimming 121, 195, 203
Distributed pack 213
Distributed solution 202
Diversity 105
Diversity factor 71
Diversity rule 250
DMX 46, 49, 50, 51, 100, 131, 143, 157, 208
DMX 512 A (2004) 142
DMX address 69, 213
DMX address selection 162
DMX address setting 175
DMX channel address 149
DMX control 133, 149, 269
DMX controlled contactor 274
DMX controlled dimmer 274
DMX controlled luminaire 218
DMX controlled non dim relay 155
DMX data outlet 200, 202, 209
DMX input 120, 134
DMX network 79, 146

DMX receiver 146
DMX standard 1990 46
DMX terminator 146
DMX universe 104
Double processor 175
Downlighter 128
Drama 95
Drama space 264
Dry hire TV studio 152
Dry ice machine 101
Dual DMX input 176
Dutch Government 215
Duty cycle 190
Dynalite 113, 120
D class MCB 235

Earthing problem 221
Earth conductor 221
Earth loop 221
Earth loop impedance 237, 262
ECB - Earth Circuit Breaker 236
ECG - Electronic Control Gear 126
Edison, Thomas 27
Edison connector 72, 134
Edison electric lamp 27
Educational space 203
Educational user 144
Effect lighting 93
Efficiency of dimmers 182
EIA232 121
EIA485 121
EIB European Installation Bus 121
Elation Lighting Inc. 137, 145
ELCB - Earth Leakage Circuit Breakers 236
Electrical authority 86
Electrical connection 86
Electrical containment 79
Electrical distribution 144
Electrical disturbance 221
Electrical diversity 265
Electrical intake 126
Electrical interference 188, 212
Electrical phases 162
Electrical pollution 210, 214
Electrical power distribution 193

Electrical protective device 79
Electrical regulations 143
Electrical riser cupboard 80
Electrical risk assessment 58
Electrical safety 144, 218
Electrical supply 20, 86, 105
Electrical switchgear 75
Electrical system 218
Electricity At Work Regulations 235
Electro-magnetic coil 234
Electromagnetic interference 100
Electronics Diversified Inc. 47, 74, 133,
    147, 148, 206
Electronics Diversified Scrimmer II Power
    Pack 74
ElectronicTheatre Controls 196
Electronic control gear 126
Electronic dimmer shutters 18
Electronic soft-start 113
Electronic Theatre Controls Inc.
    136, 189, 191
Emergency tripping coil 231
Energy supplier 193
Engineering 28
Entertainment dimmer 58, 120
Entertainment Technology Bakpak 130
Entertainment Technology Capio Plus
    173, 178
Entertainment Technology Inc. 25, 113,
    130, 131, 137, 186, 192, 194,
    196, 206, 207, 208, 244
Entertainment venue 121, 218
Erco Lighting 113
ERMA patch cord 43
ETC - Electronic Theatre Controls
    46, 137, 150, 161
ETC Europe Ltd. 25, 133, 138, 150, 152,
    156, 157, 163, 170, 186, 192,
    206, 214, 244
ETC Group 52
ETC Matrix 173
ETC Matrix II dimmer cabinet 54
ETC Powerbar 244
ETC Sensor dimmer 51
ETC SmartPack 134, 136, 147

ETC Source 4 215, 219
ETC Unison 49, 120, 162
Ethernet 51, 79, 208, 215
Ethernet based network 121
ET Intelligent Strip 194
ET Raceway 207
Eurolight Ltd. 46
Europe 43, 45
European electrical standards 69
European harmonisation 47, 73
European market 147
European Opera House 212
Ex-Or Ltd. 120
Exeter University UK 54
Exhibition centre 48, 88
Exhibition stand 132
Extended lamp life 115, 195
Extracted air 263

Facility panel 255
Fader level setting 65
Fader per channel 49
Fade down time 115
Fade up time 115
Fall time 183, 185
Fan cooling 149
Faraday dark spaces 126
Feeder supply cable 45
Filament failure 189
Filament resonance 183
Filament sing 26
Filament stretch 115, 184
Film dimmer 147
Filtering circuit 58
Filter choke 226
Fire door 78
Fire extinguishing system 78
Fire hazard 205
Fire risk 71
Firing 149
Firing angle 66
First fix 255
Fixed dimming installation 152
Flight cased dimmer 79, 134, 147, 152
Floor level circuits 99

Floor mounting rack 51
Fluke inc. 224
Fluorescent ballasts 193
Fluorescent dimmer law 69
Fluorescent fitting 223, 269, 276
Fluorescent installation 120
Fluorescent tube 40, 126
Fly floor 204
FOH bridge 97
Followspot 130
Followspot position 102
Forced cooling 58, 71
Forestage 97
Forestage area 95, 103
Forestage elevator 95
Forestage extension 95
Forward phase control 188
Forward phase mode 195
Forward phase SCR dimmer 185
Freedom range of luminaires 130
Free standing cabinet 49
Fresnel 65
Front of house 203, 207, 249
Front of house lighting 99
Front of house lighting bridge 95, 101
Front of house side lighting 103
Full rated load 147
Fundamental frequency 223, 224
Fund raising 47
Fuse 149

Galvanic isolation 223
Gas lighting 26
Gate current 182
General Electric 26, 29
General purpose studio 106
Generator 188
Generic luminaire 101
Genltye Group 113
Genlyte Group 186, 194
Germanium transistor 37, 41
GE Lighting 219
GLS lamp 113
Gobo 265
Grand Master 30

Grand Master switchboard 30
Green Ginger Ltd. 39, 46
Green Ginger Micropack 39, 48
Green Ginger Microrack touring dimmer 46
Green Ginger Microset 20 39, 40
Green Ginger Wallrack 49
Grounded stage pin connector 72
Groundrow 87, 103
Groundrow lighting 99, 208, 253

Half cycle 183, 184, 185
Hamilton Ltd. 120
Hard fired pulse 60
Hard wired dimmer 112, 120
Hard wired solution 213
Hard wired wall mounted cabinets 18
Harmonic 188
Harmonic current 183, 184, 188, 226
Harmonic distortion 62, 65, 188, 214,
    221, 223, 224
Harmonic emission 214
Harmonic free zone 193
Harmonic interference 182
Harmonic neutral current 185
Harmonic pollution 227
Harmonic problems 177
Harting connector 135
Heating cycle - luminaire 206
Heat dissipation 184
Heat dissipation considerations 70
Heat emission 144
Heat extraction system 71
Helvar 120
High density cabinet 51
High density dimmer 51, 112, 120
High density solution 18
High frequency filtering 190
High impedance mains supplies 187
High peak current 184
High rise time choke 207
High rise time dimmer 64
High school 203
Hindle, Don 130
Home theatre 112, 118
Horizontal feeder 259

Horizontal hum bars 221
Horseshoe shaped auditorium 102
Hotel 132
Hotel ballroom 203
Hotel dimming 65
House curtain 95
House lighting 218, 266
House lights 269, 275
HRC fuse 233
Hum bars 257

IEE - Institute of Electrical Engineers 188
IEE 16th Edition regulations 252
IES bV 22, 186
IES Holland 52
IES PM4 Power Module 187
IGBT - Insulated Gate Bi-polar Transistor
    182, 184, 188
IGBT dimmer 196
IGBT reverse phase 185
IGBT reverse phase solution 188
IGBT transistor dimmer 195
IGBT transistor technology 130
iLight Ltd. 113, 120
Incandescent lamp 113
Incoming feeder 219
Indication of connected load 143
Indication of fuse failure 143
Indirect contact 236
Individual dimmer 105, 130
Inductive choke 62
Inductive load 82, 226
Inrush current 82, 100
Installation cost 48
Installed dimmer 90, 118
Institute of Electrical Engineers 236, 260
Insulated gate bi-polar transistor 18
Intelligent Power Strip 244
Intensity controls 143
Interference reduction circuitry 62
Interference suppression 153
IPS- Intelligent Power System 195
Iris 18

Jands 151, 156, 161

Jesus Christ Superstar 22, 40, 126
Johnson Controls 52
Junior 8 32

Kenyon, William 54
Kliegl Bros 29, 35, 41, 46
Kliegl Collection USA 54
Kliegl Motorised Autotransformer 33
Kliegl Performer 45
Kliegl R66 dimmer 37
Kliegl safpatch system 55

Lamp characteristic 49
Lamp filament 184, 188
Lamp life 116
Lamp rating 72
Lamp sing 65
Lamp technology 219
Large scale dimmer system 193
Leading edge 62
Leading edge dimming 182
Leakage current 235
Leax 113, 120
LED fixture 193
LED lighting 276
Leprecon LLC 38, 133, 138, 148
Leviton Dimensions 4200 118
Leviton Dimension 8000 118
Leviton Inc. 113, 135, 148
Lightfactor Ltd. 142, 167
Lighting angle 87
Lighting area 87, 91
Lighting bar 48, 94, 100, 199, 207, 209,
    243, 262
Lighting boom 262
Lighting bridge 203, 207
Lighting console 208
Lighting consultant 164
Lighting control network 100
Lighting cue 100
Lighting data network 218
Lighting designer 86, 95
Lighting grid 209
Lighting ladder 99, 101
Lighting level 87

Lighting Methods Inc. 45, 52
Lighting slot 203
Lighting solution 102
Lighting stand 145, 203
Lighting Systems for TV Studios 20
Lighting Technology Ltd. 46
Lighting telescope 108, 203
Lighting throw distance 94
Lighting zone 94, 97, 99
Lightolier Compli 118
Lightolier Controls Inc. 113, 116, 125
Lightolier Lytemode 118
Lightolier Scenist 118
Lightronics Inc. 133, 135, 139, 147, 148
Light a venue 87
Light Console 29, 30
Light Processor Ltd. 120, 138
Light Processor Paradim 164
Light source 87
Linear performance 61
List of dimmer manufacturers 179
Lite Puter DX 1220 dimmer pack 47
Lite Puter Enterprise Co 47
Living museum 20
LMI Inc. 46
Load cabling 132
Load patching 48
Local distribution board 126
Local level setting 143
Local memories 149
Local memory 176
LON 121
Lonworks 121
Loss across power device 184
Loss of DMX data 149, 176
Loudspeaker 221
Lower cost pack 149
Low harm mode 195
Low impedance mains supply 187
Low voltage lighting 113
Low voltage panel 100
Low voltage relay 100
LSC ePro pack 147
LSC Lighting Systems (Aust) Pty Ltd.
    139, 142, 152, 156

LSI Projects Ltd. 157, 163, 189, 270, 272
Lumen per watt ratio 72
Luminaire 87, 91, 100, 262, 265
Luminaires 43
Luminaire hanging position 87, 88
luminaire mounted dimmer 130
Luminaire stock 75
Luminaire trunion arm 130
Lumo Lighting Ltd. 46
Lutron Grafik Eye 118
Lutron Inc. 113, 116
Lux per square metre 87
Lyttelton Theatre 189

Magic Lantern 130
Magnetic ballast 126
Magnetic field 225
Mains frequency 61
Mains waveform 61, 190
Managing cabling 48
Manners, David 130
Masking leg curtain 95
Matcham theatre 205
Matrix type grid 213
Maximum demand 228
MCA Records Inc 40
MCB 239
MCB protection 133
McGraw Collection 19, 33, 55, 68
Medium density dimmer 79
Medium density hard wired cabinet dimmer
    161
Medium density wall dimmer 130
Medium sized school hall 88
MEM/Delta Electrical Ltd. 229, 233
MEM Low Voltage Products 239
Menlo Park, New Jersey 27
Merlin Gerin Ltd. 229, 236, 240
Metropolitan Opera House 29
Microprocessor technology 59
Miniature circuit breaker 229
Minimum load 195
MK Electric Ltd. 113, 114, 134, 221
Mode Electronics 113
Modular dimmer 41, 43, 185

Modular plug-in high density dimmer 101
Modular plug in dimmer 130
Mood 112
MOSFET - Metal Oxide Silicon Field Effect
  Transistor 177, 182, 187
Moss Mitchell clutch 29
Motorised instrument 205
Motorised luminaire 100
Motorised wash light 100
Moulded case circuit breaker 229
Moving structure 203
MR range of dichroic lamps 276
Multi-Channel Controller 122
Multi-preset wall-box dimmer 58
Multi-purpose theatre 102
Multi-purpose venue 152, 275
Multicore cable 45
Multiform 38, 139
Multiway connector 45
Museum 88, 91, 130, 132, 203, 265
Musical 95
Musical recital 102

Negative half cycle 59
Negative sequence harmonic 225
Neon 193, 195
Neoprene 163
Neoprene gasket 59
Neutral conductor 252, 262
Neutral earth short 222
Neutral harmonic 195
Newcastle-upon-Tyne 28
Night mode 271
Noise damping mount 59
Noise reduction 147
Noise reduction choke 133, 174
Noise transmission 263
Non-linear loads 192
Non dim 99, 100, 101, 261, 267
Non dimmed outlet 218
Non dim contactor 50
Non dim law 67
Non dim switch 155
Non linear load 226
Non linear relationship 66

Non saturated studio 108
Northern State University 54
NSI USA 140, 148, 151
Nu, Andrew 276
Nuisance tripping 226, 238, 240
Nulec Switchgear 232
Number of outlets 99

Office complex 127
Offord, John 44
Off line diagnostics 80, 177
Ohm's law 224, 260
Olivier Theatre 38
On-site transformer 232
One-stop shop 46
On line diagnostics 80, 177
On stage power supplies 218
Opera 95
Opera house 210
Optical isolation 223
Opto-coupler 223
Orchestra 102
Oscilloscope 61, 188
Osram GmbH 113, 127
Output voltage 176
Over-current protective device 236
Over-heat problems 81
Over-stage circuits 99
Over-Stage Intelligent Raceway 208
Overload protection 113
Over Stage Bar 101
Over stage bar 100, 207
Over stage circuit 103
Over stage lighting bar 99

Pantograph 203
PARs 275
Par can 45, 65
Patch bay 154, 209
Patch cord 43
Patch panel 43
Patt 123 31
Patt 23 31
Patt 45 31
Payne, Alan 39

PC 51
Peak demand 240, 252
Peak electrical demand 221
Pearlman, Gordon 194
Pennsylvania State University 54
Performance area 91, 265
Performance space 152, 264
Performance venue 72, 104, 219, 232
Phase conductor 262
Phase control 189
Phase controlled dimmer 193
Phase rotation 224
Phase segregation 43, 250
Phase separation 251
Philips Lighting 113
Photo transistor 223
Pilbrow, Richard 205
Planning a distributed solution 213
Planning stage 95, 153
PLB - production lighting box 255
Plug-in dimmer 41, 50
Plug-in module 193
Polaron Group 113, 120
Portable pack 18, 79, 130, 132
Portable pack market 40
Positive half cycle 59
Positive rotation sequence harmonic 225
Powercon connector 74
Powered bar 207
Powerlock connector 134, 153, 155
Power bar 211
Power control device 149
Power control section 22
Power cycle 192
Power factor 226
Power factor correction 227
Power flying system 198
Power levels per square metre 108
Power rating 147
Power supply 188
Power transistor 183
Practicals 99, 265, 269
Practical Control 41
Practical DMX 20
Preheat 49, 67

Preset 115, 120
Preset capabilities 115
Preset level 115
PRG Europe 85
Primary building earth 220
Primary protective device 231
Primary school 203
Production Arts Inc. 46
Production lighting desk 273
Product launch 102
Professional theatre 87
Profile 65
Projection room 102
Projector 101
Prolonged lamp life 116
Proscenium 97
Proscenium header 102
Proscenium opening 94, 102
Proscenium stage 91
Protective device 221
Pulsar 140
Pulsar Datarak 49
Pulsar Light of Cambridge Ltd.
      38, 46, 47, 73, 142
Pulsar Mini Pak 143
Pulsar Rackpak 136
Pulsar Rakpack 73
Pulse width modulation 190
Pulse width modulation circuit 190
Push fit terminal 168

QIS Ltd 100
Quantity of dimmers 95

r.m.s. electrical supply 61
r.m.s. measurement technique 63
Rack mounted pack 130
Rack mounting 49
Rack mount packs 147
Radio City Music Hall 29
Radio frequency interference 212
Rako Controls Ltd. 128
Rank Organisation 37
Rank Strand Environ 118
RCBO 211, 213, 239

RCCB - Residual Current Circuit Breaker
   218
RCD 155, 235, 236, 239, 253, 262, 268
RCD device 154
RCD protection 50, 154
RDM 215
RDM - Remote Device Management
   standard 158
Reactive power component 188
Redundancy 213
Rehearsal lighting 218
Rehearsal mode 271
Remote programming 186
Remote tripping coil 231
Rental companies 152
Rental company 48
Repertory theatre 248
Replaceable fuse 134
Residential property 121
Resident company 95
Residual current breaker 146
Residual current device 235
Resistance dimmer 27
Resistive component 70
Resistive dimmer 18, 26, 224
Response speed 175
Reverse-phase dimming 177
Reverse phase 193, 201, 208, 213
Reverse phase angle dimmer 185
Reverse phase dimmer 185, 193, 207
Reverse phase mode 185, 195
Reverse phase solution 214
Reyrolle Lloyds register marine fuse 37
Rigging system 218, 219
Rig bleed 67
Ring intercom 221
Rise time 62, 113, 133, 134, 147, 154, 1
   62, 174, 183, 185
Rock and roll industry 187
Royal Court Theatre, Liverpool 30
Royal National Theatre 38, 189
Rugged package 147
Runking 259
Running cost 265
Rupture current rating 232, 233

Saturated lighting studio 108
Saturated reactor 26
Saturation voltage 183
Savoy Theatre 28
Scandinavia 76
School 47, 48, 49, 65
School hall 229, 265
School hall lighting layout 89
School hall luminaire positioning 90
Screw-down terminal 166
Scrims 18
Seating rake 95
Second fix 255
Second World War 30
Self-climbing hoist 108, 203
Set dressing 107
Sharp Theatre, Mahwah 274
Shopping mall 132, 250
Short circuit fire protection fuse 185
Showlight, Munich 2005 205
Show Mode 271
Shuko connector 72, 135
Side lighting 87
Side lighting position 99
Side stage ladder 209
Siemens Brothers and Company
   28, 35, 229
Silicon controlled rectifier 35
Sine wave 52, 182, 188
Sine wave dimmer 185, 188, 190, 201,
   207, 252
Sine wave distortion 177
Sine wave distributed pack 193
Sine wave inductor 190
Sine wave pack 208
Sine wave solution 207
Sine wave technology 18, 193
Single gang electrical plate 113
Six lamp bar 154
Slider control 115
Small news studio 107
Small stage 88
Small theatre 65
Small weather set 107
Smoke machine 101

Socapex connector 134
Socket box 48, 101, 262, 264
Soft-start 115, 186
Soft patching 49
Solid state relay 100
Sound amplifier 45
Sound distribution amplifier 223
Sound system 100
Special effects 87
Special lighting 93
Special mode 271
Speed of response 185
Square D 229
Square law 66
Square law curve 69
Stafford King Controls Ltd. 39
Stafford King Controls Minipack 39
Stage 95
Stage area 95, 203, 263
Stage bar 130
Stage Electrics Ltd. 46
Stage extension 97, 99
Stage floor 207
Stage floor circuit 211
Stage left 99
Stage pin connector 134
Stage right 99
Stage side light 98
Stage temporary supply 231
Stage wall 207
Standby generator 225, 228
Standing electrical supply 219
Standing wave 259
STLD Archive 21, 25, 31
Strand 300 Series console 41
Strand Archive 30
Strand CD80 dimmer 52
Strand CD80 pack 147
Strand CD90 High Density dimming system
    52, 53
Strand CD Dimming system 31
Strand CD system 40
Strand Century 37
Strand Century archive 54
Strand EC21 dimmer 52, 190, 193

Strand Electric 32
Strand Electric and Engineering Co. Ltd 29
Strand Electric Company 36
Strand Environ 2 118
Strand JP control desk 37
Strand JTM cabinet 37
Strand JTM dimmer 113
Strand JTM dimmer cabinet 51
Strand Junior 8 32
Strand Junior HA switchboard 32
Strand LD90 49, 50
Strand Lighting 113, 141
Strand Lighting Accent 120
Strand Lighting CD80 173
Strand Lighting EC21 173
Strand Lighting LD24 164
Strand Lighting Ltd. 25, 46, 119, 142,
    145, 148, 152, 162, 167, 171,
    172, 175, 189, 190, 191, 192,
    193, 214
Strand Lighting SLD96 52, 173
Strand Lighting SL luminaire 219
Strand MCM dimmer 41
Strand Microdim 118
Strand Mini 2 dimmer pack 37, 48
Strand Mini 2 Plus dimmer pack 38
Strand MTU Dimmer 116
Strand Outlook 118, 120
Strand Permus 49
Strand PIP dimmer 41
Strand Premier 118
Strand Resistance Dimmer banks 1956 21
Strand STM dimmer 113
Strand STM dimmer cabinet 37, 51
Studio theatre 130, 132
Sub-distribution board 221
Substation 228
Supply authority 188
Supply transformer 188, 219
Suppression choke 182
Surrey Advertiser 32
Suspension system 219
Swan, Joseph 27
Swan lamp 28
Switched circuit 82

Switchfuse 233
Switchgear 231
Switch mode power supply 223
Synchronisation section 59
S characteristic 66

Task lighting 270
Taylor, David 205
TBA Ltd. 130
Technical cabling 257
Technical earth 220, 221
Television 47
Television dimmer 43, 147
Television studio 87
Temporary show 152
Theatre 49, 101, 199, 203, 208, 263
Theatre-in-the-round 91, 199, 250
Theatre boom 130
Theatre console 115
Theatre dimmer 147
Theatre diversity 249
Theatre grid 95
Theatre stage 94
Themed restaurant 20
Theme park 20
Theodore Fuchs Collection 54
Thermal protection 233
Thermal runaway 182
Thermal shock 67
The Art of Stage Lighting 30
The Strand Archive 54
The third wire 126
Thorn modular dimmer 41, 42
Thorn Q File control desk 41
Three phase electrical supply 104
Three phase motor 225
Thyratron 18, 26
Thyristor 18, 35, 41, 52, 59, 149, 162, 1
    82, 183, 185, 193, 213
Thyristor dimmer 35, 113
Thyristor dimmer circuit 60
Thyristor gate 60
Top cyc lighting 208
Touring circuit 95
Touring company 95

Touring dimmers 43, 45
Touring rack 46
Touring show 45, 101
Touring system 45
Touring venue 176
Touring world 46
Tracking lighting grid 202
Trailing edge dimming 182
Transformer 263, 265
Transformer - building 126
Transformer - electronic 113
Transformer - wire-wound 113
Transformer size 189
Transient 221
Transistor 26, 45, 52
Transistor dimmer 18
Transistor dimming 182
Transtechnik FDX90 dimmer 52
Triac 18, 26, 52, 59, 183, 213
Triac dimmer 113, 182, 186
Trim pot 118
Tripping hazard 146
True r.m.s. breaker 226
True r.m.s. measuring meter 63
Trunking system 259
Truss 262
Tungsten lamp 113
Turn-around time 199, 200
TV application 202
TV camera 18
TV company 100
TV dimmer law 67
TV law 67
TV lighting 100
TV recording 100
TV studio 108, 132, 173, 187, 189, 199,
    203, 208, 263
TV studio grid 130
TV venue 67
Twist Lock connector 72, 134
Two way switching 113
Typical News Studio 106
Typical rise times for buildings 64
Typical UK Wall Box formats 114

UK 20
UK electrical regulations 43
UK Rental List 1970 34
Uniform lighting level 86
Unistrut 79
Unit dimmer 113, 130, 213
University 91
UPS - Uninterrupted Power Supply 228
USA 20, 43, 45
User interface 271
USITT 46
US market 147

Valve 26
Vari-Lite 26
Vent Axia extractor fan 78
Vertex solid stage relay 100
Vertical riser 259
Video distribution amplifier 223
Video equipment 221
Video signal 221
Voltage compensation 131
Voltage drop 182, 195
Voltage efficiency 63
Voltage spike 261
Voltage stabilisation 174
Voltmeter 154

Wall box dimmers 58, 112, 113
Wall dimmers 113
Wall mounting 49
Wall mount dimmer 120
Warm colour 88
Watts per square metre 105
Waveform degradation 224
Waveform diagram 190
Waveform distortion 65
WhiteLight Ltd. 46
Wieland connector 153
Wild, Larry 54
Wings 99
Working lights 218, 269
Working light system 270
Wrap around cyclorama 107
Wurlitzer organ 29

Zero 88 Alpha Pak 143
Zero 88 Betapack 133
Zero 88 Lighting Ltd. 38, 47, 120, 141, 148, 152, 172
Zero crossing point 100, 184, 225

ENTERTAINMENT TECHNOLOGY PRESS

FREE SUBSCRIPTION SERVICE

Keeping Up To Date with

Practical Dimming

Entertainment Technology titles are continually up-dated, and all major changes and additions are listed in date order in the relevant dedicated area of the publisher's website. Simply go to the front page of www.etnow.com and click on the BOOKS button. From there you can locate the title and be connected through to the latest information and services related to the publication.

The author of the title welcomes comments and suggestions about the book and can be contacted by email at: books@nickmobsby.com

Titles Published by Entertainment Technology Press

ABC of Theatre Jargon *Francis Reid* **£9.95** ISBN 1904031099
This glossary of theatrical terminology explains the common words and phrases that are used in normal conversation between actors, directors, designers, technicians and managers.

Aluminium Structures in the Entertainment Industry *Peter Hind* **£24.95**
ISBN 1904031064
Aluminium Structures in the Entertainment Industry aims to educate the reader in all aspects of the design and safe usage of temporary and permanent aluminium structures specific to the entertainment industry – such as roof structures, PA towers, temporary staging, etc.

AutoCAD – A Handbook for Theatre Users *David Ripley* **£24.95** ISBN 1904031315
From 'Setting Up' to 'Drawing in Three Dimensions' via 'Drawings Within Drawings', this compact and fully illustrated guide to AutoCAD covers everything from the basics to full colour rendering and remote plotting.

Basics – A Beginner's Guide to Lighting Design *Peter Coleman* **£9.95** ISBN 1904031412
The fourth in the author's 'Basics' series, this title covers the subject area in four main sections: The Concept, Practical Matters, Related Issues and The Design Into Practice. In an area that is difficult to be difinitive, there are several things that cross all the boundaries of all lighting design and it's these areas that the author seeks to help with.

Basics – A Beginner's Guide to Special Effects *Peter Coleman* **£9.95** ISBN 1904031331
This title introduces newcomers to the world of special effects. It describes all types of special effects including pyrotechnic, smoke and lighting effects, projections, noise machines, etc. It places emphasis on the safe storage, handling and use of pyrotechnics.

Basics – A Beginner's Guide to Stage Lighting *Peter Coleman* **£9.95** ISBN 190403120X
This title does what it says: it introduces newcomers to the world of stage lighting. It will not teach the reader the art of lighting design, but will teach beginners much about the 'nuts and bolts' of stage lighting.

Basics – A Beginner's Guide to Stage Sound *Peter Coleman* **£9.95** ISBN 1904031277
This title does what it says: it introduces newcomers to the world of stage sound. It will not teach the reader the art of sound design, but will teach beginners much about the background to sound reproduction in a theatrical environment.

Building Better Theaters *Michael Mell* **£16.95** 1904031404
A title within our Consultancy Series, this book describes the process of designing a theater, from the initial decision to build through to opening night. Mr. Mell's book provides a step-by-step guide to the design and construction of performing arts facilities. Chapters discuss: assembling your team, selecting an architect, different construction methods, the architectural design process, construction of the theater, theatrical systems and equipment, the stage, backstage, the auditorium, ADA requirements and the lobby. Each chapter clearly describes what to expect and how to avoid surprises. It is a must-read for architects, planners, performing arts groups, educators and anyone who may be considering building or renovating a theater.

A Comparative Study of Crowd Behaviour at Two Major Music Events
Chris Kemp, Iain Hill, Mick Upton **£7.95** ISBN 1904031250
A compilation of the findings of reports made at two major live music concerts, and in particular crowd behaviour, which is followed from ingress to egress.

Copenhagen Opera House *Richard Brett and John Offord* **£32.00** ISBN 1904031420
Completed in a little over three years, the Copenhagen Opera House opened with a royal gala performance on 15th January 2005. Built on a spacious brown-field site, the building is a landmark venue and this book provides the complete technical background story to an opera house set to become a benchmark for future design and planning. Sixteen chapters by relevant experts involved with the project cover everything from the planning of the auditorium and studio stage, the stage engineering, stage lighting and control and architectural lighting through to acoustic design and sound technology plus technical summaries.

Electrical Safety for Live Events *Marco van Beek* **£16.95** ISBN 1904031285
This title covers electrical safety regulations and good pracitise pertinent to the entertainment industries and includes some basic electrical theory as well as clarifying the "do's and don't's" of working with electricity.

The Exeter Theatre Fire *David Anderson* **£24.95** ISBN 1904031137
This title is a fascinating insight into the events that led up to the disaster at the Theatre Royal, Exeter, on the night of September 5th 1887. The book details what went wrong, and the lessons that were learned from the event.

Fading Light – A Year in Retirement *Francis Reid* **£14.95** ISBN 1904031358
Francis Reid, the lighting industry's favourite author, describes a full year in retirement. "Old age is much more fun than I expected," he says. Fading Light describes visits and experiences to the author's favourite theatres and opera houses, places of relaxation and re-visits to scholarly intitutions.

Focus on Lighting Technology *Richard Cadena* **£17.95** ISBN 1904031145
This concise work unravels the mechanics behind modern performance lighting and appeals to designers and technicians alike. Packed with clear, easy-to-read diagrams, the book provides excellent explanations behind the technology of performance lighting.

Health and Safety Aspects in the Live Music Industry *Chris Kemp, Iain Hill* **£30.00** ISBN 1904031226
This title includes chapters on various safety aspects of live event production and is written by specialists in their particular areas of expertise.

Health and Safety Management in the Live Music and Events Industry *Chris Hannam* **£25.95** ISBN 1904031307
This title covers the health and safety regulations and their application regarding all aspects of staging live entertainment events, and is an invaluable manual for production managers and event organisers.

Hearing the Light – 50 Years Backstage *Francis Reid* **£24.95** ISBN 1904031188
This highly enjoyable memoir delves deeply into the theatricality of the industry. The author's almost fanatical interest in opera, his formative period as lighting designer at Glyndebourne and his experiences as a theatre administrator, writer and teacher make for a broad and unique background.

An Introduction to Rigging in the Entertainment Industry *Chris Higgs* **£24.95**
ISBN 1904031129
This book is a practical guide to rigging techniques and practices and also thoroughly covers safety issues and discusses the implications of working within recommended guidelines and regulations.

Let There be Light – Entertainment Lighting Software Pioneers in Interview
Robert Bell **£32.00** ISBN 1904031242
Robert Bell interviews a distinguished group of software engineers working on entertainment lighting ideas and products.

Lighting for Roméo and Juliette *John Offord* **£26.95** ISBN 1904031161
John Offord describes the making of the Vienna State Opera production from the lighting designer's viewpoint – from the point where director Jürgen Flimm made his decision not to use scenery or sets and simply employ the expertise of LD Patrick Woodroffe.

Lighting Systems for TV Studios *Nick Mobsby* **£45.00** ISBN 1904031005
Lighting Systems for TV Studios, now in its second edition, is the first book specifically written on the subject and has become the 'standard' resource work for studio planning and design covering the key elements of system design, luminaires, dimming, control, data networks and suspension systems as well as detailing the infrastructure items such as cyclorama, electrical and ventilation. Sensibly TV lighting principles are explained and some history on TV broadcasting, camera technology and the equipment is provided to help set the scene! The second edition includes applications for sine wave and distributed dimming, moving lights, Ethernet and new cool lamp technology.

Lighting Techniques for Theatre-in-the-Round *Jackie Staines* **£24.95**
ISBN 1904031013
Lighting Techniques for Theatre-in-the-Round is a unique reference source for those working on lighting design for theatre-in-the-round for the first time. It is the first title to be published specifically on the subject, it also provides some anecdotes and ideas for more challenging shows, and attempts to blow away some of the myths surrounding lighting in this format.

Lighting the Stage *Francis Reid* **£14.95** ISBN 1904031080
Lighting the Stage discusses the human relationships involved in lighting design – both between people, and between these people and technology. The book is written from a highly personal viewpoint and its 'thinking aloud' approach is one that Francis Reid has used in his writings over the past 30 years.

Model National Standard Conditions *ABTT/DSA/LGLA* **£20.00** ISBN 1904031110
These *Model National Standard Conditions* covers operational matters and complement *The Technical Standards for Places of Entertainment*, which describes the physical requirements for building and maintaining entertainment premises.

Mr Phipps' Theatre *Mark Jones, John Pick* **£17.95** ISBN: 1904031382
Mark Jones and John Pick describe "The Sensational Story of Eastbourne's Royal Hippodrome" – formerly Eastbourne Theatre Royal. An intriguing narrative, the book sets the story against a unique social history of the town. Peter Longman, former director of The Theatres Trust, provides the Foreword.

Pages From Stages *Anthony Field* **£17.95** ISBN 1904031269
Anthony Field explores the changing style of theatres including interior design, exterior design, ticket and seat prices, and levels of service, while questioning whether the theatre still exists as a place of entertainment for regular theatre-goers.

Practical Dimming *Nick Mobsby* **£22.95** ISBN 19040313447
This important and easy to read title covers the history of electrical and electronic dimming, how dimmers work, current dimmer types from around the world, planning of a dimming system, looking at new sine wave dimming technology and distributed dimming. Integration of dimming into different performance venues as well as the necessary supporting electrical systems are fully detailed. Significant levels of information are provided on the many different forms and costs of potential solutions as well as how to plan specific solutions. Architectural dimming for the likes of hotels, museums and shopping centres are included. Practical Dimming is a companion book to Practical DMX and is designed for all involved in the use, operation and design of dimming systems.

Practical DMX *Nick Mobsby* **£16.95** ISBN 19040313668
In this highly topical and important title the author details the principles of DMX, how to plan a network, how to choose equipment and cables, with data on products from around the world, and how to install DMX networks for shows and on a permanently installed basis. The easy style of the book and the helpful fault finding tips, together with a review of different DMX testing devices provide an ideal companion for all lighting technicians and system designers. An introduction to Ethernet and Canbus networks are provided as well tips on analogue networks and protocol conversion. This title has been recently updated to include a new chapter on Remote Device Management that became an international standard in Summer 2006.

Practical Guide to Health and Safety in the Entertainment Industry
Marco van Beek **£14.95** ISBN 1904031048
This book is designed to provide a practical approach to Health and Safety within the Live Entertainment and Event industry. It gives industry-pertinent examples, and seeks to break down the myths surrounding Health and Safety.

Production Management *Joe Aveline* **£17.95** ISBN 1904031102
Joe Aveline's book is an in-depth guide to the role of the Production Manager, and includes real-life practical examples and 'Aveline's Fables' – anecdotes of his experiences with real messages behind them.

Rigging for Entertainment: Regulations and Practice *Chris Higgs* **£19.95**
ISBN 1904031218
Continuing where he left off with his highly successful *An Introduction to Rigging in the Entertainment Industry*, Chris Higgs' second title covers the regulations and use of equipment in greater detail.

Rock Solid Ethernet *Wayne Howell* **£24.95** ISBN 1904031293
Although aimed specifically at specifiers, installers and users of entertainment industry systems, this book will give the reader a thorough grounding in all aspects of computer networks, whatever industry they may work in. The inclusion of historical and technical 'sidebars' make for an enjoyable as well as informative read.

Sixty Years of Light Work *Fred Bentham* **£26.95** ISBN 1904031072
This title is an autobiography of one of the great names behind the development of modern stage lighting equipment and techniques.

Sound for the Stage *Patrick Finelli* **£24.95** ISBN 1904031153
Patrick Finelli's thorough manual covering all aspects of live and recorded sound for performance is a complete training course for anyone interested in working in the field of stage sound, and is a must for any student of sound.

Stage Lighting Design in Britain: The Emergence of the Lighting Designer, 1881-1950 *Nigel Morgan* **£17.95** ISBN 190403134X
This book sets out to ascertain the main course of events and the controlling factors that determined the emergence of the theatre lighting designer in Britain, starting with the introduction of incandescent electric light to the stage, and ending at the time of the first public lighting design credits around 1950. The book explores the practitioners, equipment, installations and techniques of lighting design.

Stage Lighting for Theatre Designers *Nigel Morgan* **£17.95** ISBN 1904031196
This is an updated second edition of Nigel Morgan's popular book for students of theatre design – outlining all the techniques of stage lighting design.

Technical Marketing Techniques *David Brooks, Andy Collier, Steve Norman* **£24.95** ISBN 190403103X
Technical Marketing is a novel concept, recently defined and elaborated by the authors of this book, with business-to-business companies competing in fast developing technical product sectors.

Technical Standards for Places of Entertainment *ABTT/DSA* **£30.00** ISBN 1904031056
Technical Standards for Places of Entertainment details the necessary physical standards required for entertainment venues.

Theatre Engineering and Stage Machinery *Toshiro Ogawa* **£30.00** ISBN 1904031021
Theatre Engineering and Stage Machinery is a unique reference work covering every aspect of theatrical machinery and stage technology in global terms, and across the complete historical spectrum.

Theatre Lighting in the Age of Gas *Terence Rees* **£24.95** ISBN 190403117X
Entertainment Technology Press has republished this valuable historic work previously produced by the Society for Theatre Research in 1978. *Theatre Lighting in the Age of Gas* investigates the technological and artistic achievements of theatre lighting engineers from the 1700s to the late Victorian period.

Theatre Space: A Rediscovery Reported *Francis Reid* **£19.95** ISBN 1904031439
In the post-war world of the 1950s and 60s, the format of theatre space became a matter for a debate that aroused passions of an intensity unknown before or since. The proscenium arch was clearly identified as the enemy, accused of forming a barrier to disrupt the relations between the actor and audience. An uneasy fellow-traveller at the time, Francis Reid later recorded his impressions whilst enjoying performances or working in theatres old and new and this book is an important collection of his writings in various theatrical journals from 1969-2001 including his contribution to the Cambridge Guide to the Theatre in 1988. It reports some of the flavour of the period when theatre architecture was rediscovering its past in a search to establish its future.

Theatres of Achievement *John Higgins* **£29.95** ISBN: 1904031374
John Higgins affectionately describes the history of 40 distinguished UK theatres in a personal tribute, each uniquely illustrated by the author. Completing each profile is colour photography by Adrian Eggleston.

Walt Disney Concert Hall – The Backstage Story *Patricia MacKay & Richard Pilbrow* **£28.95** ISBN 1904031234
Spanning the 16-year history of the design and construction of the Walt Disney Concert Hall, this book provides a fresh and detailed behind the scenes story of the design and technology from a variety of viewpoints. This is the first book to reveal the "process" of the design of a concert hall.

Yesterday's Lights – A Revolution Reported *Francis Reid* **£26.95** ISBN 1904031323
Set to help new generations to be aware of where the art and science of theatre lighting is coming from – and stimulate a nostalgia trip for those who lived through the period, Francis Reid's latest book has over 350 pages dedicated to the task, covering the 'revolution' from the fifties through to the present day. Although this is a highly personal account of the development of lighting design and technology and he admits that there are 'gaps', you'd be hard put to find anything of significance missing.

Go to www.etbooks.co.uk for full details of above titles and secure online ordering facilities.